Forestry Commission Booklet Nc

FOREST MENSUR HANDBOOK

by G. J. Hamilton, M SC

FORESTRY COMMISSION

London: Her Majesty's Stationery Office

First published 1975
Third impression 1988

ISBN 0 11 710023 4

ODC 5:(021)

Keywords: Forestry, Mensuration

ACKNOWLEDGEMENTS

The production of the various tables and charts contained in this publication has been very much a team effort by members of the Mensuration Section of the Forestry Commission's Research & Development Division.

J. M. Christie has been largely responsible for initiating and co-ordinating the development and production of the tables and charts.

A. C. Miller undertook most of the computer programming required to produce the tables and was responsible for establishing some form height/top height and tariff number/top height relationships, and for development work in connection with assortment tables and the measurement of stacked timber.

R. O. Hendrie prepared the single tree tariff charts and analysed various data concerning timber density, stacked timber, and bark.

M. D. Witts established most of the form height/top height and tariff number/top height relationships and investigated bark thickness in the major conifers.

Assistance in checking data was given by Miss D. Porchet, Mrs N. M. Johnson and E. J. Fletcher. The provision of information on stacked timber measurement by A. W. Simpson of the Forestry Division of the Department of Agriculture for Northern Ireland is gratefully acknowledged.

Thanks are also due to many Commission staff who offered constructive comments on various parts of the booklet.

The Forestry Commission is indebted to the Literary Executor of the late Sir Ronald A. Fisher, FRS, to Dr. Frank Yates, FRS, and to Longman Group Ltd., London, for permission to reprint Table 13 from their book *Statistical Tables for Biological, Agricultural and Medical Research.*

Minor amendments prior to reprinting in 1985 have been advised by T. J. D. Rollinson.

Contents

PART IV

MEASUREMENT OF STANDING TIMBER

PART V

MISCELLANEOUS

PART VI

TABLES

Page numbers only

Tables *continued*

Tariff Number/ Top Height	Top Height Mean Height	Double Bark Thickness	Bark Percent	Bark as percent of underbark Volume
112	146	148	150	161
112	146	148	150	161
112	146	148	151	161
112	146	148	152	161
112	146	148	152	161
None	None	Use SS	Use SS	Use SS
112	146	148	153	161
112	146 Use JL	148	153	161 Use JL
113	146	148	154	161
113	146	148	154	Use SS
113	146	148	155	Use SS
None	None		155	Use SS
113	146	148	156	Use SS
113	146	148	156	Use SS
113	None	148	157	None
Use oak	None	148	157	None
Use Birch	None	148	158	None
Use Oak	None	148	158	None
113	None	148	159	
Use Oak	None	148	159	None
Use Oak	None	148	160	None

Forest Mensuration Handbook

INTRODUCTION

Measurement of timber is required for several purposes. The most obvious of these, perhaps, is the need to quantify forest produce for sale. Measurement of timber is also required in management, notably for planning purposes and for control of resources.

There are many different ways in which timber can be measured, some being more appropriate for one purpose than others. In addition the choice of method may be influenced by the size and quantity of produce, its value and possibly by the local conditions and facilities available.

This publication is intended to provide the information necessary to meet the needs of measurement for most purposes and conditions in British forestry. The main components are, first, a *key* (front inside cover) which enables the user to choose the measurement procedure most appropriate for the purpose intended. The principles involved in producing this key, together with explanatory notes, are given in Part I, immediately following. Secondly, detailed measurement procedures are given separately for felled and standing timber in Part III, page 20 and Part IV, page 44. Essential background information is given with each of the procedures which are individually numbered. The tables required to carry out some of these procedures are produced at the back of the book in Part VI, page 201.

Miscellaneous aspects of measurement, together with conversion factors, abbreviations, etc are brought together to form Part V, page 117.

PART I GENERAL ASPECTS OF MEASUREMENT

Expression of Quantity

Timber quantity can be expressed in terms of solid volume, stacked volume, green weight, dry weight, length, number of pieces, etc. Traditionally timber quantity has mostly been expressed in terms of solid volume and there are good reasons why this should be so. In the first place, many timber products, following conversion, are sold by solid volume. Sawn timber is an obvious example. Just as important, however, is the fact that solid volume can be relatively easily assessed for both felled and standing timber. Alternative measures which sometimes have a more direct bearing on the requirements of the consumer, such as dry weight for pulp manufacture, are generally restricted in their use on account of the practical difficulties in assessing them. For example the measurement of the weight of dry matter in timber is a complex process. Furthermore, weight measurements of any kind are impossible in standing timber. Even when parameters other than solid volume are assessed, for example stacked volume or weight, these are frequently converted to solid volume estimates for management purposes.

In general, therefore, the traditional measure of solid volume remains the basic reference quantity in timber measurement.

The Need for Conventions

A characteristic feature of measurement in forestry is that by the nature of the products, very precise measurement is rarely practicable and one is invariably dealing with volume *estimates*. There are many different ways of estimating timber volume with inevitable differences in the estimate arrived at. Even the smallest log can be measured in several different ways. It is thus a fundamental necessity to describe the method of measurement and the *measurement conventions* used when ascribing volumes to timber in order to convey the full meaning of such estimates. Standard measurement conventions are described in Part II, page 17.

Cost/benefit Aspects of Measurement

Given that an estimate of quantity is required for a particular purpose, a decision has to be made about the degree of precision which should be sought. Virtually any forest product may be measured to varying degrees of precision and to arrive at an appropriate level it is necessary to consider the costs and benefits associated with these different levels of precision.

In the first place greater precision generally costs more per unit volume. For example, the volume of a single log may be estimated as the product of its length and its mean cross-sectional area. The mean cross-sectional area may be estimated from one measurement taken at the mid point of the log. A more precise estimate of the mean cross-sectional area may be determined by taking the average of a number of measurements taken at regular intervals along the length of the log. The more frequent the measurements, the more precise will be the estimate. A second example might be, say, finding the mean diameter of a stand by sampling. The more trees sampled, the more precise will be the estimate of mean diameter. In both of these examples greater precision involves more work and hence costs more per unit of volume.

In broad terms also, greater precision produces greater benefits. As an example, consider the situation of a prospective buyer of timber confronted by two lots, of say, 500 logs. In one lot the volume of each individual log has been measured, whilst the volume of the second lot has been derived from a 5% sample of randomly selected logs. Depending on how accurately the sample represents the total population of logs, the true volume may be greater than, less than, or exactly equal to the volume estimated from the sample. Although the chances of an underestimate of volume are equal to the chances of an overestimate, the risk of a shortfall in volume may be one which the buyer is unwilling or unable to accept. The elimination of the element of risk is consequently of some value to him and the lot of logs where measurement is complete consequently becomes a more attractive proposition. This will be reflected in his willingness to pay a slightly higher price for this lot. The difference between the two prices could be regarded as an insurance premium against the risk of loss. Thus it follows that increases in price may be expected with increasing precision.

The relationship of price to precision, however, will be rather different from the relationship of cost of measurement to precision. Figure 1 depicts what might be regarded as the typical situation. The error of estimate can be regarded here as a standard error or as confidence limits at a specified level of probability (see page 123 for further explanation). Whereas cost rises rapidly as the error approaches ±0% the price curve tends to level out in the same area. An optimum level of precision can then be identified at the point where the difference between the two curves is greatest. In practice the establishment of a price/precision curve can rarely be based on factual information, but the generalised shape will apply in most situations.

There are two further important factors to be considered here which influence the shape of these curves and hence the optimum level of precision applying in a given situation. The first of these is the value of the product per unit of volume. For a given quantity and method of measurement the cost/precision curves may be similar for high and low value products but the price/precision curves may be expected to vary. In the case of a low value product the financial risk is clearly lower than with high value products at a given level of precision (other than ±0%). The net result is a relatively lower 'insurance premium' against loss, and consequently a rather flatter price/precision curve as shown in Figure 2. With lower timber values the optimum level of precision becomes lower also.

The same principles apply where measurement is carried out for purely management purposes. In these cases the 'price' becomes a value considered by management as appropriate for the purpose. The critical factor here however is again the rate of change of this value with changing precision, bearing in mind here that the 'risk' attached to varying levels of precision is a risk to management. For purposes like inventory for production forecasting,

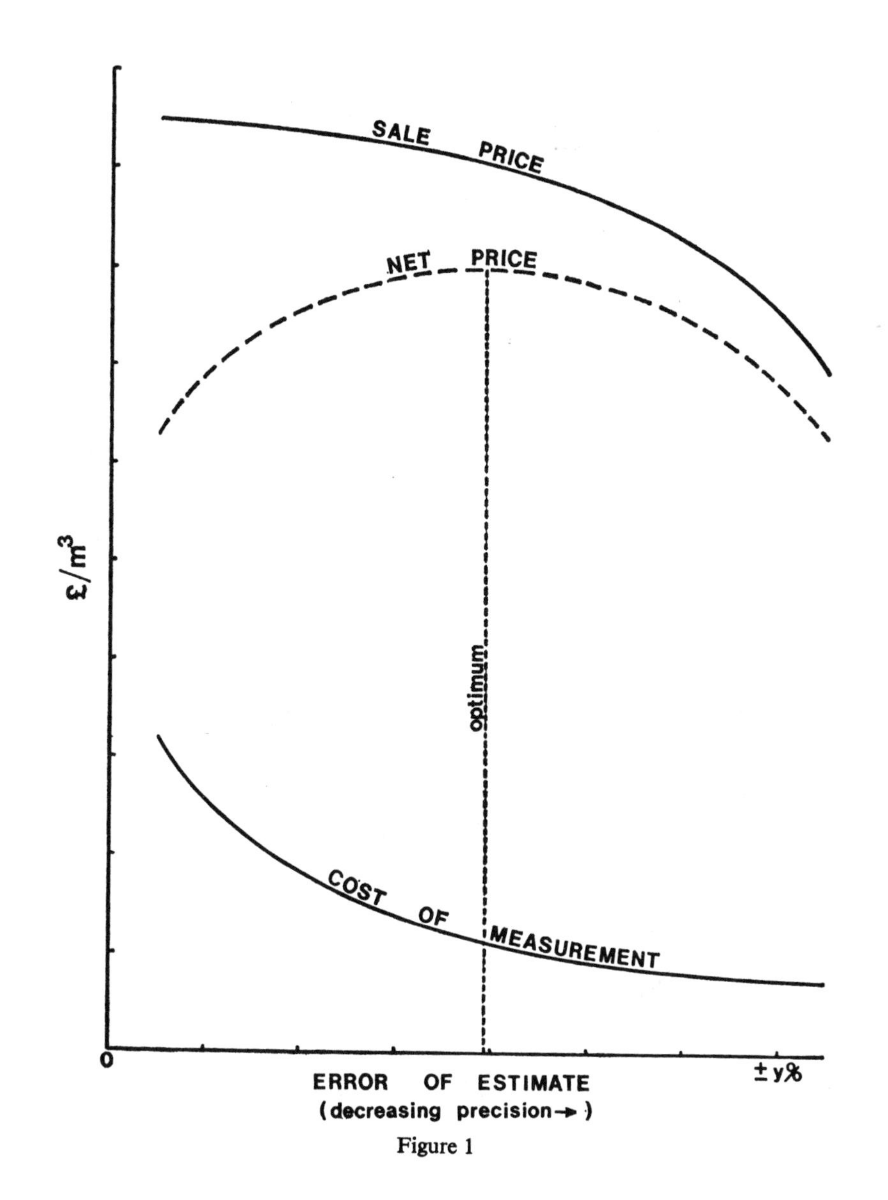
SALE PRICE
NET PRICE
optimum
COST OF MEASUREMENT
£/m³
0
± y%
ERROR OF ESTIMATE
(decreasing precision→)
Figure 1

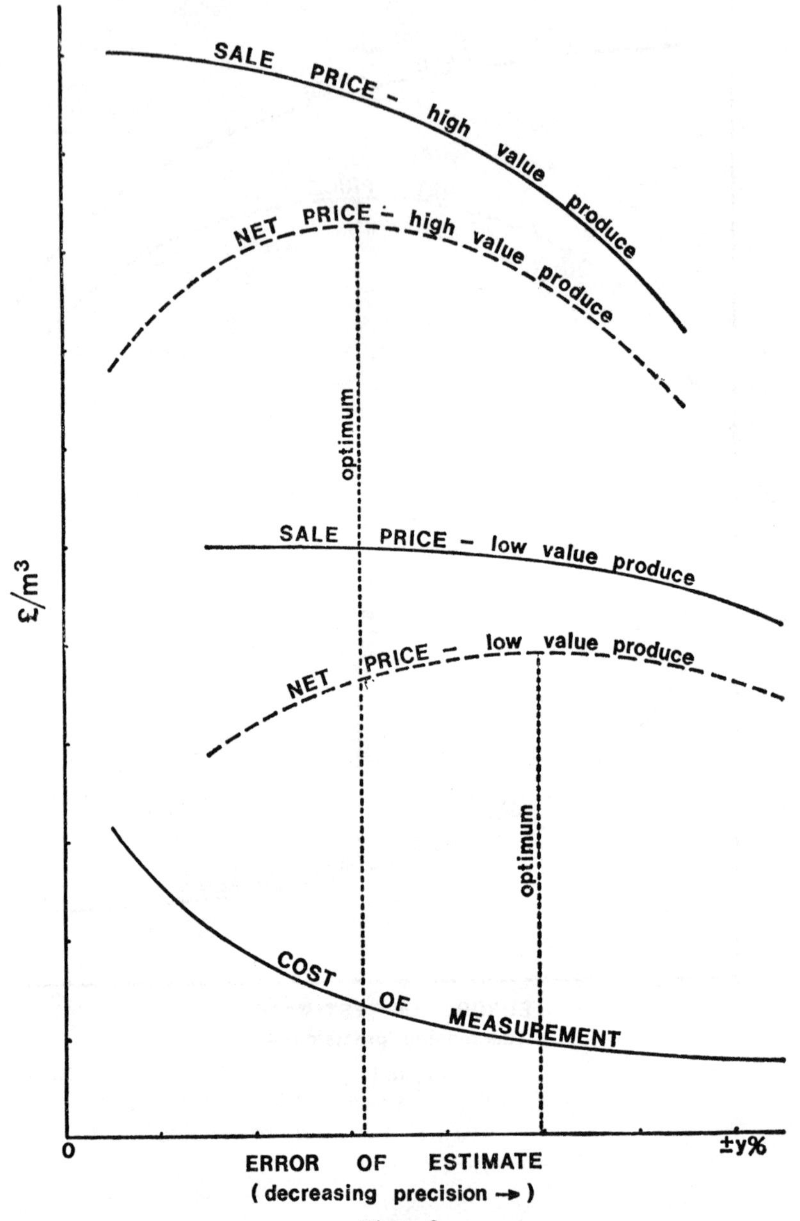
SALE PRICE - high value produce
NET PRICE - high value produce
optimum
SALE PRICE - low value produce
NET PRICE - low value produce
optimum
COST OF MEASUREMENT
£/m³
0
±y%
ERROR OF ESTIMATE
(decreasing precision →)

Figure 2

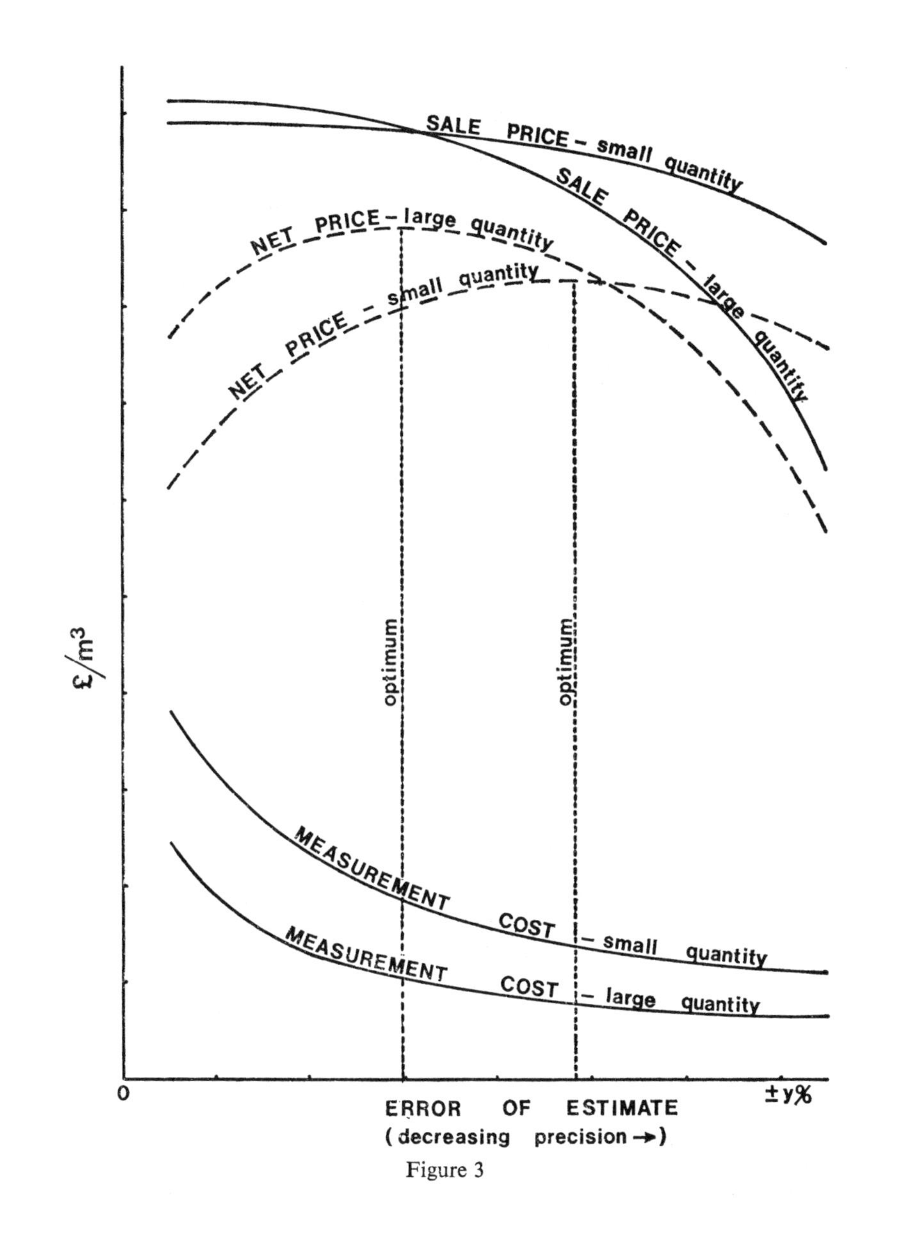
SALE PRICE – small quantity
SALE PRICE – large quantity
NET PRICE – large quantity
NET PRICE – small quantity
optimum
optimum
£/m3
MEASUREMENT COST – small quantity
MEASUREMENT COST – large quantity
0
±y%
ERROR OF ESTIMATE
(decreasing precision →)

Figure 3

the implications of under or over estimates are of relatively little importance compared with similar estimates for sale purposes. Consequently 'insurance premiums' are low and the resulting 'price'/precision curve tends to be relatively flat over a wide range of precision. The net result is that a modest level of precision is indicated as optimal.

The second important factor influencing the optimum level of precision is *quantity*. From the buyers point of view the risk of loss associated with a given level of precision has more serious financial or contractual implications for large quantities than for small, and so he will tend to pay higher 'insurance premiums' for higher levels of precision in situations where large quantities are involved. From the point of view of cost of measurement, sizeable quantities usually entail sampling. A given level of precision can be obtained from proportionately fewer samples from large populations than from small. Consequently the absolute cost per unit volume is less for larger quantities. In general, the rate of change will also be smaller over the range of precision levels important in practice.

The net effect, therefore, is that a higher level of precision for larger quantities is desirable as shown in Figure 3.

Another point to be considered in connection with quantity is that its effect on unit costs varies according to the method of measurement used. For example, a sizeable element of the cost associated with the measurement of stacked timber is the physical measurement of every stack. The proportion of the total cost, which varies according to the quantity, is therefore confined to the cost of establishing a solid/stacked conversion factor. Consequently, the difference between the unit costs of measuring large and small quantities is less marked than, for example, the respective costs of estimating volume from weight measurements. In the latter case the cost of weighing each load of timber is relatively small. A relatively more significant element of the unit cost would be the establishment of volume weight ratios. This could be a relatively expensive procedure for small quantities, whereas for large quantities the cost per unit volume would be small. If the cost of weighbridge facilities were to be considered, clearly the differences in unit costs of large and small quantities would be further accentuated.

Figure 4 demonstrates typical relative unit costs in relation to quantity, for different methods of measurement. (This is a purely notional representation of what might reasonably be expected to apply in one particular situation and is not based on factual information).

It is recognised that a detailed cost benefit analysis, however desirable, is not feasible in practice for each required task of measurement. The features mentioned above however, form the basis of the guidelines contained in this book for selecting an appropriate measurement procedure for a given purpose.

Choice of Method

The key to procedures (front inside cover) indicates an appropriate procedure for a given purpose. For some purposes a choice of method is presented.

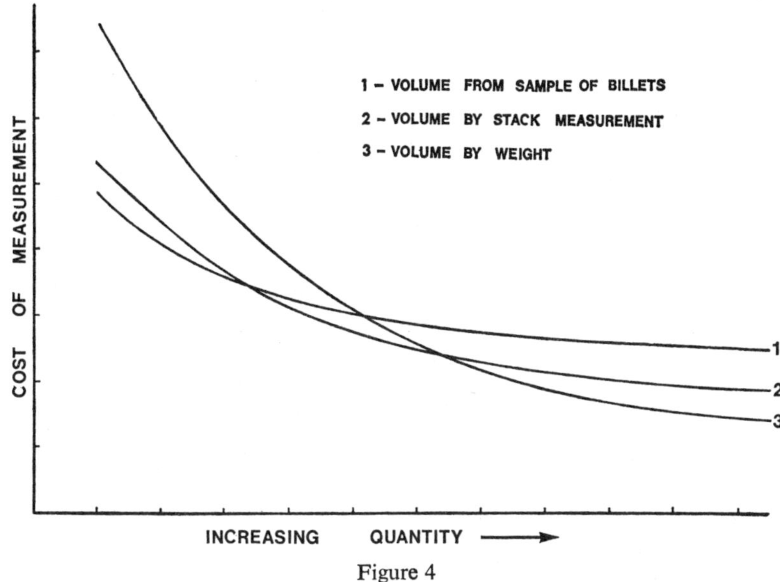

Figure 4

The choice in these cases usually depends on one or more of the following factors: a. quantity; b. the availability of suitable facilities, eg a weighbridge for weight measurement, and c. the acceptability of the method to all parties concerned. The particular situations where a choice is presented are considered below:

(i) **Felled or Standing?**

In selling timber the choice of whether the timber be measured standing or felled tends to depend on who is responsible for the felling and extraction. Where this is done by the buyer, the tendency is to measure standing, but if the grower is responsible, felled measure is more usual. In most cases this approach is usually justified, but there is no reason why it should always be so. If, for a required level of precision, the unit cost of measurement is very high, for example in these situations:

a. small lots of timber,

b. very diverse crops,

c. high value produce, eg veneer timber,

it may be better to provide a very rough and cheap estimate of standing volume (Procedure 9) in order to attract the interest of the prospective buyer, but to agree to sell on the basis of an appropriate felled measure.

(ii) **Standing Timber**

Apart from the situations outlined above the choice of method for measuring standing timber is clearly indicated in the key and requires no further explanations.

(iii) **Felled Timber**

A choice of methods is indicated for sawlogs and for timber destined for fragmentation (pulpwood, chipwood, woodwool):

a. *Sawlogs.* The mid-diameter and length method (Procedure 1) is the most accurate and is the standard method by which others are judged. It is most appropriate for small lots, for particularly valuable produce, and for long log lengths.

The top diameter (underbark) and length method (Procedure 2) is less accurate because a standard rate of taper has to be assumed. Average taper may be expected to vary from stand to stand, and within a given stand significant variation around the mean taper is usual. The method is more suitable for shorter, uniform log lengths already stacked, eg at roadside, where the cost of measurement is less than by the first method.

Weight measurement is very much cheaper than other methods for large quantities of material, and is the preferred method in these situations. As the labour content in weight measurement is low, increases in labour cost can be expected to lead to an increased use of weight measurement.

b. *Pulp, chipwood, woodwool etc.* Timber which is to be fragmented tends to be of small diameter, shorter length and often of less value than other products. These features imply cheaper measurement and the alternatives given are stack or weight measurement. Assuming in either case the objective is an estimate of the solid *volume* of the timber, weight measurement tends to be more efficient, in terms of precision achieved per unit cost, for large quantities, and has the further advantage of being the more objective method of the two. For more moderate quantities however, stack measure can produce greater precision per unit cost where billets are uniform, straight and properly stacked. Poor stacking, poor quality and very varied sizes lead to precision of a significantly lower level.

PART II MEASUREMENT CONVENTIONS

1. The measurement conventions listed below are those currently established as standard in British forestry. In certain measurement procedures, conventions other than standard may be required. These are considered under the appropriate paragraphs which follow. Conventions employed in research applications are not included here.

Diameter

2. Tree and log diameters will normally be measured overbark by girthing tape, rounding down to the nearest whole centimetre. Rounding down is achieved automatically with the classifying tapes of the type used by the Forestry Commission. (The zero point in these tapes is the extreme edge of the brass rectangle or the point of the hook, according to the fitment, as shown in Figure 5. In cases where the zero point is found to fall on the dividing line between two diameter classes, the higher diameter class is read).

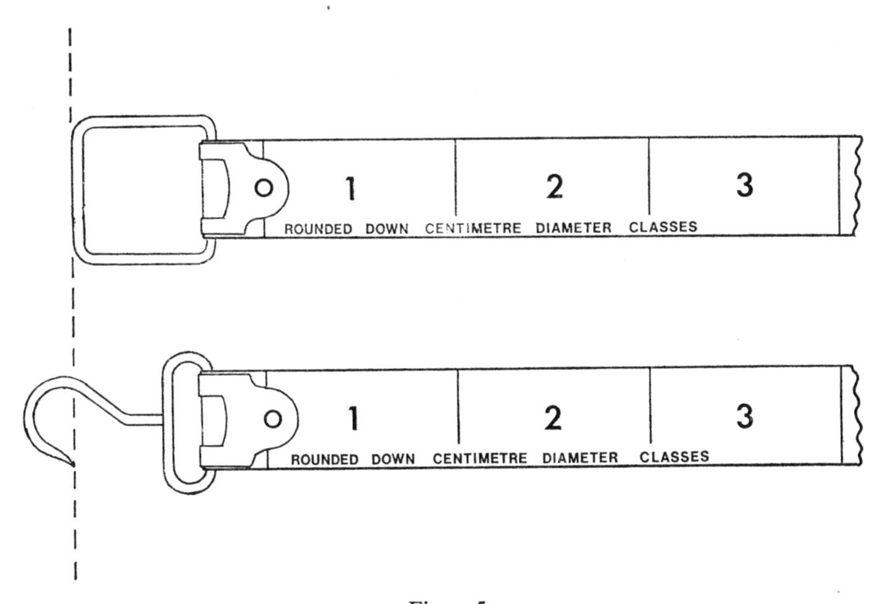

Figure 5

a. Diameter at Breast Height (dbh)

(i) Always ensure that trees are girthed at a point on the tree 1·3 m above ground level, which is the *breast height point.*

(ii) The diameter tape must be taut and at right-angles to the stem.

(iii) On *sloping ground* always measure the diameter at 1·3 m from ground level on the upper side of the tree.

(iv) On *leaning trees* (on level ground) always measure the diameter at 1·3 m from ground level on the under-side of the tree, parallel to the axis of the stem.

(v) Where trees are planted on *turfed or ploughed ground*, the diameter should be measured 1·3 m from the root collar or present ground level, whichever is the higher.

(vi) Where a *swelling* occurs at 1·3 m above ground level, measure the diameter below the swelling or deformity, at the point where the diameter is smallest.

(vii) Where the stem *forks* below 1·3 m treat each limb as a separate tree. Where a stem is forked at 1·3 m, treat the stem as one tree and measure the diameter below the fork at the point where it is smallest.

(viii) *Coppice* crops should be girthed at 1·3 m from ground level, not from stool level.

(ix) Trees of less than 7 cm dbh are considered to have no measurable volume.

b. Mid-sectional Diameter

(i) The diameter is measured at the mid point of the rounded down length section (see 3 (iii) and 3 (iv)).

(ii) If the mid-diameter falls on a whorl or swelling the diameter should be measured immediately above it (ie towards the small end).

(iii) If the mid-diameter of a timber length falls below the breast height point of the standing tree, the dbh should be regarded as the mid-diameter.

c. Top Diameter

(i) The timber point is the point furthest from the butt at which the overbark diameter is not less than 7 cm. (Using a rounded down centimetre class tape as in Fig 5, the 7 cm point is the dividing line between the 6 and 7 cm classes.)

(ii) Where top diameter (the diameter at the small end) is measured on pitwood or smallwood, a rule should be used in preference to a girthing tape. The diameter is rounded down to the nearest whole centimetre.

(iii) Where top diameter (underbark) is required for sawlog measurement (by Procedure 2) the diameter should be measured across the smallest diameter.

Length

3. (i) Length measurement will not normally include material beyond the timber point (7 cm diameter), or beyond the point at which no main stem is distinguishable.

   (ii) The minimum timber length to 7 cm top diameter which is considered to have measurable volume is 1·3 m.

   (iii) Lengths, measured from the butt-end, should be rounded down to the nearest 0·1 m for lengths up to 10 m and to the nearest whole metre for lengths greater than 10 m.

   (iv) Where the rounded down length exceeds 20 m it should be measured in two sections for volume assessment. Measured from the butt end, the butt section will be the rounded down length divided by two but rounded down to the nearest whole metre. The top section will be the remaining length.

   Example:

   Timber length 25 m (rounded down)

   Butt section $\frac{25}{2}$ = 12 m (rounded down)

   Top section 25 — 12 = 13 m

   (v) Special length conventions apply to pitwood (see Procedure 4, page 25).

   (vi) On curved stems, lengths will be measured along the curvature and not in a direct line from end to end.

Volume

4. (i) The conventional top diameter limit for volume is 7 cm overbark, or the point at which no main stem is distinguishable, whichever comes first.

   (ii) The smallest timber length to 7 cm top diameter considered to have measurable volume is 1·3 m.

   (iii) The minimum dbh of a tree considered to have measurable volume is 7 cm.

   (iv) Where trees are forked at or above breast height, the butt will be measured as one log. The volume of each stem of the fork will also be measured separately and may be added to that of the butt to give the volume of the tree.

   (v) Where trees are forked below breast height each limb is treated as a separate tree and will be girthed as such. The volume of the tree is therefore the volume of the appropriate limb. The volume of the butt piece will be ignored, its length being excluded in determining the volume of the tree.

PROCEDURE 1

THE ASSESSMENT OF VOLUME FROM LENGTH AND MID-DIAMETER

GENERAL

1. This is the traditional method of assessing the volume of timber lengths, sawlogs, selected poles, billets etc.

2. The volume is derived from the product of the length of the log or section and its mean cross-sectional area. The latter is assumed to be approximately equal to the cross-sectional area at the mid point of the section. (There are alternative ways of finding an estimate of mean cross-sectional area, but this principle is the only one considered here.) In practice it is the *diameter* at the mid point which is actually measured.

3. The volume is derived from the following formula which is known as Huber's formula:

$$V = \frac{\pi \, d_m{}^2}{40\,000} \times L$$

where V = volume in cubic metres
L = length in metres
d_m = mid diameter in centimetres
π = 3·1415927

PRACTICE

4. The length of the section is measured observing the rounding conventions specified on page 19.

5. The diameter (overbark) at the mid point of the rounded down length is measured according to the normal conventions (page 18).

6. Table 64 (pages 202–241) is used to estimate the volume from these measurements. The lengths are tabulated from 1·0 to 10 m. For lengths greater than 10 m the decimal place in the lengths and volumes is moved one place to the right.

7. **Examples**

(i) *Actual length:* = 7·36 m
Rounded down length = 7·3 m
Rounded down diameter at
$\left(\frac{7 \cdot 3}{2}\right)$ m = 3·65 m from butt end = 18 cm
Volume from Table 64 (page 205) = 0·186 m^3

(ii)	*Actual length:*	= 12·85
	Rounded down length	= 12 m
	Rounded down diameter at 6 m from butt end	= 25 cm
	Volume from Table 64 (page 206) (enter 1·2 m length, move decimal point)	= 0·59 m^3
(iii)	*Actual length:*	= 25·7 m
	Rounded down length	= 25 m
	1st (butt) section length	= $\frac{25}{2}$
	,, ,, ,, ,, (rounded down)	= 12 m
	2nd section length (25 — 12)	= 13 m
	1st section mid diameter (at 6 m from butt)	= 29 cm
	1st section volume from Table 64 (page 206) (enter 1·2 m, move decimal point)	= 0·79 m^3
	2nd section mid diameter (at 6·5 m from large end of section or 18·5 m from extreme butt end)	= 16 cm
	2nd section volume from Table 64 (page 204) (enter 1·3 m, move decimal point)	= 0·26 m^3
	Total volume of timber length	= 0·79 + 0·26 m^3
		= 1·05 m^3

PROCEDURE 2

THE ASSESSMENT OF UNDERBARK VOLUME OF SAWLOGS FROM LENGTH AND TOP DIAMETER

General

1. The use of this method is confined to softwood sawlogs. It is a method which is less time consuming and consequently cheaper than Procedure 1 and is best suited to batches of uniform length logs. The description of logs in terms of top diameter and length provides a more useful basis for size classification and can often be more meaningful to the potential buyer.

2. Because of the need to assume a standard rate of taper, volume estimates derived by this method are subject to greater errors than by the mid-diameter and length method.

3. A standard taper of 1: 120, ie 1 cm diameter in 1·2 m length has been used in constructing the tables (Table 65, pages 242–249). This rate, which refers to the taper between the top and mid point of a log, is considered to be reasonably appropriate for softwood sawlogs in Britain. The taper of individual logs may be expected to differ significantly from the standard rate, and for this reason the tables will tend to be less reliable for small numbers of logs or when butt or top logs predominate.

4. The formula used in calculating the tables is:

$$V = L \times \left(\frac{\pi}{40\,000} \times \left(d_t + \frac{(L \times 0{\cdot}5)}{1{\cdot}2} \right)^2 \right)$$

where V = volume in cubic metres
L = length in metres
d_t = top diameter in centimetres
π = 3·1415927

5. Lengths will normally be rounded down to the nearest 0·1 m. The international sawn softwood standard length specifications range from 1·8 m to 6·3 m in steps of 0·3 m (see page 186). In order to provide for those cases where logs are cross-cut to conform to these specifications, the length intervals in the tables have been grouped in threes so that the standard 0·3 m multiples appear as the first entry in each group. In such cases a small extra allowance of 0·05 m will be made on the sawlog length to permit subsequent cross-cutting and should be agreed with the buyer beforehand.

6. The top diameter entries in the tables are tabulated in 2 cm intervals from 10 cm to 72 cm. The diameter values at the head of each column refer to the lower limit of each diameter class, eg the 14–16 class is headed 14.

7. The specified volumes are based on the mean diameter of each class. For example the 14–16 cm class is headed 14, but volumes are calculated using 15 cm top diameter. This is based on the assumption that the top diameters of individual logs will be distributed evenly over the range of each 2 cm class. It follows therefore that if logs are cut to specified top diameters the volumes in the tables will be more appropriate if the specified diameters accord with the *mean* top diameter of the 2 cm class.

8. It is intended that the tables be used with underbark top diameter to give underbark volumes, but estimates of overbark volume can be obtained from the tables by using overbark rather than underbark top diameter.

9. It is advisable to confine the use of this method to log lengths under 8·4 m.

PRACTICE

10. Measure the length, following the convention of rounding down to the nearest 0·1 m.

11. The top diameter underbark should be measured across the smallest diameter. (Plastic rules incorporating an abbreviated version of the tables are available and are graduated in terms of the 2 cm classes).

12. Table 65 is entered by the appropriate top diameter class and length in order to find the volume.

Example:

Actual length = 6·67 m

Rounded down length = 6·6 m

Actual u.b. diameter 23·5 cm = diameter class 22 cm.

Volume (from Table 65, page 243) = 0·34 m^3

PROCEDURE 3

THE ASSESSMENT OF SMALLWOOD VOLUMES FROM TOP DIAMETER AND LENGTH

General

1. This method is applicable for small lots of small diameter material, eg stakes, garden poles, etc where other methods, eg weight, are not practicable.

2. A standard taper of 1: 84, ie one centimetre diameter in 84 cm length, has been assumed in constructing the tables on pages 250-253 (Table 66). This rate of taper is also used in the pitwood volume tables (Procedure 4) and is regarded as suitable for small material which is taken from the uppermost part of trees where the taper rate is generally above average. The taper is that between the top and mid-point of the billet.

3. Top diameters are given in centimetre classes and lengths in intervals of 0·1 m. The formula used in calculating the tables is:

$$V = L \times \left(\frac{\pi}{40\,000} \times \left(d_t + \frac{(L \times 0{\cdot}5)}{0{\cdot}84} \right)^2 \right)$$

where V = volume in cubic metres

L = length in metres

d_t = top diameter in centimetres

π = 3·1415927

4. Volumes shown are for 100 pieces of the specified dimensions.

5. For top diameters of less than 7 cm the specified volumes *include* the material beyond the conventional top diameter limit for measurable volume of 7 cm overbark.

6. Where top diameters are measured overbark the volumes indicated will be overbark. Likewise underbark volumes are implied from the use of underbark measurements of top diameter.

Practice

7. Top diameters should be measured with a rule and rounded down to the nearest whole centimetre. One measurement taken in a random direction across the diameter is sufficient.

8. Lengths should be rounded down to the nearest 0·1 m.

9. Volumes are obtained from Table 66 (pages 250–253).

Example:

Actual top diameter — 7·6 cm, rounded down top diameter —7 cm.

Actual length — 2·67 m, rounded down length 2·6 m.

Volume — 1·49 m^3 per 100 pieces (page 250).

or 0·0149 m^3 per piece.

PROCEDURE 4

THE MEASUREMENT OF PITWOOD

General

1. The principles of measurement of pitwood are similar to those described in Procedure 3. However, the size specifications of pitwood are unique, requiring specially prepared tables.

2. Two tables are provided for pitwood measurement (pages 254-259). The first (Table 67) provides volumes for given top diameters and lengths, and assumes a taper between the top and mid-point of the billet of 1: 84, ie 1 cm diameter in 84 cm length. Volumes shown are for 100 pieces of the specified dimension.

3. The second (Table 68) provides volumes per 100 lineal metres of a given size specification and is used where orders for pitwood are specified in terms of lineal metres.

4. The size specifications are the minimum dimensions of top diameter and length. Pitwood is normally specified in terms of *underbark* top diameter. Measurements of underbark top diameter will give underbark volumes.

5. The sizes covered by the tables are confined to those required by the National Coal Board.

Practice

6. In practice, pitwood is cut to given specifications, and a limited range of sizes will apply in any one situation. Particularly for smaller sized material, the cutter will find it most convenient to use a measuring stick marked at the specified lengths.

7. The billets of each specified size category will be separately piled and the only assessment then required is to count the numbers of each size, and apply the appropriate table.

8. If the pitwood tables presented here are used to calculate unit prices, minor differences may be expected from those calculated by the National Coal Board, which uses tables with values expressed to a greater number of decimal places.

9. Examples of the use of pitwood tables are shown below.

Example (1):

263 props of 7 cm top diameter by 1·05 m length.

$$\text{Volume} = \frac{263}{100} \times 0{\cdot}479 \text{ m}^3 = 1{\cdot}260 \text{ m}^3$$

(from Table 67, page 254).

Example (2):

560 linear metres of 8 cm top diameter by 1·025 m length.

$$\text{Volume} = \frac{560}{100} \times 0{\cdot}582 \text{ m}^3 = 3{\cdot}259 \text{ m}^3$$

(from Table 68, page 257).

PROCEDURE 5

MEASUREMENT OF STACKED TIMBER

GENERAL

1. This method is applicable to uniform length timber, mostly material intended for fragmentation, eg for pulp, woodwool, chipboard, and is an alternative to measurement by weight. (The relative merits of weight and stacked measurement are considered in Part I, pages 14 and 16).

2. In some situations the stacked volume, derived from the average height, width and length of a stack, may be used directly in sales. It is more usual, however, to convert the stacked volume to solid volume by applying an appropriate conversion factor (solid/stacked volume ratio) and to value the material on the basis of a price per unit solid volume.

3. The establishment of solid/stacked volume conversion factors is considered separately from the measurement aspects of stacked timber.

Measurement of Stacks

THEORY

4. The ease and accuracy of measuring stacks depend largely on the regularity of the external surfaces of the stack. The more irregular these are, the more time consuming or alternatively the less precise is the measurement. Two other aspects are to be considered here, namely, the size of the stack and the arrangement of stacks (on vehicles).

a. Shape

Strictly rectangular stacks present least problems and require the minimum number of measurements of height, width and length. Stacks which are not strictly rectangular, but which have nonetheless regular straight sides, faces and tops require a few more measurements to establish reliable average dimensions. Any degree of curvature requires more attention. As an example, the most commonly occurring situation, a convex top, is illustrated below in Figure 6.

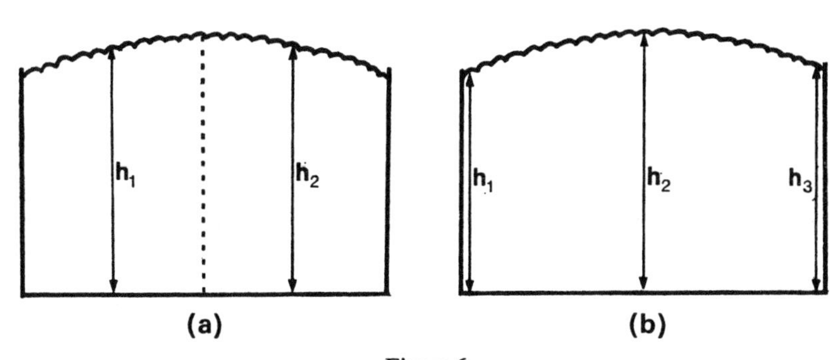

Figure 6

"In (*a*) heights are taken at the mid point of sections of equal width. and averaged. The shorter the interval the more accurate the mean height. In (*b*) heights are taken at the extremities (but given half weighting) and at equal intervals along the width of the stack. The mean height is calculated thus:-

$$h = \frac{\frac{1}{2}(h_1 + h_3) + h_2}{2}$$

This method provides a slight underestimate of the mean height.

b. Size of Stack

Timber piled between posts or bolsters contains less solid volume than an equal face area within a stack of greater overall dimensions. This follows from the fact that gaps are created at the perimeters of the stack which would be occupied by portions of billets in an infinitely large stack. This effect can be clarified by visualising one stack piled on top of another. Because of the intermeshing of the piles the overall dimensions of the combined pile will be less than the sum of the two individually measured piles. This effect is not very important with large stacks but of course increases in importance with decreasing stack size. The effect can be reduced, but not eliminated, by measuring to a point on the common tangents of adjacent billets, rather than to the extreme edge of the most prominent billet. (See Fig 7.)

c. Arrangement of Stacks (on vehicles)

Generally, the most satisfactory arrangement for the loading of vehicles, from the measurement point of view, is where billets rest at right angles to the platform of the vehicles, exposing both faces. Where stacks are arranged parallel to the lorry platform, faces of individual stacks may be obscured and measurement made more difficult.

Given the above points it must be recognised that the arrangement of stacks may be dictated by size specification or other factors which may transcend measurement considerations.

Practice

5. Owing to the possible variation in the uniformity, size and shape of stacks there can be no single measurement procedure applicable in every situation. The principles of measurement to be adopted are outlined in the following paragraphs.

6. The *length* of the stack should be taken as the specified length of the material. It will be necessary to check lengths on a sample of billets to ensure that these accord with the specifications. In the absence of specified lengths the average length should be taken as the mean of the sample. Length should not be measured as an overall dimension of the stack.

7. The *width* of the stack should be measured parallel to the base of the stack.

8. The *height* should be measured at right angles to the base of the stack.

9. In measuring height and width, the extremities of each measurement line should be taken at the point at which the line crosses the common tangent of adjacent billets as shown in Fig 7.

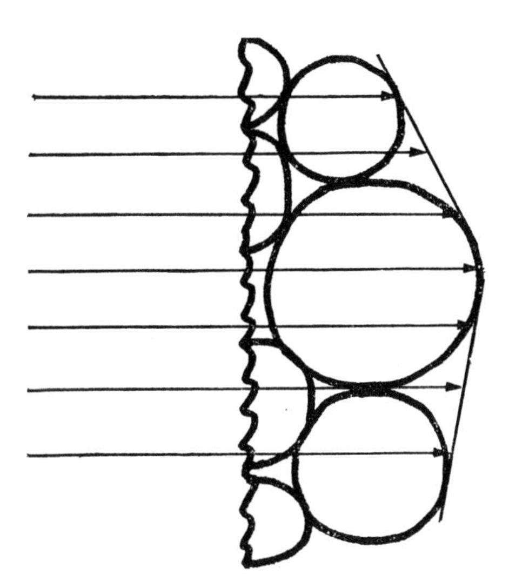

Figure 7

10. The number of measurements of height and width depend on the individual stack's size and shape. In assessing mean height the practical problem of dividing very wide stacks (of variable width) into equal parts can be time consuming and can result in awkward sub-multiples. In these circumstances it is prudent to select a fixed width interval appropriate to the width and irregularity of the stack, to take the first measurement at half of this interval from one end of the stack, and to take further height measurements at the selected intervals thereafter. This will normally mean that the final height measurement may not correctly represent the mean height of the last width section but this error is usually acceptable in the interests of expediency.

11. The various shapes and their measurement are illustrated in Fig 8 in which the specified length is denoted as L.

12. All dimensions should be measured to the nearest centimetre and expressed in metres, to two decimal places.

13. The volume of the stack is calculated as mean length multiplied by mean height, multiplied by mean width, and expressed in cubic metres to two decimal places.

14. As required, an appropriate solid/stacked conversion factor can be applied to the stacked volume to obtain the solid volume content.

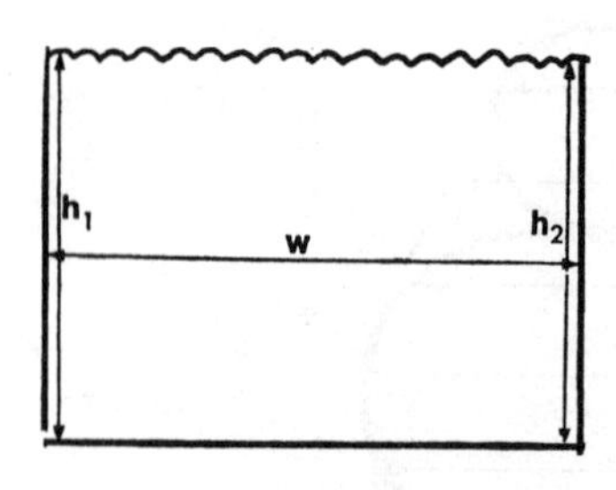

$$\text{VOLUME} = \frac{(h_1 + h_2)}{2} \times w \times L$$

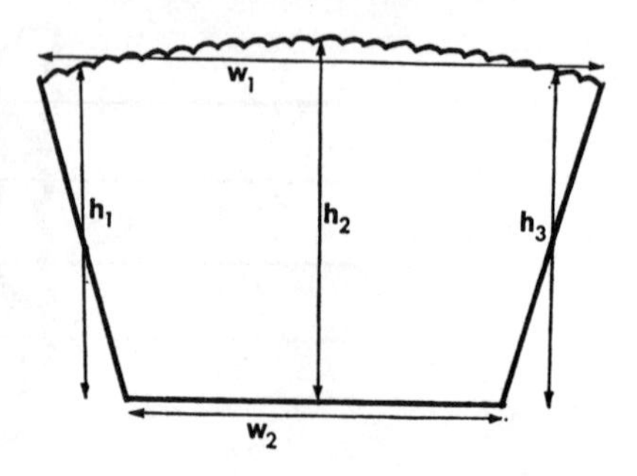

$$\text{VOLUME} = \frac{(h_1 + h_3)/2 + h_2}{2} \times \frac{w_1 + w_2}{2} \times L$$

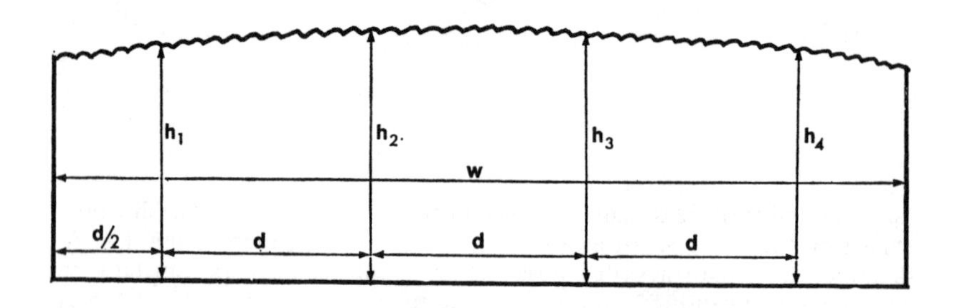

$$\text{VOLUME} = \frac{h_1 + h_2 + h_3 + h_4}{4} \times w \times L$$

Figure 8

Solid Volume/Stacked Volume Conversion Factors

THEORY

15. The solid/stacked volume conversion factor is the volume of solid timber divided by the volume of solid timber plus airspaces contained in a unit of volume within a stack of timber.

16. Solid/stacked conversion factors in practice vary considerably depending on a number of circumstances which are considered below.

a. Construction of stack

Two methods of stacking cylinders, uniform in length and diameter, are depicted in Figure 9.

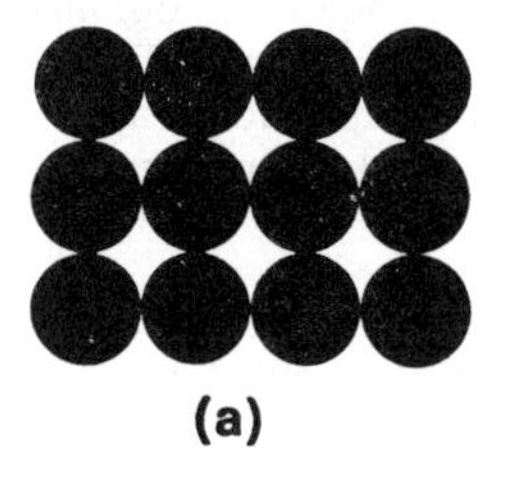

(a)

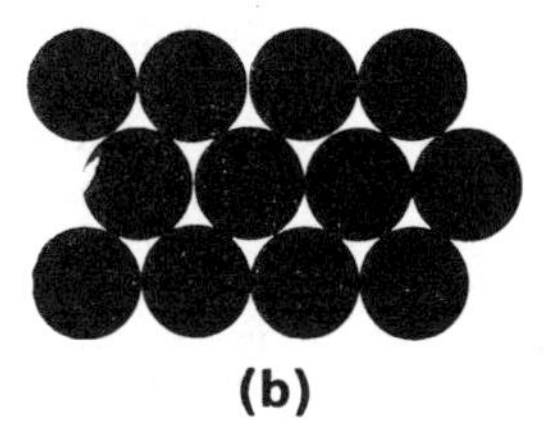

(b)

Figure 9

With square stacking (a) the solid/stacked conversion factor is 0·78 whilst with octagonal stacking (b) the factor is 0·91. Neither of these strictly uniform methods of stacking are feasible with roundwood billets, which are tapered and inevitably varied in diameter. Although conversion factors of 0·91 are not attainable in practice, it is frequently possible to produce stacks where the solid volume is over 80% of the stacked volume (conversion factors greater than 0·80) with relatively short, straight and generally high quality material (see Fig. 10). More usually, however, appropriate conversion factors are in the region of 0·70-0·75.

Whilst in theory it would be possible to raise the value of the conversion factor by skilful building, in practice the scope for this is limited and it is more realistic to assume that billets are placed on the stack at random, particularly where machine loading is concerned.

b. Billet Straightness

Curved billets, randomly stacked, occupy a greater volume of a stack than do straight billets of equal volume and consequently effect a reduction on the conversion factor. Indeed this is probably the most influential factor. Curvature can be expressed in terms of the displacement of the central axis at the mid point of the billet from the line joining the centre points of the ends of the billet, as a percentage of the billet length. The effect is roughly to reduce the conversion factor of stacks of straight billets by 2% for every 5% of average curvature.

c. Stem Irregularities—such as prominent nodes also have the effect of lowering the conversion factor.

d. Diameter

The range in diameter of billets in a stack has relatively little impact on the conversion factor. Likewise the value of the mean diameter in the stack is inconsequential.

e. Taper

Given varied diameters, varied tapers and random stacking, the mean rate of taper has a modest effect on the conversion factor. If taper is expressed as one centimetre reduction in diameter in 'x' centimetres length, then the conversion factor can be expected to be diminished by about 0·6% for an average reduction of 'x' of 10 cms. Thus stacked timber with an average taper of 1 : 90 will usually produce a conversion factor some 0·6% less than stacked timber with an average taper of 1 : 100, other factors being constant.

f. Bark

This factor is relatively unimportant but can in some species, by its removal, accentuate stem irregularities and thereby reduce the conversion factor. With soft barked species mutual compression can increase the factor very marginally but this can usually be discounted.

g. Settling in Transit

Where timber is transported stacked, stack movement induces a degree of settling which frequently causes a reduction of 3–8% in the height of the stack, and hence of stack volume. Consequently conversion factors will be lower prior to transportation.

PRACTICE

17. A conversion factor should be established for each type of material adhering to a set of specifications dictated by the consumer. In most cases this means one conversion factor per consumer but where two or more categories are recognised and differentiated by the consumer, eg conifer and hardwood, the appropriate conversion factors should be calculated for each. Likewise any marked regional or quality differences will require separate conversion factors.

18. It may be necessary to set a provisional conversion factor prior to the establishment, through sampling, of an appropriate specific factor. For average quality coniferous material 0·70 will be a reasonable first approximation. Hardwoods may be expected to be in the range 0·55–0·65.

19. There are basically two methods of determining the solid/stacked conversion factor for a single stack.

Method 1

20. The first is the traditional method of measuring the stacked volume, dismantling the stack, and measuring the solid volume of the individual billets. The conversion factor is calculated simply as the total volume of the individual billets divided by the original volume of the stack.

21. The procedure used in assessing the volume of the stack is outlined in paras 5–14 (pages 28-29).

22. The volume of each billet is assessed from the *specified* length and the diameter at a point half the specified length, measured from the large end of the billet. Diameters will be measured by tape rounding down to the nearest whole centimetre. Specified lengths will normally be expressed in metres including the first decimal place. Table 64 (or FC Booklet 26) should be used to determine the volume from the length and diameter measurements.

23. In many cases the solid volume of the stack may be estimated from measurements of the solid volume of a sample of billets, the sample size depending on the number of billets in the stack. The volume of the stack is calculated as the volume of the sample multiplied by:

$$\frac{\text{Total number of billets}}{\text{Number of billets in sample}}\cdot$$

24. The number of stacks sampled in order to estimate the solid/stacked conversion factor depends on the level of precision desired. This will usually be a matter for agreement between buyer and seller, but as a general guide the estimate of the mean solid/stacked conversion factor should have confidence limits at the 95% probability level at least within ±10% of the estimate in the case of small quantities (a few hundred cubic metres or less). For large quantities, eg annual supplies to a processing plant, the confidence limits might be expected to be in the region of ±1–3%.

Guidance on the method of calculating an appropriate sampling intensity is given in Part V (1), page 131. This involves estimating the *coefficient of variation*. Although it is best to do this by undertaking a preliminary sample, values for the coefficient of variation can be expected to be in the range 5–10% depending on the size of sample and the quality of the material. For particularly poor quality material and/or poor stacking the value of the coefficient of variation may be higher.

Method 2

25. This method entails measurements of the face of a stack only, is much less labour intensive, consequently cheaper, and often more convenient.

26. The method involves calculating the area on the face of a stack occupied by the ends of billets per unit of total area on the face of the stack.

27. This can be assessed by placing a rectangular grid or dot grid against the stack face. The number of intersections or dots falling on billet ends counted relative to the number of intersections or dots falling on both billet and airspaces provides a very easily obtained estimate of the conversion factors. This is demonstrated in Fig 10. The number of intersections falling on billet ends is approximately 80, which relative to a total number of intersections of 100 suggests a conversion factor of $\frac{80}{100} = 0{\cdot}80$.

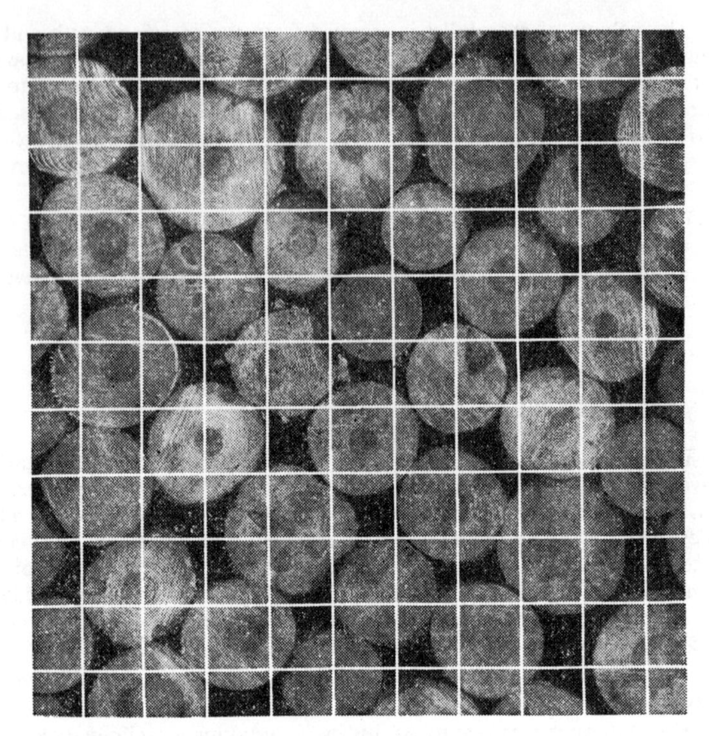

Figure 10

28. Although it is possible to construct a full scale grid of one form or another to use in this fashion, it is more usual to photograph the stack face and assess the conversion factor from the photographic print overlain by a small grid. (A dot grid of the type commonly used for area measurement on maps is suitable and readily available).

29. The most obvious first requirement is that the face of the stack is visible, and this imposes restrictions on the method of loading vehicles.

30. For convenience, the spacing between dots on the grid should be about $\times \frac{1}{2}$ to $\times$ 1 the average 'diameter' of the billets.

31. In the case of the photographic method this relationship can be influenced by:

(i) the actual mean diameter of the billets,

(ii) the degree of enlargement of the photograph,

(iii) the distance of the camera from the stack,

(iv) the focal length of the camera lens and

(v) the scale of the grid.

The actual diameter of the billets is of course not a controllable factor. The possibility of enlarging photographs to various degrees in order to meet the conditions of para 30 is not a practical proposition. Given a camera of fixed focal length the question of distance from the stack is of some importance. With shorter distances a problem of parallax arises. The images at the perimeters of the photograph are recorded, not at the desired plane perpendicular to the face of the stack, but at a significant deviation from the perpendicular. No problem exists where all the ends of the billets are strictly in the same plane (flush) but this seldom occurs in practice. The result is that the correct ratio of solid timber and airspace is not presented to the camera. The solutions to this problem are either:

a. to use a camera with a lens of greater focal length, or

b. to assess the conversion factor by sampling the central portion of the photograph only.

The most suitable combination of the above factors is easily determined from trials.

32. The photographic method has a further advantage in that permanent records of the stacks are provided. A camera of the 'Polaroid' type can be used to provide an immediate assessment of the conversion factor.

33. The question of sampling intensity is discussed in para 24 and the recommendations given apply equally to this method, except that in estimating the appropriate coefficient of variation, a preliminary sample *must* be taken.

PROCEDURE 6

MEASUREMENT BY WEIGHT

GENERAL

1. In the Forestry Commission weight measurements may be used:

   a. directly as a means of quantifying produce for sale, ie payment is made in terms of a price per tonne

   b. indirectly to estimate the volume of the produce. In this case payment is made in terms of a price per cubic metre.

2. The first alternative, ie the use of **weight as a direct measure of quantity** is largely confined to regular bulk supplies of small roundwood destined for processing, eg pulp, chipboard, fibreboard, etc and occasionally small sawlogs.

3. The attraction of weight measurement in this situation is that it is cheap, is not labour intensive, and is objective. The major drawback is that the notorious variability in the density of felled timber can result in weight measurement being a less reliable indicator of the quantity of end-product available than the more conventional measure of timber quantity, namely volume.

4. One source of variation is particularly important in this connection. It is the drying-out effect of the period occurring between felling and weighing the timber. Since the effect is obviously one-way, that is, the timber invariably becomes less dense with time, and could consequently be used to the advantage of the buyer, it is essential that the period of delay between felling and weighing is made subject to reasonable controls.

5. Provided these controls are exercised, the use of weight as a direct measure of quantity for the kind of produce described above, is satisfactory.

6. The second alternative, ie the use of **weight measurement to estimate volume**, is generally more appropriate for more valuable produce, eg sawlogs, or roundwood contracts which are of limited duration in any one area, or where variation in density of timber is known to be a notably troublesome factor.

7. Suitable volume/weight conversion factors are required in order to estimate the volume of timber measured by weight. Variation in green (fresh felled) density, which of course affects volume/weight ratios, exists not only between species but between and within individual trees, stands, regions, etc. There are many factors which influence the green density of timber, some of which are local in origin and are not completely understood.

8. At present it is not considered practical to derive suitable volume/weight ratios merely by assessing the various contributing factors. The procedure recommended here is the more reliable but more costly alternative of establishing the volume/weight ratios applying in a given situation, empirically

from samples. Here too, however, some of the important factors contributing to variation have usually to be considered.

9. The following paragraphs describe the variation in green density and the factors affecting it.

Variation in Green Density

10. *Green density* (ie fresh felled density) is the sum of two components, namely, basic density and moisture content. Basic density (nominal specific gravity) is the weight of oven dried wood expressed relative to its green volume. Moisture content is the weight of the green timber less the oven dry weight, expressed as a percentage of the oven dry weight.

Thus if:

V = green volume (cc)

W = green weight (gm)

w = oven-dry weight (gm)

then:

$$\text{basic density (d)} = \frac{w}{V} \text{ (gm/cc)}$$

$$\text{moisture content (mc)} = \frac{W - w}{w} \times 100(\%)$$

$$\text{green density (D)} = \frac{W}{V} \textit{ or } d\left(\frac{mc + 100}{100}\right) \text{ (gm/cc)}$$

So that if the basic density sample of timber is 0·34 gm/cc and the moisture content is 130%, the green density is

$$D = 0{\cdot}34 \left(\frac{130 + 100}{100}\right) = 0{\cdot}78 \text{ gm/cc}$$

or, expressed as a volume/weight ratio:

$$\frac{1}{0{\cdot}78} \text{ cc/gm} = 1{\cdot}28 \text{ cc/gm or } 1{\cdot}28 \text{ m}^3\text{/tonne.}$$

Variation Between Regions

11. Undoubtedly differences in average green density, in any given species, exist between regions. These are not yet sufficiently well documented for significantly different regions to be clearly identified. It must be stressed that the average density values given in the tables below may not be appropriate in particular regions.

Variation Between Species

12. The following tables provide typical values of basic density, moisture content and green density for most commercial species in Britain. In the absence of any single comprehensive survey or authoritative source of information in this area, these tables have been compiled from many different sources. Consequently, the values given should be regarded only as reasonable estimates and not definitive. The tables give yearly averages and refer to the properties of timber immediately after felling. For the purpose of deriving provisional volume weight ratios (para 21) it may be assumed that the values relate to a mean diameter of 20 cm. The tables may be applied to both barked and unbarked timber (see para 17).

Table 1

Basic Density

Species	Basic Density	Species	Basic Density	Species	Basic Density
SP	0·41	JL/HL	0·41	Oak	0·56
CP	0·40	DF	0·43	Beech	0·55
LP	0·39	WH	0·36	Ash	0·53
SS	0·35	RC/LC	0·32	Syc	0·49
NS	0·34	GF	0·30	Birch	0·53
EL	0·45	NF	0·31	Elm	0·43
				Poplar	0·36

Table 2

Moisture Content

Species	M/C(%)	Species	M/C(%)	Species	M/C(%)
SP	149	JL/HL	103	Oak	89
CP	150	DF	103	Beech	88
LP	145	WH	160	Ash	48
SS	164	RC/LC	180	Syc	69
NS	183	GF	185	Birch	76
EL	100	NF	200	Elm	140
				Poplar	150

Table 3

Green Density

Species	Density (gm/cc)	Vol/Wt Ratio (m^3/tonne)	Species	Density (gm/cc)	Vol/Wt Ratio (m^3/tonne)
SP	1·02	0·98	RC/LC	0·89	1·12
CP	1·00	1·00	GF	0·85	1·17
LP	0·95	1·05	NF	0·93	1·07
SS	0·92	1·08	Oak	1·06	0·94
NS	0·96	1·04	Beech	1·03	0·97
EL	0·90	1·11	Ash	0·78	1·28
JL/HL	0·83	1·20	Syc	0·83	1·20
DF	0·87	1·15	Birch	0·93	1·07
WH	0·93	1·07	Elm	1·03	0·97
			Poplar	0·90	1·11

Variation Between and Within Trees

13. In any stand significant variation occurs in the average green density between individual trees. Within individual trees the pattern of variation is rather complex. In general green density tends to increase from the pith to the cambium. The average density in cross-section decreases slightly from the butt to about 20% of the height, and thereafter increases towards the top.

Diameter

14. As a result of the pattern of variation within a tree, timber of smaller diameter tends to have greater green density. The effect of mean (mid) diameter is more marked in spruces than in pines. For an increase in mean diameter of 10 cm the volume/weight ratio can be expected to increase by about 0·11 m^3/tonne in spruces and by about 0·02 m^3/tonne in pines.

Season

15. Higher moisture contents in winter induce slightly greater green densities in this season compared with summer. Season is much more important however in terms of rate of drying (para 16).

Delay Between Felling and Weighing

16. It is convenient to recognise two periods in the year in which reasonable assumptions may be made on the average rate of drying. These periods are spring/summer (April–September) and autumn/winter (October–March).

The following table shows the increase in volume/weight ratio in unbarked timber which can be expected for a period of delay between felling and weighing of 20 days.

Table 4

Species	April-September	October-March
Spruces, Douglas fir	+7%	+1½%
Pines, larches	+5%	+1%

The average rates of drying specified cannot, of course, be maintained indefinitely and would be expected to decline after a total period of 70–80 days. It will also be obvious that the rate of drying is markedly influenced by the prevailing weather conditions during the period of delay, and also to some extent by the average dimensions of the timber, so that the values given above must be regarded only as typical averages.

Bark

17. In some species there may be small differences in the volume/weight ratio applying to barked (without bark) and unbarked (with bark) timber. These differences, however, have not yet been adequately quantified so no recommendations can be made at present. A feature of greater importance, however, is that the rate of drying may be twice as fast in barked timber compared with unbarked timber. Weight measurement of barked timber is consequently inadvisable where significant delays between felling and weighing occur.

18. The factors discussed above have been considered independently of each other, but in practice they frequently interact, adding to the complexity of the subject.

PRACTICE

Weight measurement

19. The weight of a vehicle load of timber is simply determined as the total weight of the vehicle plus load less the weight of the vehicle.

20. A certified public weighbridge must be used.

Volume/weight ratios based on standard assumptions

21. A provisional volume/weight ratio may be required for planning purposes

prior to obtaining a satisfactory estimate by sampling. For this purpose, provisional estimates can be made by considering:

(i) the notional average green density of the species

(ii) the mean diameter of the material

(iii) the expected average delay between felling and weighing.

Example

Consider a situation where the timber supply to a mill consists of Sitka spruce billets, averaging 12 cm (mid) diameter and with an expected delay between felling and weighing of 14 days. The expected volume/weight ratio for summer deliveries would be calculated as follows:

(i) Notional volume/weight ratio (Table 3)—1·08 m^3/tonne

(ii) Diameter correction. The notional value given in Table 3 refers to a mean diameter of 20 cm (para 12). Given that the volume/weight ratio increases by 0·11 m^3/tonne for an increase in 10 cm mean diameter (para 14) the correction will be:

$$0{\cdot}11 \times \frac{12 - 20}{10} = -0{\cdot}088 \text{ m}^3/\text{tonne}$$

and the corrected ratio: 1·08 – 0·088 = 0·992 m^3/tonne.

(iii) Correction for delay. The notional value refers to fresh felled timber. Given that the volume/weight ratio increases by 7% for every 20 days delay (para 16) the proportional increase for 14 days will be:

$$7 \times \frac{14}{20} = 4{\cdot}9\%$$

and the corrected ratio: $0{\cdot}992 \times \frac{104{\cdot}9}{100} = 1{\cdot}041$ m^3/tonne.

Establishing Volume /weight Ratios from Sample Measurements

22. The volume/weight ratio required to estimate the volume of timber from weight measurements is calculated from a sample which is measured both by weight and by volume.

23. The size of the sampling unit will depend to some extent on the type of produce and the weighing facilities available. In many cases a complete load will be the most convenient sample. With small uniform length material it will often be more efficient to use samples of about 20 billets, which may require separate weight scales.

24. Procedure 1 (page 20) should be used to assess the volume of each piece in the sample. (With standard length billets where the whole load is weighed the volume of the whole load can be estimated from a sample, although this generally means that in order to achieve a given level of precision more loads must be sampled.)

25. The volume/weight ratio should be calculated for each sample and expressed in terms of cubic metres per tonne.

26. The intensity of sampling adopted is dependent on the level of precision of measurement required. This will be a matter for agreement between the buyer and seller, but will be influenced in the main by the total quantity of timber involved. For very large or continuing supplies of timber the questions of precision and sampling intensity must form part of the sales contract and agreed sampling schemes will be drawn up to meet the individual circumstances. For more limited contracts the 95% *confidence limits* of the total volume estimate will be in the region of ±2% to ±4%.

27. Basic aspects of sampling intensity and precision are considered in more detail in Part V (1) page 117.

28. To assess the number of samples required, in addition to the desired level of precision, an estimate of the coefficient of variation is required (see page 131). The table below lists likely values of the coefficient of variation for a number of different situations.

Table 5

Values of Coefficient of Variation

Size of sampling units, measurements, and specifications	Coefficient of variation	
	Pines	Other conifers
1. Random log lengths, volume and weight of complete loads	6%	11%
2. Uniform lengths, volume and weight of complete loads	5%	9%
3. Uniform lengths, volume and weight of 20 billets	8%	14%
4. Uniform lengths, weight of complete load, volume of 20% sample	7%	12%

29. The required sample number (n) is then calculated as:

$$n = \frac{(\text{coefficient of variation})^2}{(\text{standard error of mean vol/weight ratio})^2}$$

(*NB:* The value of the standard error follows from the desired confidence limits (see page 123).)

30. Using a notional value for the coefficient of variation carries a certain risk. It is therefore prudent to sample the first, say 10% of the contract at twice the sampling intensity indicated. The samples thus obtained can be used to calculate a more reliable estimate of the coefficient of variation and the sampling intensity recalculated and used as indicated for the remaining 90% of the contract volume.

31. To accommodate systematic variation, eg seasonal, the sampling should be done systematically. For example, if the total contract volume is in the region of 40,000 cubic metres and the required sample number is about 100, each sample being a load of about 20 cubic metres, the sampling intensity is about 5%, so every 20th vehicle entering the weighbridge should be taken as a sample.

Estimating Volume from Weight Measurements

32. The volume of the timber may be assessed periodically using the average volume/weight ratio calculated from samples taken in the same period. Alternatively the volume may be calculated as a cumulative total using the sum of all weights and the average volume/weight ratio of all samples. In this case it is important that the samples used are in the same proportion to the volume of timber throughout the period. If, in the example given above (para 30), the first 10% of the contract volume has been sampled at 4% intensity whereas the remaining 90% was sampled at 3%, then only ¾ of the samples taken from the first 10% should figure in the cumulative average. These should be taken systematically, ie in this case every 4th sample would be ignored.

PART IV MEASUREMENT OF STANDING TIMBER

PROCEDURE 7

ESTIMATING VOLUME OF SINGLE STANDING TREES

GENERAL

1. This method is applicable where volume estimates of individual trees and small groups of trees are required. The method becomes unduly expensive where a large number of trees are involved.

2. The measurements required are the dbh and height of each tree. An assumption on form is therefore implicit.

3. Variation in form between individuals of the same height and dbh, induced by various locality factors, can effect considerable differences in their volumes. The method described here therefore provides estimates of individual tree volumes with relatively moderate precision only.

4. The volumes derived from the procedure outlined below are based on measurements of individual trees grown under a wide range of conditions from locations throughout Britain.

5. Volumes indicated for conifers are to 7 cm top diameter o.b. (timber height).

6. Volumes indicated for hardwoods are to timber height, ie 7 cm diameter o.b. or to the point at which no main stem is distinguishable, whichever comes first.

7. Branchwood is not included in the specified volumes.

PRACTICE

8. Measure the dbh of the tree, observing the usual conventions (see page 17).

9. Measure the height of the tree. With conifers this is the height to tip whereas with hardwoods it is the timber height, ie 7 cm diameter or the point at which no main stem is distinguishable, whichever comes first. (A note on measurement of tree height is given in Part V (4) page 143.)

10. According to the species, select the appropriate Single Tree Tariff Chart from charts 1–19 and find the tariff* number indicated for the measurements taken. This is achieved by laying a straight edge on the chart, lining up the dbh and height values and reading the tariff number from the right hand scale.†

* An explanation of the tariff system is given on page 65.

† With Poplar, timber height only is required to estimate tariff number.

Example:

Given that the tree is a Sitka spruce of 30 cm dbh and 21 m height, the appropriate tariff number from the chart on page 49 is found to be 33.

11. Consult the tariff tables on pages 261–271 to find the volume of the tree from the dbh and the tariff number deduced above. In the example the volume given for a dbh of 30 cm in the tariff table numbered 33 is 0·70 cubic metres (page 266).

Single Tree Tariff Chart

SCOTS PINE

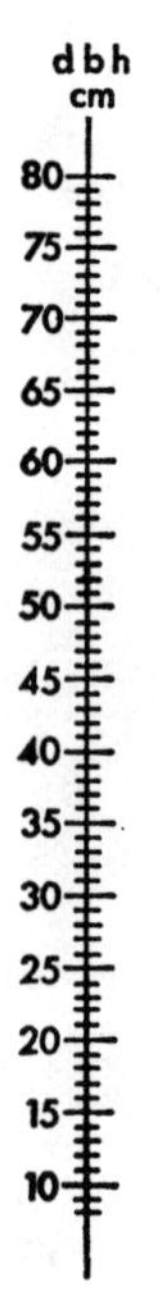

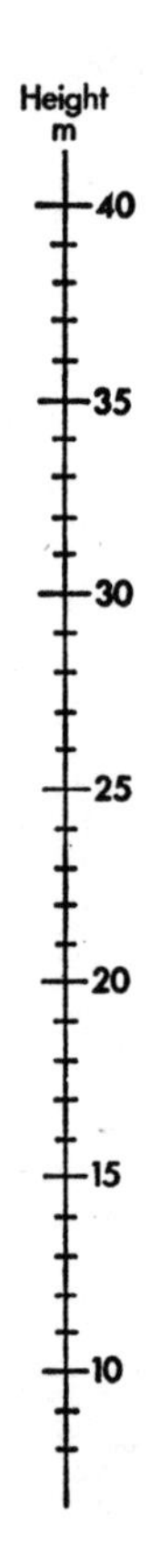

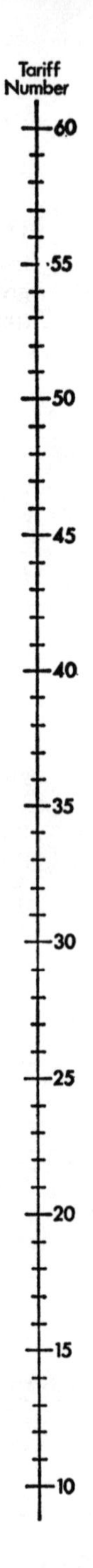

CORSICAN PINE

d b h
cm

80
75
70
65
60
55
50
45
40
35
30
25
20
15
10

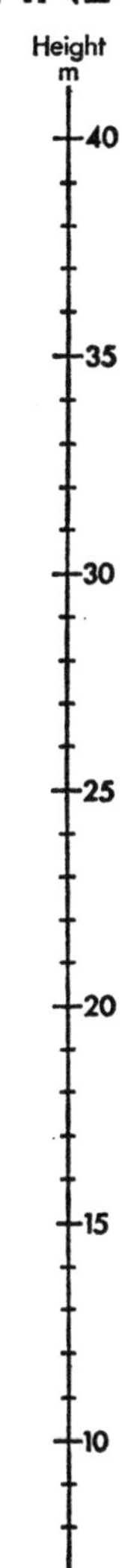

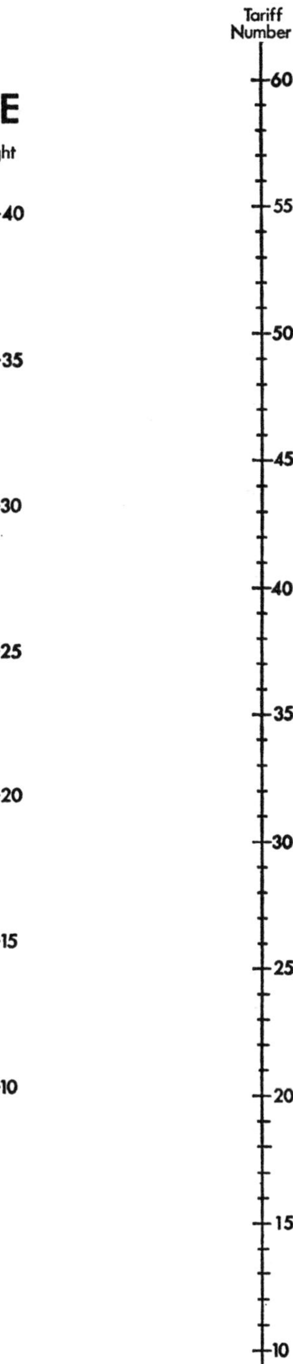

LODGEPOLE PINE

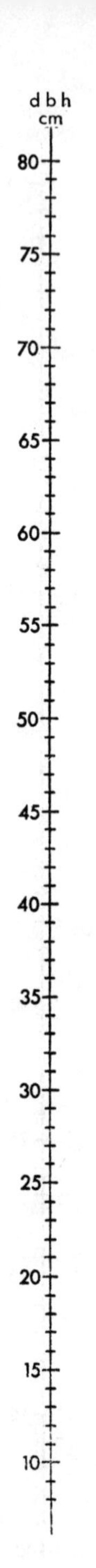

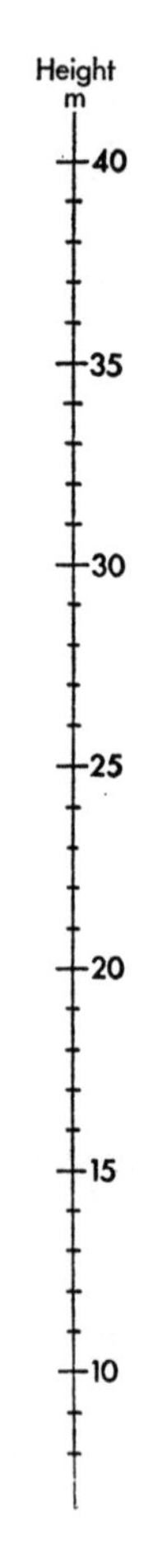

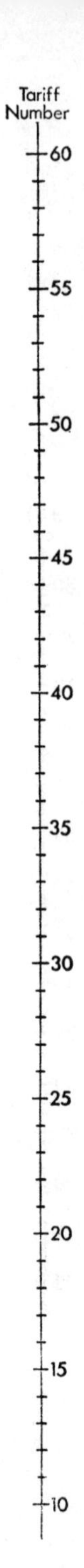

SITKA SPRUCE

d b h
cm
80
70
60
50
40
30
20
10
8

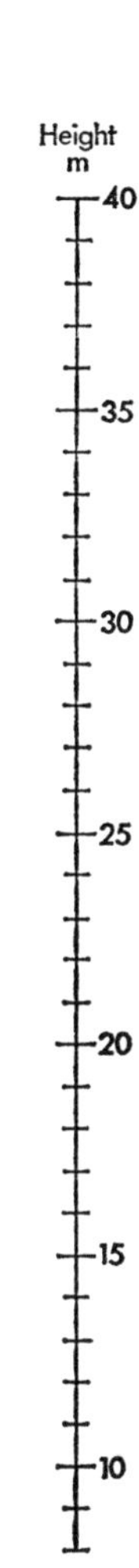

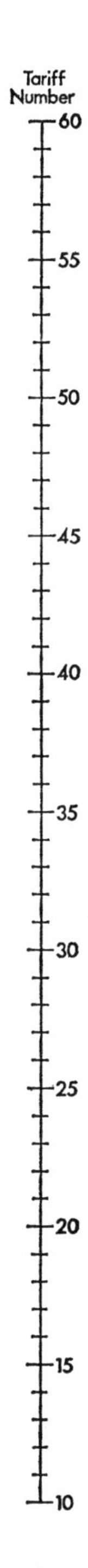

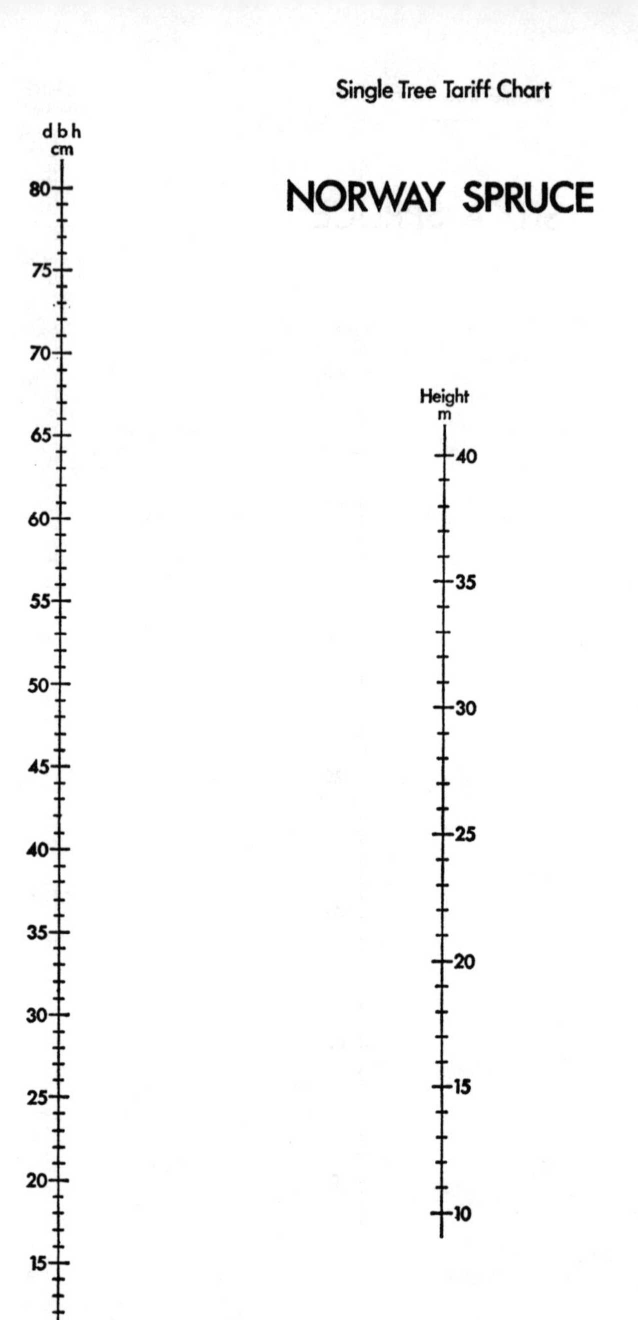
Single Tree Tariff Chart
NORWAY SPRUCE
d b h
cm
80
75
70
65
60
55
50
45
40
35
30
25
20
15
10
Height
m
40
35
30
25
20
15
10

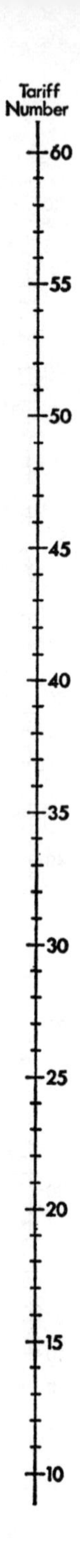
Tariff
Number
60
55
50
45
40
35
30
25
20
15
10

EUROPEAN LARCH

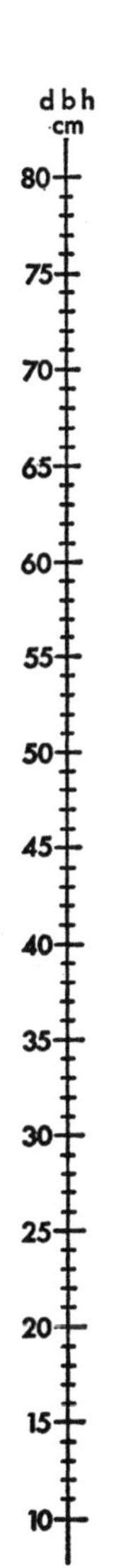

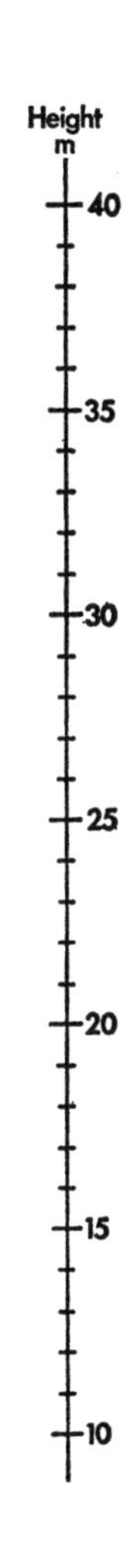

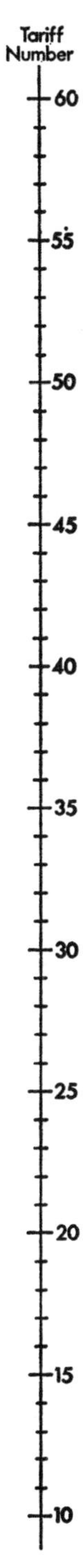

JAPANESE AND HYBRID LARCH

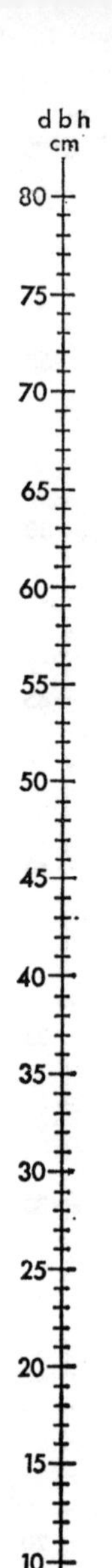

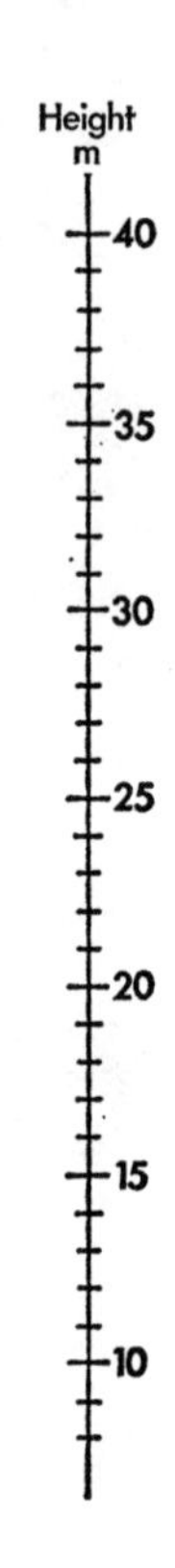

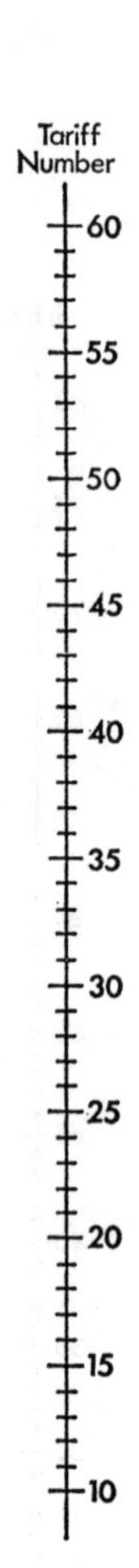

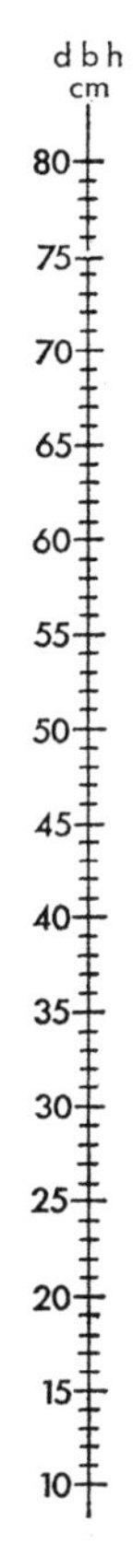

Height
m
40
35
30
25
20
15
10

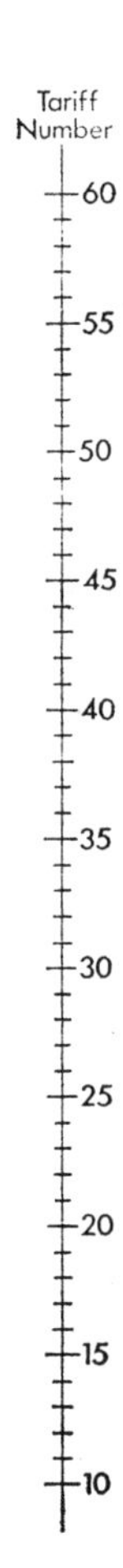

Single Tree Tariff Chart

WESTERN HEMLOCK

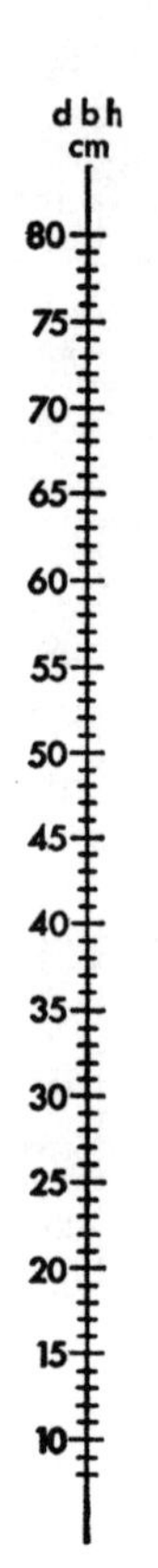

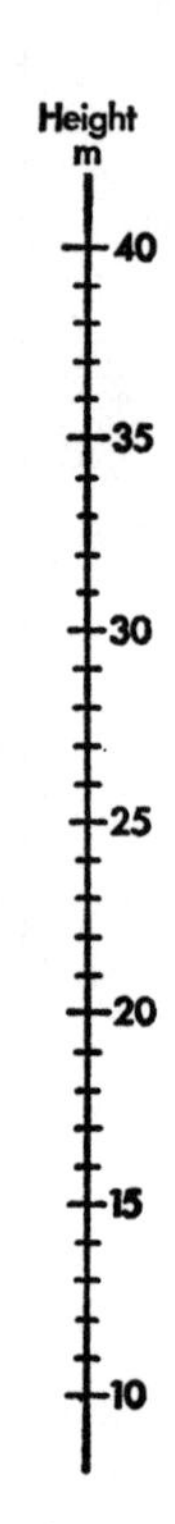

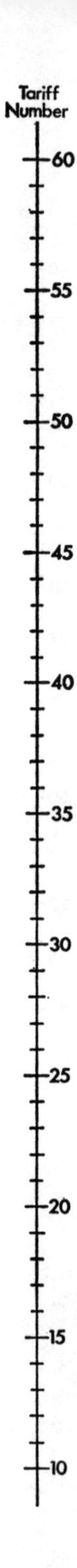

Single Tree Tariff Chart

d b h
cm
80
75
70
65
60
55
50
45
40
35
30
25
20
15
10

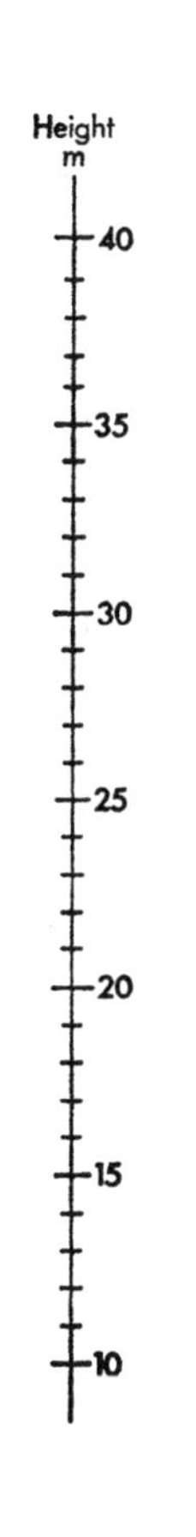

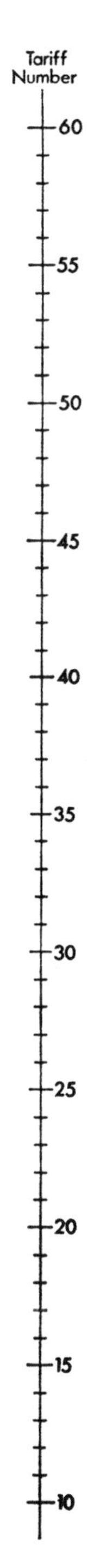

Single Tree Tariff Chart

GRAND FIR

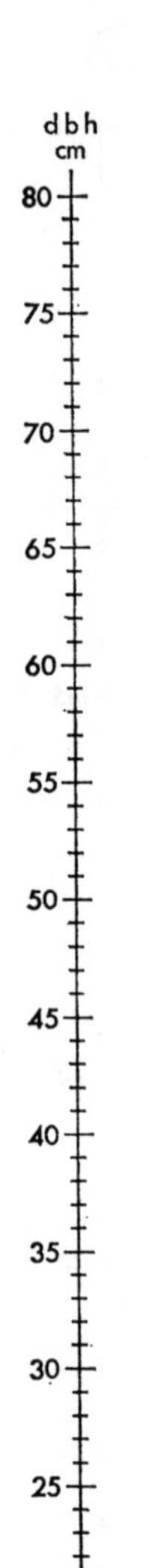

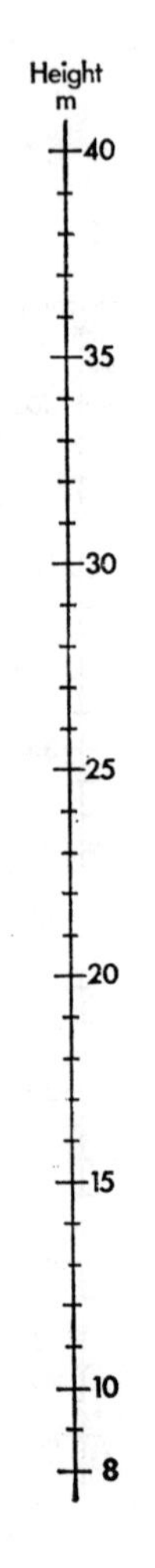

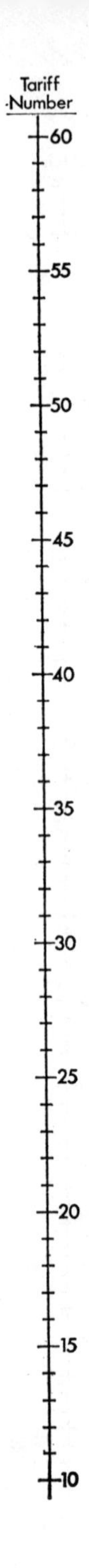

NOBLE FIR

dbh
cm

80
75
70
65
60
55
50
45
40
35
30
25
20
15
10

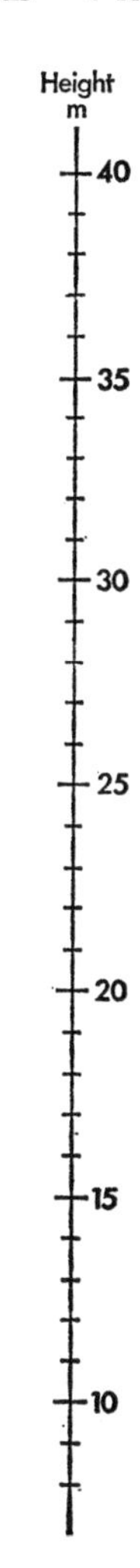

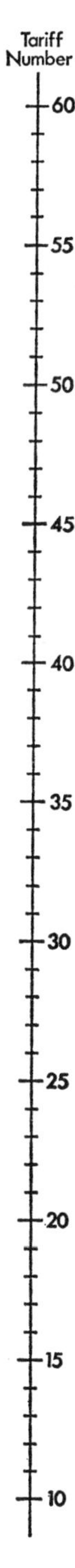

Single Tree Tariff Chart

OAK

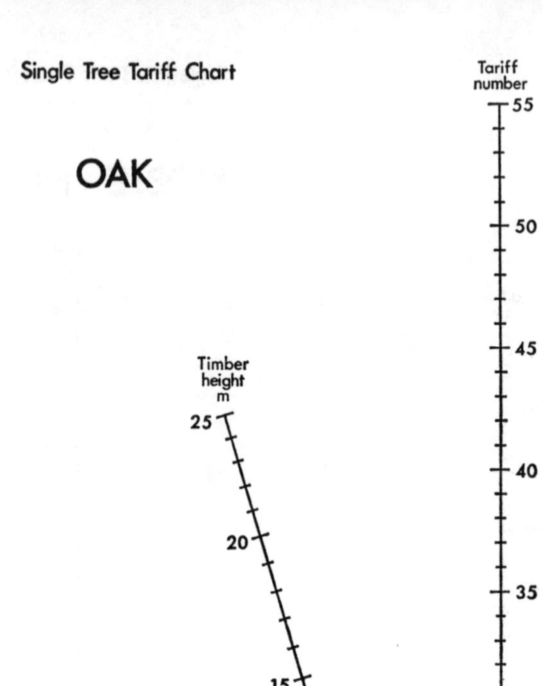

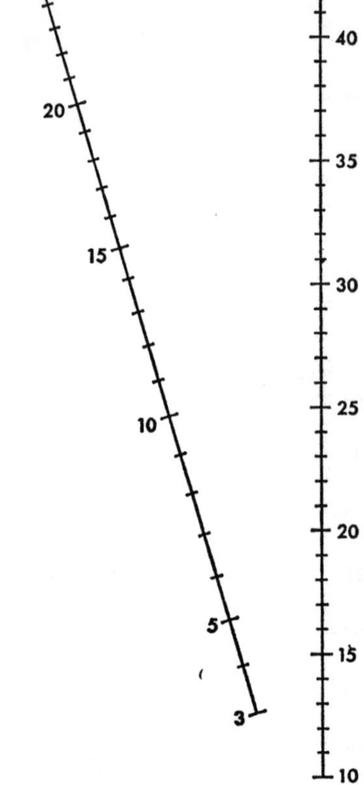

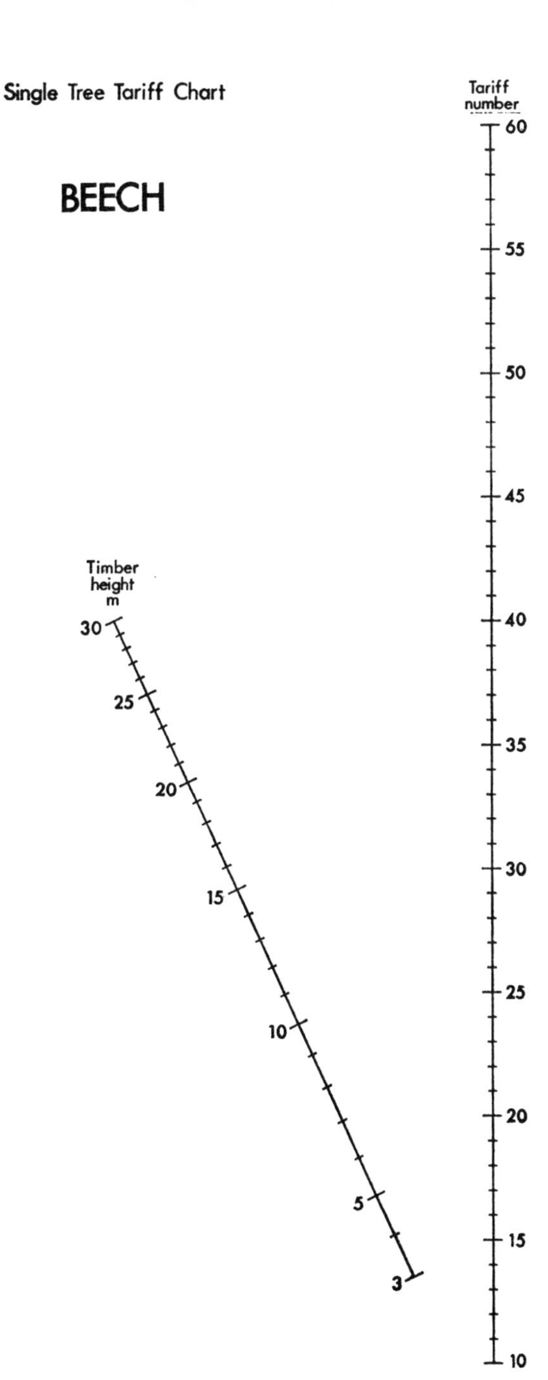
Single Tree Tariff Chart
BEECH
Tariff number
60
55
50
45
40
35
30
25
20
15
10
Timber height m
30
25
20
15
10
5
3
dbh cm
120
110
100
90
80
70
60
50
40
30
20
10

Single Tree Tariff Chart

SYCAMORE

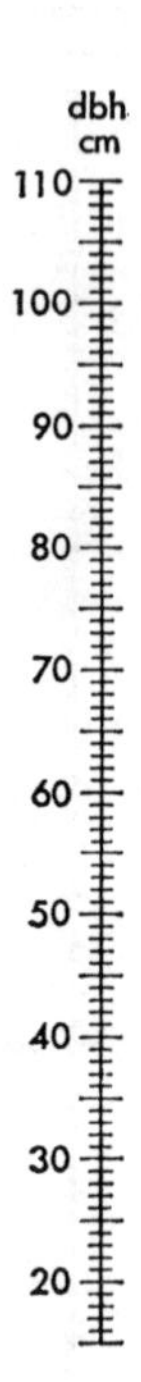

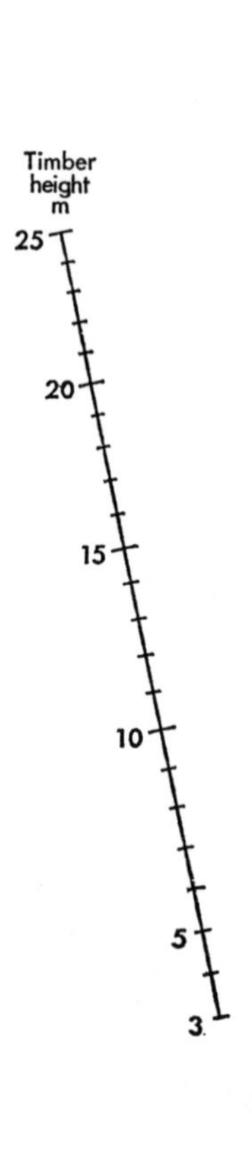

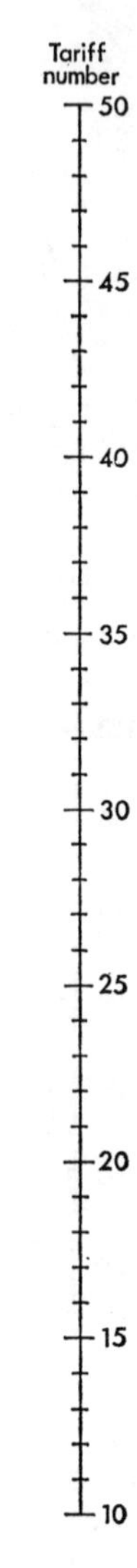

Single Tree Tariff Chart

ASH

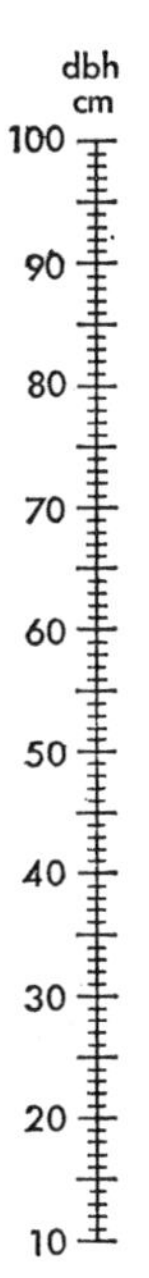

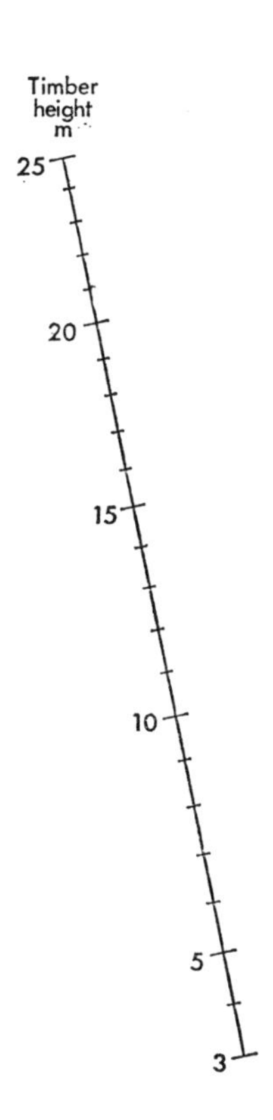

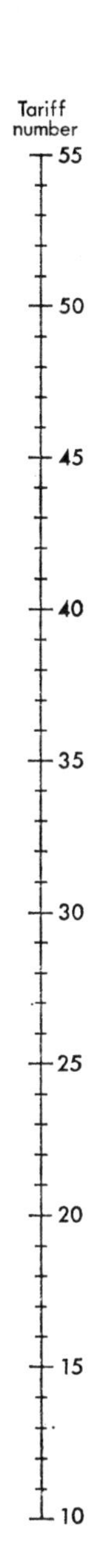

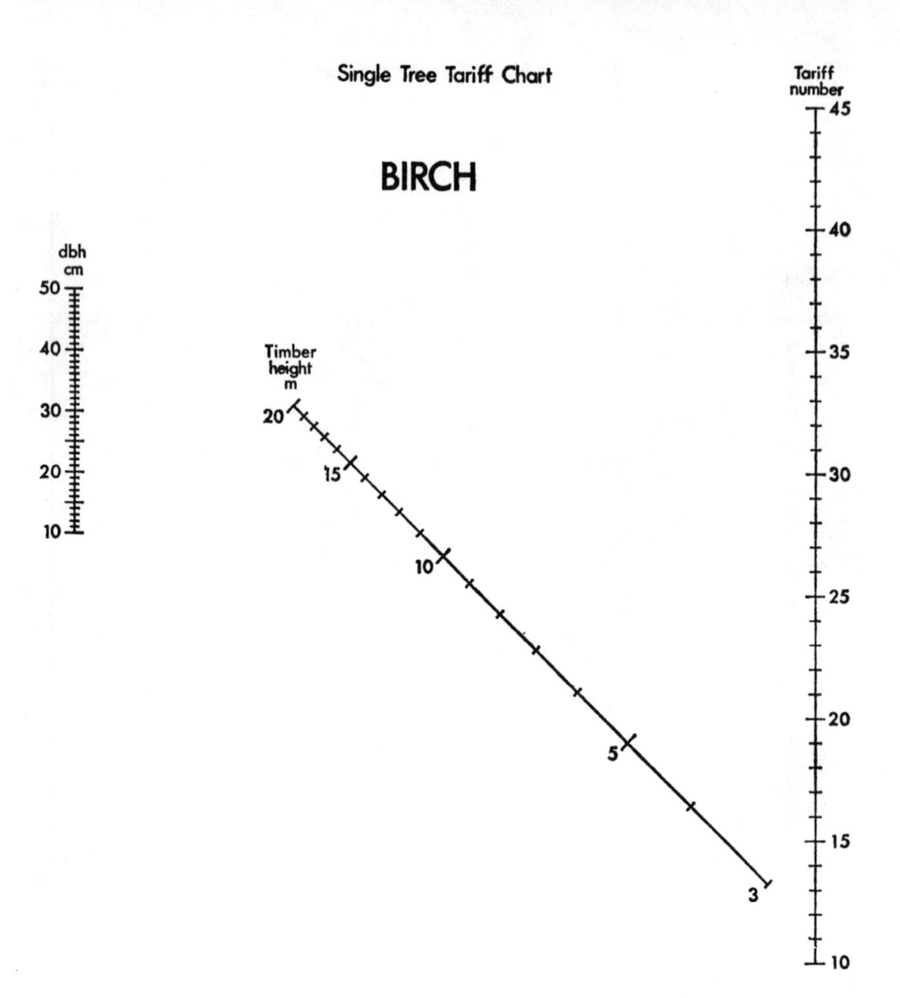
Single Tree Tariff Chart
BIRCH
dbh
cm
50
40
30
20
10
Timber
height
m
20
15
10
5
3
Tariff
number
45
40
35
30
25
20
15
10

Single Tree Tariff Chart

ELM

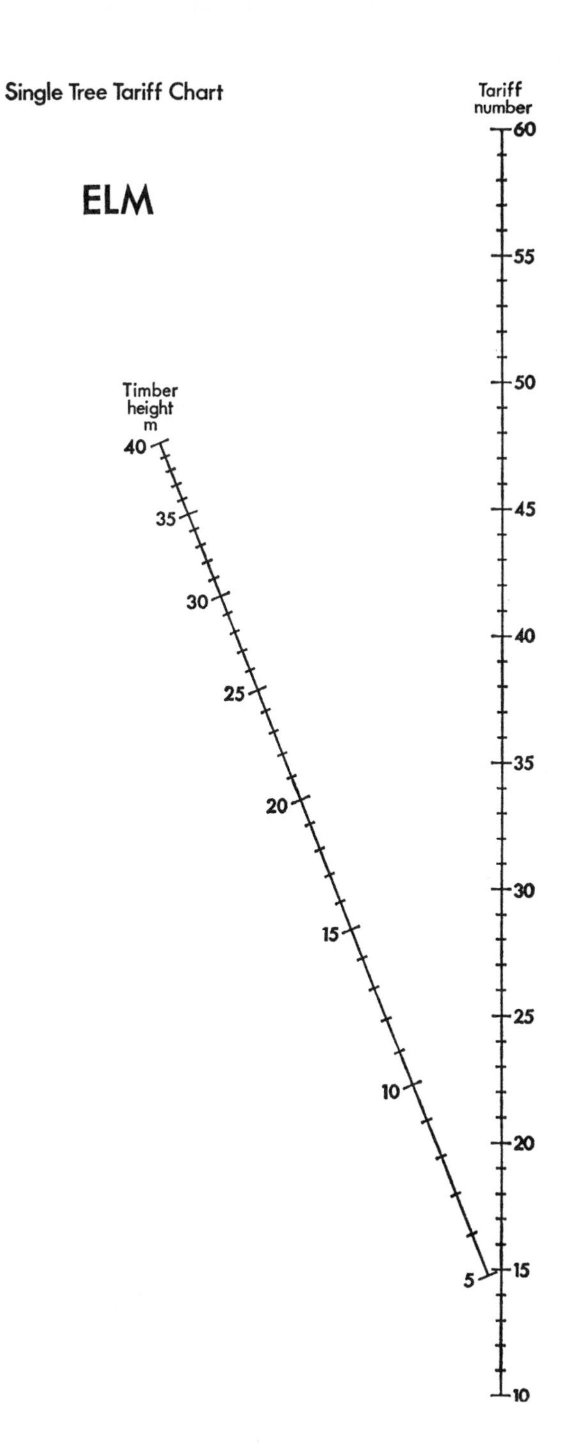

POPLAR

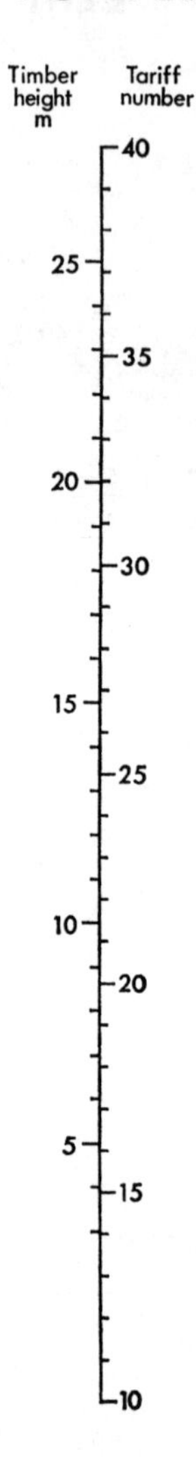

PROCEDURE 8

MEASUREMENT FOR STANDING SALES USING TARIFF TABLES

General

1. The methods of measurement described here are intended to be used in connection with the *sale* of standing timber.

2. The procedures described involve the use of tariff tables (pages 261-271) which have been used for this purpose by the Forestry Commission since 1956. The tariff system of measurement has subsequently proved efficient and reliable provided that the recommended procedures have been correctly followed.

3. Whereas previously the use of the tariff system was confined to certain clearly defined conditions, it is now considered better to use the tariff system than any other method of measuring standing timber, in almost any kind of crop.

4. The system described here can be applied to both thinnings and fellings.

5. It cannot be too strongly emphasised that, in order to produce reliable results, each step in the procedure must be carried out with care. This entails giving proper attention to detail both in fieldwork and calculations and requires competent supervision at each stage and in subsequent checking.

6. The Tariff System

Rudiments

There are basically three steps in estimating the volume of a parcel of trees using the tariff system. The first is to count all trees. Secondly, the trees are classified in terms of diameter at breast height (dbh), in most cases by measuring dbh on a sample of the total population. The third step is to convert the tally of trees thus obtained to volumes using an appropriate single-entry volume table, ie a table giving a volume for each dbh class. Such tables can be regarded as 'local' volume tables in this context. Tariff tables are simply a series of pre-constructed 'local' volume tables. In order to determine which tariff table is appropriate for a given stand it is necessary to fell a sample of trees and to measure their volume. Though it is more usual, with thinnings, to combine the initial selection and marking of trees in the parcel with the measurement procedure in one operation, these can be carried out separately.

Theory

A feature of any pure even-aged stand is that if the volume of each tree is plotted against its basal area, the points are scattered along a clearly defined straight line. The slope of this line varies with species, age, height, and other factors, but all such lines tend to converge at a common point which, using metric conventions, has been empirically determined at a volume of 0·005 m^3 for a basal area of 0·004 m^2 (7 cm diameter). (See Fig 11.) Each of these lines can be converted to a single-entry volume table. Each of the tariff tables

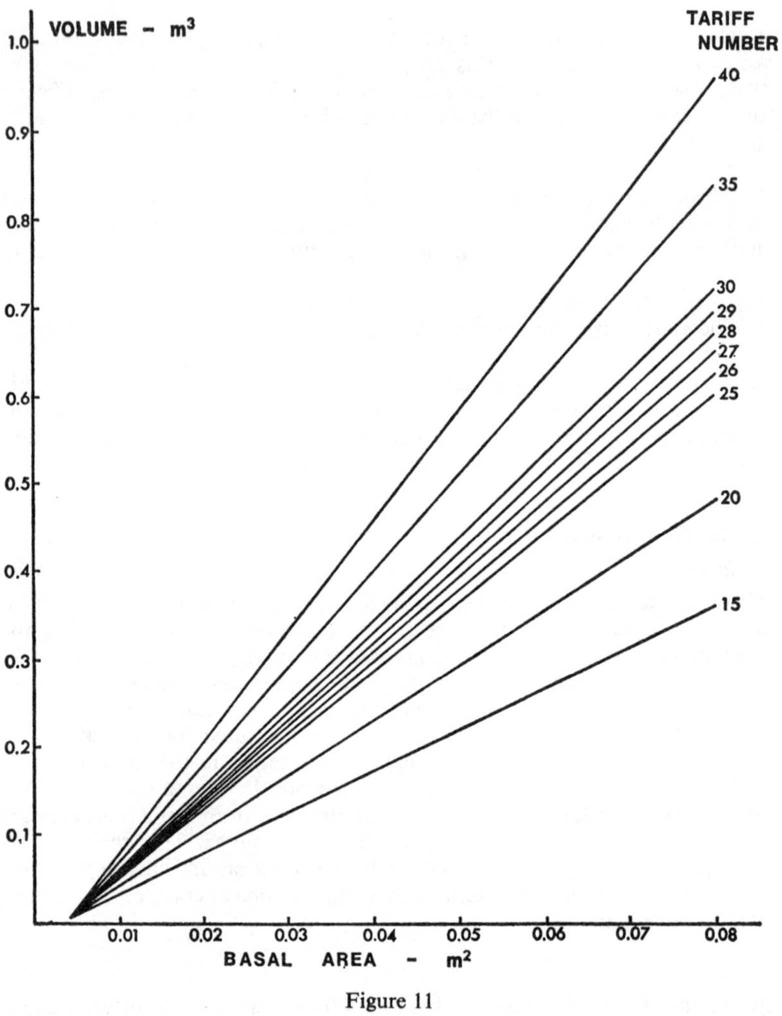
VOLUME - m³
TARIFF NUMBER
1.0
0.9
0.8
0.7
0.6
0.5
0.4
0.3
0.2
0.1
40
35
30
29
28
27
26
25
20
15
0.01
0.02
0.03
0.04
0.05
0.06
0.07
0.08
BASAL AREA - m²

Figure 11

represents one such line. The higher the tariff number the higher the volume for a given dbh. The practical implications of the volume/basal area theory are first, that since each volume/basal area line has one known point in common, not only is the pre-construction of lines (and hence volume tables) possible, but it is easier to establish which volume/basal area relationship (tariff table) to apply to a given crop than would otherwise be the case. Secondly, the fact that the average tariff number is basically the same for all trees within a given crop irrespective of dbh means that sampling is simplified. Taken together these features enable a suitable volume table to be identified from a relatively small number of felled sample trees and it is this fact that accounts for the efficiency of the system.

Application

The tariff method was originally designed for pure even-aged crops. The principle can, however, be extended to other crop types provided that, in order to attain the normal level of precision (see Note b, page 76), the method of sampling is adapted to suit the conditions. In some circumstances the method of computation also requires modification. In certain cases, crops which are not pure and even-aged can be divided into components each of which by themselves can be regarded as pure and even-aged and each component separately measured. For example, in a mixture of two species of the same age, the volume of each species should be sampled, recorded, and measured separately.

Where it is impracticable to deal with each component separately on the ground, a higher intensity of sampling is required for the crop as a whole, together with a modified method of calculation involving sub-division of the crop on paper.

There are also certain crop types of abnormal variability which require a higher sampling intensity than normal.

The following paragraphs describe these situations in greater detail.

Stratification and Sampling

7. It is essential that the stands to be measured are first *correctly stratified*, ie divided into parts (strata) each consisting of acceptable uniformity. This broadly entails separating species, storeys and areas of different height or age and measuring each of these strata independently.

8. When the stands have been stratified as far as is practical it is necessary to decide on the level of *sampling intensity* which should be applied to each stratum. Three sampling schemes are provided, designated 'A', 'B' and 'C' the lowest intensity being 'A', the highest 'C'. The selection of the appropriate sampling scheme is dependent on the nature of the crop in each stratum.

9. The various aspects to be considered in correctly stratifying and sampling stands are presented in a series of logical steps in the key below. More detailed notes on each stage of the key are given on page 69.

10. The sampling scheme appropriate to each stratum is determined from the key and is incorporated in the measurement procedure which is outlined in paragraphs 11-36 on pages 72-75.

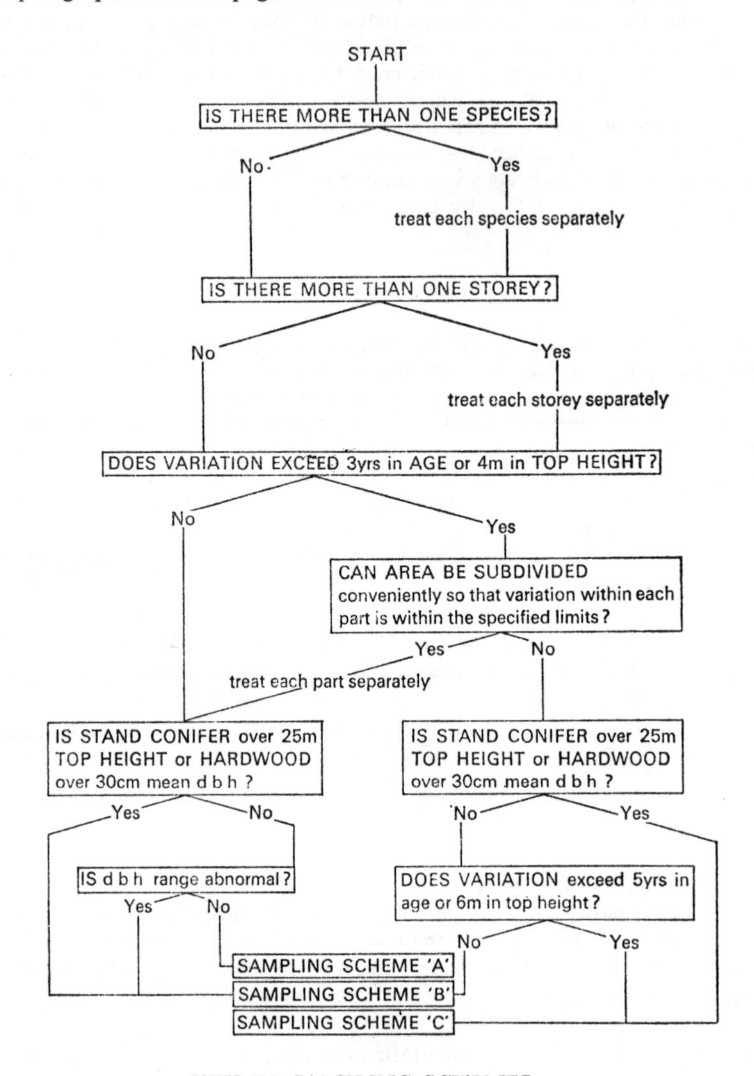

KEY TO SAMPLING SCHEMES

Notes on Key

(i) *Is there more than one species?*

Normally each component species will be sampled and recorded separately except when, *from prior experience in that area,* it is known that the tariff numbers of different species of the same age and height are similar. Situations such as this will tend to occur in early pole stage crops of closely related species, eg Scots and Corsican pine. To group species together in this way also assumes that no species differentiation is required in the volume estimate, by the potential buyer for example.

(ii) *Is there more than one storey?*

In two-storied crops each component, if not of a different species, will usually be of markedly differing ages. Occasionally situations will arise where a 'two storied' situation has been achieved by thinning. Whenever two 'storeys' can be clearly discerned, then each one should be measured separately.

(iii) *Does variation exceed* 3 *years in age or* 4 *m in top height? If so, can area be subdivided . . .? etc.*

This is the final stage in separating out strata to be treated individually, in sampling, recording and computation. Having separated out species and storeys, each component must be examined for variation in height or age. Where variation exceeds the specified limits, the area should if possible be sub-divided into parts such that variation within each part is contained within the specified limits. If the variation occurs locally such that sub-division is not practical, then the problem must be tackled by raising the level of sampling intensity. It is advisable also to treat separately stands which have had markedly different thinning histories.

(iv) *Is the stand to be assessed a conifer over* 25 *m top height or a hardwood of more than* 30 *cm mean dbh?*

A higher intensity of sampling is required where stands exceed these limits.

(v) *Is the diameter range unusually wide?*

A higher sampling intensity will be required in stands where a wider than usual range in dbh is encountered. This situation is more common with crops to be clearfelled, and particularly where little thinning has been carried out, or with thinnings where all sizes of trees are removed, eg line thinnings. A *rough* estimate as to whether the dbh range is exceptional in this respect can be obtained by measuring the dbh of the largest and smallest marked measurable trees (by dbh) in a sample of 20, taken consecutively in a line through the stand. Add the diameters together and consult Table 6 to find the normal maximum dbh range associated with this figure (eg smallest 14 and largest 50, total 64—normal maximum range 27). If the tabulated range is less than that actually obtained by sampling, ie the difference between the largest and smallest tree measured, then the dbh distribution can be regarded as unusually wide. In the above example the *actual* range exceeds the tabulated value, hence the dbh range is unusually wide. It is advisable to repeat this at least three or four times to get a reasonable impression of the dbh range in a stand.

Table 6

Largest + smallest dbh	Maximum dbh range	Largest + smallest dbh	Maximum dbh range	Largest + smallest dbh	Maximum dbh range
18	7	46	19	74	32
20	7	48	20	76	33
22	8	50	21	78	34
24	9	52	22	80	35
26	10	54	23	82	36
28	11	56	24	84	37
30	12	58	25	86	38
32	13	60	26	88	39
34	14	62	27	90	40
36	15	64	27	92	41
38	16	66	28	94	42
40	16	68	29	96	43
42	17	70	30	98	44
44	18	72	31	100	45

N.B. Where 'largest + smallest' is an odd number, take next higher even number.

(vi) *Is variation greater than 5 years in age or 6 metres in top height?*

Variation exceeding this requires a higher sampling intensity than would otherwise be the case. The volume estimate may also have to be calculated by subdividing the dbh distribution and calculating the volume of each part of the distribution. This is dealt with in para 36 (ix), page 75.

(vii) The sampling Schemes A, B and C are shown on page 71 (Table 7). The sampling scheme appropriate to each separately measured component is determined from the Key and incorporated in the measurement procedure which is outlined in the next section.

Table 7

Sampling Schemes

ESTIMATED NOS. OF TREES (of 10 cm dbh and above)	GIRTH SAMPLING FRACTION A	B	C
100— 150	1 : 1	1 : 1	1 : 1
151— 200	1 : 1 (15)	1 : 1	1 : 1
201— 300	1 : 1 (15)	1 : 1	1 : 1
301— 400	1 : 1 (20)	1 : 1 (12)	1 : 1
401— 500	1 : 2	1 : 1 (15)	1 : 1
501— 600	1 : 2	1 : 1 (15)	1 : 1 (12)
601— 800	1 : 3	1 : 2	1 : 1 (15)
801— 1 000	1 : 4	1 : 3	1 : 2
1 001— 1 200	1 : 5	1 : 3	1 : 2
1 201— 1 400	1 : 6	1 : 4	1 : 3
1 401— 1 600	1 : 7	1 : 4	1 : 3
1 601— 1 800	1 : 8	1 : 5	1 : 4
1 801— 2 000	1 : 9	1 : 6	1 : 4
2 001— 2 400	1 : 10	1 : 6	1 : 5
2 401— 3 000	1 : 12	1 : 8	1 : 6
3 001— 4 500	1 : 15	1 : 10	1 : 7
4 501— 6 000	1 : 20	1 : 15	1 : 10
6 001— 8 000	1 : 25	1 : 18	1 : 12
8 001—10 000	1 : 30	1 : 20	1 : 15
10 001+	1 : 40	1 : 25	1 : 20

Notes

a. Use the Key on page 68 to determine which sampling scheme to use for each separately measured parcel, ie whether A, B or C.

b. The girth sampling fraction to use will be determined according to the estimated number of trees in the parcel, eg if the sampling scheme indicated by the key is 'A' and the estimated numbers of trees in the parcel is 1 500 then the appropriate girth sampling fraction will be 1: 7, ie every seventh tree in the stand will be girthed.

c. Normally *every 10th* girth sample tree will be felled and measured for volume. The figures above shown in brackets indicate the exceptions to this, and these concern cases where all trees are girthed. For example, if sampling scheme 'A' is indicated and the estimated number in the parcel is 180 then all trees will be girthed but *every 15th* tree will be selected as a volume sample tree.

d. For parcels of fewer than 100 trees, see Note (*e*) (page 77).

Fieldwork

11. Use the Key on page 68 to ensure that the area has been properly stratified and to determine the sampling scheme(s) to be applied.

12. The measurement team should consist of 1 booker and a number of markers depending on the conditions (see Note (a) on page 76). If marking, in the sense of initial selection and blazing of trees, is done separately from measurement, 'marking' of the same trees with scribe, chalk, or crayon etc is still required for enumeration in the measurement procedure.

13. The special assessment form (FC U15) shown on pages 78–80 to illustrate a worked example should be used by the booker for recording the data.

14. The total number of trees of 10 cm dbh and above in each separately assessed parcel must be estimated. Some care taken at this stage may avoid the necessity of extra work later. In this respect it is better to *underestimate* rather than overestimate the numbers. A convenient way of estimating the number of trees is to lay down a series of plots throughout the area counting the trees marked or likely to be marked in each plot, finding the average stocking per plot and deriving a total from the total area of the stand being measured. A plot size of 0·01 ha may be adequate for early thinnings whereas for older crops plots of 0·05 ha may be more suitable. (In the worked example the estimate was 1,900.)

15. The girth sampling fraction $\left(\frac{1}{\text{'n'}}\right)$ is determined from table 7 on the previous page using the appropriate sampling scheme and the estimated number of trees. (In the worked example this is 1 : 9, the sampling scheme required being 'A'.)

16. The marking of those trees to be felled proceeds normally. On marking each tree the marker calls 'mark' to the booker who records this in Part B of the form, and returns the call. Trees of less than 7 cm dbh are not entered here, and may either be ignored or, if required, recorded separately. The gate method of recording marked trees is most convenient, and where the sampling fraction is not a multiple of five, trees should be tallied in groups as shown in the worked example.

The accuracy of the number of trees counted is of fundamental importance and where large numbers of trees are involved it makes it easier for the prospective buyer to check the record of trees marked (Part B) if this is arranged in sections, each section corresponding to an area easily identified on the ground, eg by roads, rides, streams etc.

17. *After* the 'n'th tree is marked and recorded in Part B, the booker calls 'girth'. The dbh of this tree must then be measured by the marker and called to the booker who records it in the appropriate part of Section C, and confirms the measurement by returning the call to the marker. Normal conventions apply in measuring the dbh of these *girth sample trees* (see page 17).

18. After the 10th* girth sample tree has been marked and girthed, the booker calls 'sample', indicating that this tree is a *volume sample tree.* The point at which the diameter was measured *must be scribed,* and the trees numbered above breast height point in the sequence in which they are encountered, and entered in Part D. (Roman numerals are normally more convenient.) These volume sample trees, with the exception of trees of 7, 8 and 9 cm dbh, may either be felled and measured immediately, or alternatively distinctively marked as a volume sample tree and felled and measured later.

19. The volume of each felled sample tree must be assessed using Procedure 1 (page 20). It is important that the rounded-down timber length point and the point at which the mid-diameter is measured should be clearly scribed. (It is customary to scribe the timber point with an arrow and so avoid confusion with chain saw marks.) The timber length(s) and mid-diameter(s) are entered in columns 3 and 4 of part D. Trees of 7, 8 and 9 cm dbh which are selected as volume sample trees must be entered in Part D of the assessment form but their volumes should not be calculated and they should not be used in calculating average tariff numbers. For subsequent checking purposes they should be distinctly marked and numbered.

20. Apart from situations where all trees in the parcel have been girthed, it is necessary to check that a sufficient number of volume sample trees of 10 cm dbh and above have been measured. If the numbers are less than 16 (Sampling Scheme A), 25 (Scheme B), 34 (Scheme C), additional sampling should be carried out (see Note (*c*) page 76).

Calculations

21. Add up the total number of girth sample trees in part C of the assessment form and enter in column 3.

22. Multiply the numbers in each class by the sampling fraction denominator 'n' (in the worked example this is 9) and enter in col 4 of part C, this column providing the dbh distribution of the total number of trees in the stand.

23. The tariff number of each volume sample tree (ie Part D col 6), must be obtained from the tariff tables, using the dbh and volume of each tree. In the worked example, volume sample tree No 1 has a volume of 0·21 cubic metres for a dbh of 18 cm. Reference to the tariff tables shows that the table showing a volume nearest to that of the sample tree for this dbh is tariff table 30 which indicates a volume of 0·208 cubic metres (page 264). Tariff number 30 is thus entered in column 6. If the volume falls exactly halfway between two tariffs then the lower tariff number is taken.

24. The tariff numbers are then summed and divided by the total number of entries in this column to give an average tariff number which should be rounded *down* to the nearest whole number.

**See* Note c under Table 7, page 71.

25. The tariff table volumes indicated by this average tariff number are then entered in column 5 (Part C) against the appropriate dbh class.

26. The volume in each dbh class (col 6 Part C) is then simply the product of cols 4 and 5.

27. The grand totals in Part C are then completed and transferred to Part A. Average volume per tree is derived by dividing the total volume (col 3) by the number of trees (col 2). Owing to its derivation as a multiple of the number of girth sample trees, the total number of trees shown at the bottom of column 4, Part C, may differ from the total actually marked (Part B). No adjustment should, however, be made to the volume estimate.

28. The final step which may or may not be required is to estimate the volume to 18 cm (col 6) and 24 cm (col 7) top diameter. This information is obtained using one of the stand volume assortment tables (tables 48-51) which are entered using the mean dbh of the marked trees. The choice of table depends on the minimum length required. In the worked example table 49 on page 173 has been used. This assumes a minimum length of 2 m. The figures obtained are to be regarded only as a guide to the volume breakdown and cannot be guaranteed. The mean dbh is that equivalent to the average volume using the appropriate tariff table. (In the worked example the mean volume of 0·202 m^3 is equivalent to 18 cm dbh).

29. An estimate of the number of tops of trees, or unmeasurable trees, can be entered in the boxes provided in Part A if required.

30. Checks i-v (page 75) must be carried out as part of the procedure.

31. Where Sampling Scheme 'C' has been used, check (ix) must be carried out and the volume calculated as indicated if necessary.

Sources of Error

32. *Girthing Standards.* It is imperative that the same standard of girthing should apply to both girth sample trees and volume sample trees. For this reason the procedure must always be such that the dbh should be measured, called and recorded *before* the marker is told that the tree is also a volume sample tree. On no account must the measurement be subsequently changed. Consistent standards are best obtained using a stick of 1·3 m or by attaching a pin to one's clothing at 1·3 m from ground level.

33. *Bias.* If the procedure is followed correctly there will, in general, be little opportunity for biased selection of girth or volume sample trees. The risk of bias is greater if there is only one marker or if the booker attempts to act as a marker. Risk of bias is also related to the sampling fraction $\left(\frac{1}{\text{'n'}}\right)$. Where 'n' is small the marker can more easily be aware that the next tree is a girth sample tree before marking it. Scribing all girth sample trees in these circumstances provides a useful basis for checking the occurrence of bias.

34. *Measurement errors.* Whilst volume sample tree measurements can be easily checked, girth sample tree measurements are more difficult to check and errors occurring here usually require new girth samples to be taken. Girthing tapes should be checked periodically and those which are found to be inaccurate or worn should be discarded.

Checks

35. The following *routine checks* must be undertaken:

(i) Check all calculations and ensure that the total number of trees, the sampling fraction and the number of sample trees are compatible with one another.

(ii) Check that all trees of less than 7 cm dbh have been excluded from all calculations.

(iii) Check that no trees less than 10 cm dbh have been used in calculating average tariff number.

(iv) Check that any volume sample trees with a timber length of less than 2·5 m have a mid-diameter equal to their dbh.

(v) Check that the average volume is reasonable for the stand in the light of experience and observation.

36. Not all faults can be easily identified but the following *supervisors' checks* may assist where there is some doubt as to the accuracy of the estimate.

(vi) Check that the dbh of each volume sample tree is present in the tally of girth sample trees (Part C). If not this indicates failure to record the volume sample trees as girth sample trees, or that the volume sample trees have been measured on a different basis, eg after felling where the breast height point has been incorrectly estimated as 1·3 m from *the butt.*

(vii) Examine the dbh distribution of the volume sample trees against that of the girth sample trees by tallying opposite the girth sample trees in Part C of the form, and compare the quadratic mean dbh of each distribution (ie the dbh corresponding to the mean basal area).

If marked differences are apparent, the explanation may be either that a different standard of girthing has applied between girth and volume sample trees, or that bias has entered the selection of volume sample trees. The first possibility is more serious.

(viii) Bias in the selection of girth sample trees (if these have not been scribed at breast height) cannot be detected from the assessment form, and can only be checked by undertaking a new sample. Biased selection of girth sample trees is much more serious than bias in the selection of volume sample trees.

(ix) Tally the tariff numbers against dbh in Part C (or plot on graph paper). Check that there is no marked tendency for tariff number to increase or decrease with increasing dbh. If there is, it will be necessary to split the dbh distribution into two or more parts and to calculate the average tariff number appropriate to each part from the volume sample trees with dbh's falling within each sub-division of the dbh distribution. The volume of each sub-division is simply calculated using the tariff number derived for that part of the distribution. This technique is justified where there are at least 12 sample trees within each sub-division of the group and where the difference between mean tariff numbers of successive sub-divisions exceeds 3.

Notes

a. Team organisation

The most efficient system is that where initial selection of trees, marking and measurement are combined. In most cases the measurement of volume sample trees will be undertaken at a later stage, thereby avoiding the necessity of transporting a power saw and stump protection equipment throughout the operation.

The number of markers which one booker can cope with depends on the stand conditions, ie whether the stand is being thinned or being clear felled, and the stocking of marked trees. It is recommended that there should be a minimum of two markers. The optimum number will probably be 3 markers in thinnings whereas in clear fellings, marking is more rapid and as a result 2 markers will give a balanced team.

In traversing an area where acceptable variation (see Key and Notes pages 68–70) follows a detectable gradient, the traversing should be done at right angles to the gradient. For example, where variation exists between the top and bottom of a slope, the team should work across the slope.

b. Precision of volume estimate

Assuming measurement errors are minimal and that the procedure has been properly carried out the true volume will be within the range ±10% of the volume estimate, at the 95% probability level. In other words there is *at least* a 19 to 1 chance against the possiblity of the true volume lying outside the 10% limits. This level of precision may not apply to parcels of fewer than 100 trees.

c. Procedure if insufficient volume sample trees measured (para 20)

If, because of an overestimate of the number of trees to be marked in a parcel, the sampling fraction used has resulted in insufficient volume sample trees being selected, then additional samples should be taken. The simplest way of doing this is to follow a diagonal line through the area, girthing every marked tree on the line, and taking every tenth tree as a volume sample tree. This can be repeated with a second *complete* diagonal if need be. In line thinning it may be necessary to sample in a similar manner marked lines taken at random. Whichever method is used, the samples can never be truly representative of the stand, short of repeating the exercise from scratch, but some effort should be made to cover as much of the area as possible in selecting the additional volume sample trees.

The additional girth and volume sample trees should be entered in Parts C and D of the assessment form respectively but, of course, the marked trees will have already been counted and entered in Part B. The mean tariff number is calculated using all volume sample trees and the total number of girth sample trees is tallied in col 3 of Part C as usual. To find the total number of trees in each class multiply each entry in col 3 by the factor obtained by dividing the number of marked trees in the stand by the total number of girth sample trees. As a result of taking additional girth sampling trees, this fraction may prove rather awkward, and this is yet another reason why efforts should be made to avoid the need to select further samples by making careful initial estimates of numbers of trees.

d. Line thinning

A modified method of sampling is permissible in first line thinnings but only in uniform conditions where rows are clearly defined and evenly spaced, and where the line thinning pattern is strictly regular. In these situations a less costly method of sampling is to derive the total number of trees by sampling a proportion of the lines to be removed. (This proportion should not be less than 20%, ie a maximum interval of every fifth marked line.) The dbh distribution can be derived by measuring the dbh of all or a proportion of trees in these lines. For example, if the indicated girth sampling fraction is 1: 10, every fifth line would be sampled and the dbh assessed of every second tree of 7 cm dbh and above in the line. For a girth sample of 1: 8, every fourth row would be sampled and the dbh of every second tree in the line measured, and so on. In these circumstances it should be noted that the total number of trees is *estimated* and by implication this may require modification to sales contracts. The prospective buyer must be informed of such a departure from the normal method of sampling.

e. Parcels of fewer than 100 trees

Where the parcel being assessed contains fewer than 100 trees the method of assessment remains the same except that it is usually uneconomic to fell a sufficient number of trees in order to attain the normal level of precision attached to the volume estimate. (See Note b.) The dbh of all trees should be measured. Where there are 50–100 trees, every tenth tree should be taken as a volume sample tree. Where there are fewer than 50 trees, 5 volume sample trees should be selected systematically by means of an appropriate sampling fraction. The volume and tariff number of each of these should be calculated, a mean tariff number derived and thereafter the volume of the parcel calculated in the manner described above.

An alternative approach may be justifiable in small parcels which cannot be combined with larger areas and in which for one reason or another, eg two or more species, an abnormal range in dbh etc—the normal cost of measurement would be very high in relation to the value of the timber. In these cases the procedure outlined above is followed, except that instead of felling the volume sample trees the tariff number of each sample tree is obtained from its height and dbh and the use of Charts 1–19 (as appropriate) on pages 46–64 (see Procedure 7). The precision of the estimate obtained by this method is clearly lower than with the normal procedure, and cannot be guaranteed. The prospective buyer must be informed when a tariff number is calculated by this method and the assessment form noted to this effect.

WORKED EXAMPLE

FORESTRY COMMISSION

VOLUME ESTIMATE — THINNINGS / FELLINGS

CONSERVANCY WEST (WALES) FOREST CADER COMPT. NO: 68

SPECIES SITKA SPRUCE AREA 6·5 ha. AGE (Yrs) - 30 YIELD CLASS 20

SAMPLING SCHEME A DATE MEASURED 4/72 SIGNATURE S. JAMES

A.

Species	Totals		Average vol. per tree m³	Average d b h cm	Volume* m³ to	
	No. of trees	Volume m³			18 cm top diam	24 cm top diam
	(2)	(3)	(4)	(5)	(6)	(7)
SITKA SPRUCE	2169	437·8	0·202	18	122·6	4·4

Estimated No. of tops to be used	
No. of unmeasurable trees to be felled	

*From assortment tables.

D. DETAILS OF SAMPLE TREES FELLED AND MEASURED

Tree No.	d b h cm	Length to 7 cm top diam	Mid diam cm	Volume m³	Tariff No.	Tree No.	d b h cm	Length to 7 cm top diam	Mid diam cm	Volume m³	Tariff No.
(1)	(2)	(3)	(4)	(5)	(6)	(1)	(2)	(3)	(4)	(5)	(6)
1	18	12	15	0·21	30	26					
2	20	13	15	0·23	26	27					
3	21	13	17	0·30	31	28					
4	15	8·9	13	0·118	26	29					
5	21	14	17	0·32	33	30					
6	25	15	18	0·38	26	31					
7	19	14	15	0·25	32	32					
8	17	11	13	0·15	24	33					
9	15	10	13	0·133	29	34					
10	19	13	15	0·23	29	35					
11	18	12	15	0·21	30	36					
12	20	14	16	0·28	32	37					
13	19	13	15	0·23	29	38					
14	17	11	14	0 17	28	39					
15	14	9·4	12	0 106	28	40					
16	9	—	—	—	—	41					
17	12	9·5	10	0·075	30	42					
18	24	15	18	0·38	29	43					
19	20	14	15	0·25	28	44					
20	16	12	13	0·16	30	45					
21	18	13	14	0·20	29	46					
22	18	11	15	0·19	27	47					
23	16	12	13	0·16	30	48					
24	27	18	20	0·57	34	49					
25						50					
				Total c. fwd	670					Total bt. fwd	
										GRAND TOTAL	670

Mean Tariff Number = Grand Total of Tariff Nos. / No. of sample trees (Omit trees of 7, 8 and 9 cm d b h) = 670 / 23 = 29·1 = 29 (rounded down)

U15

B. RECORD OF TREES MARKED By Gate method – one gate to each square

𝍸	IIII	𝍸	IIII	𝍸	IIII	𝍸	IIII	𝍸	IIII	𝍸	IIII	𝍸	IIII	𝍸	IIII	𝍸	IIII	𝍸	IIII
𝍸	IIII	𝍸	IIII	𝍸	IIII	𝍸	IIII	𝍸	IIII	𝍸	IIII	𝍸	IIII	𝍸	IIII	𝍸	IIII	𝍸	IIII
𝍸	IIII	𝍸	IIII	𝍸	IIII	𝍸	IIII	𝍸	IIII	𝍸	IIII	𝍸	IIII	𝍸	IIII	𝍸	IIII	𝍸	IIII
𝍸	IIII	𝍸	IIII	𝍸	IIII	𝍸	IIII	𝍸	IIII	𝍸	IIII	𝍸	IIII	𝍸	IIII	𝍸	IIII	𝍸	IIII
𝍸	IIII	𝍸	IIII	𝍸	IIII	𝍸	IIII	𝍸	IIII	𝍸	IIII	𝍸	IIII	𝍸	IIII	𝍸	IIII	𝍸	IIII
𝍸	IIII	𝍸	IIII	𝍸	IIII	𝍸	IIII	𝍸	IIII	𝍸	IIII	𝍸	IIII	𝍸	IIII	𝍸	IIII	𝍸	IIII
𝍸	IIII	𝍸	IIII	𝍸	IIII	𝍸	IIII	𝍸	IIII	𝍸	IIII	𝍸	IIII	𝍸	IIII	𝍸	IIII	𝍸	IIII
𝍸	IIII	𝍸	IIII	𝍸	IIII	𝍸	IIII	𝍸	IIII	𝍸	IIII	𝍸	IIII	𝍸	IIII	𝍸	IIII	𝍸	IIII
𝍸	IIII	𝍸	IIII	𝍸	IIII	𝍸	IIII	𝍸	IIII	𝍸	IIII	𝍸	IIII	𝍸	IIII	𝍸	IIII	𝍸	IIII
𝍸	IIII	𝍸	IIII	𝍸	IIII	𝍸	IIII	𝍸	IIII	𝍸	IIII	𝍸	IIII	𝍸	IIII	𝍸	IIII	𝍸	IIII
𝍸	IIII	𝍸	IIII	𝍸	IIII	𝍸	IIII	𝍸	IIII	𝍸	IIII	𝍸	IIII	𝍸	IIII	𝍸	IIII	𝍸	IIII
𝍸	IIII	𝍸	IIII	𝍸	IIII	𝍸	IIII	𝍸	IIII	𝍸	IIII	𝍸	IIII	𝍸	IIII	𝍸	IIII	𝍸	IIII
𝍸	IIII	𝍸	IIII	𝍸	IIII	𝍸	IIII	𝍸	IIII	𝍸	IIII	𝍸	IIII	𝍸	IIII	𝍸	IIII	𝍸	IIII
𝍸	IIII	𝍸	IIII	𝍸	IIII	𝍸	IIII	𝍸	IIII	𝍸	IIII	𝍸	IIII	𝍸	IIII	𝍸	IIII	𝍸	IIII
𝍸	IIII	𝍸	IIII	𝍸	IIII	𝍸	IIII	𝍸	IIII	𝍸	IIII	𝍸	IIII	𝍸	IIII	𝍸	IIII	𝍸	IIII
𝍸	IIII	𝍸	IIII	𝍸	IIII	𝍸	IIII	𝍸	IIII	𝍸	IIII	𝍸	IIII	𝍸	IIII	𝍸	IIII	𝍸	IIII
𝍸	IIII	𝍸	IIII	𝍸	IIII	𝍸	IIII	𝍸	IIII	𝍸	IIII	𝍸	IIII	𝍸	IIII	𝍸	IIII	𝍸	IIII
𝍸	IIII	𝍸	IIII	𝍸	IIII	𝍸	IIII	𝍸	IIII	𝍸	IIII	𝍸	IIII	𝍸	IIII	𝍸	IIII	𝍸	IIII
𝍸	IIII	𝍸	IIII	𝍸	IIII	𝍸	IIII	𝍸	IIII	𝍸	IIII	𝍸	IIII	𝍸	IIII	𝍸	IIII	𝍸	IIII
𝍸	IIII	𝍸	IIII	𝍸	IIII	𝍸	IIII	𝍸	IIII	𝍸	IIII	𝍸	IIII	𝍸	IIII	𝍸	IIII	𝍸	IIII
𝍸	IIII	𝍸	IIII	𝍸	IIII	𝍸	IIII	𝍸	IIII	𝍸	IIII	𝍸	IIII	𝍸	IIII	𝍸	IIII	𝍸	IIII
𝍸	IIII	𝍸	IIII	𝍸	IIII	𝍸	IIII	𝍸	IIII	𝍸	IIII	𝍸	IIII	𝍸	IIII	𝍸	IIII	𝍸	IIII
𝍸	IIII	𝍸	IIII	𝍸	IIII	𝍸	IIII	𝍸	IIII	𝍸	IIII	𝍸	IIII	𝍸	IIII	𝍸	IIII	𝍸	IIII
𝍸	IIII	𝍸	IIII	𝍸	IIII	𝍸	IIII	𝍸	IIII	𝍸	IIII	𝍸	IIII	𝍸	IIII	𝍸	IIII	𝍸	IIII
𝍸	IIII	II																	
				=2	171														

C. TREES GIRTHED

dbh cm	Tally of girth sample trees	Sample total No.	Stand total No.*	Vol. per tree† m³	Vol. of class (Cols. 4 x 5) m³
(1)	(2)	(3)	(4)	(5)	(6)
9	IIII	4	36	0.028	1.0
10	卌 I	6	54	0.041	2.2
11	IIII	4	36	0.056	2.0
12	卌 IIII	9	81	0.073	5.9
13	卌 卌 I	11	99	0.091	9.0
14	卌 卌 卌 III	18	162	0.110	17.8
15	卌 卌 IIII	14	126	0.131	16.5
16	卌 卌 卌 卌 卌	25	225	0.153	34.4
17	卌 卌 卌 卌 卌 II	27	243	0.176	42.8
18	卌 卌 卌 卌 卌 卌 I	31	279	0.201	56.1
19	卌 卌 卌 卌 卌 III	28	252	0.228	57.5
20	卌 卌 卌 II	17	153	0.256	39.2
21	卌 卌 II	12	108	0.28	30.2
22	卌 卌 I	11	99	0.32	31.7
23	IIII	4	36	0.35	12.6
24	卌 II	7	63	0.38	23.9
25	卌 I	6	54	0.42	22.7
26	II	2	18	0.45	8.1
27	I	1	9	0.49	4.4
28	II	2	18	0.53	9.5
29	II	2	18	0.57	10.3
30					
1					
2					
3					
4					
5					
6					
7					
8					
9					
	Grand Totals	241	2169		437.8

*(Col. 4) Multiplication factor=

$$\frac{\text{No. of trees in stand}}{\text{No. of trees in sample}} \quad \frac{2171}{241} = 9$$

†(Col. 5) Volume per tree is obtained from the Tariff Tables using column appropriate for mean Tariff number

PROCEDURE 9

ESTIMATION OF STAND VOLUME FOR INVENTORY PURPOSES

General

1. This method provides suitable estimates of standing volumes for inventory purposes, for valuation, or for any purpose for which speed and low-cost is desired rather than a high degree of precision.

2. The method is less precise for crops which are very variable in species and in height, and in such crops convenient stratification into more homogeneous parts may be necessary to retain an adequate level of precision.

3. The method requires assessments of basal area per hectare, top height of the crop and the net area of the stand.

Note:

a. The *basal area* of an individual tree is the overbark cross-sectional area of the stem at breast height. *Basal area per hectare* is the sum of the basal areas of all trees in one hectare. Where volume estimates are concerned *measurable basal area* is used, ie trees of less than 7 cm dbh are excluded.

b. *Net area* is the gross area of the stand less unproductive areas such as roads, rides etc.

4. Volume estimates are derived from the product of basal area and *form height*. Form height is in turn the product of the mean height of the stand and the crop form factor. This quantity is found to be closely related to the top height of the stand, and by assessing top height, form height can be predicted.

5. Crop form heights are tabulated against top height in Table 8 (page 85). Form heights appropriate to thinnings are given separately in Table 9 for conifers only.

6. The values given here are mean values derived from permanent sample plot data. Clearly, local variations will exist depending on both climatic and stand conditions.

7. In even aged woodlands the tabulated values of form height will usually be within ±10% of the true value in 95% of cases. With most hardwoods however, the values will be less precise where top height is less than 13 m or greater than 25 m.

Practice

8. Top height should be estimated as described in Part V (4), page 144. It is important that the samples are taken throughout the area in order to obtain adequate representation of the stand.

9. Basal area per hectare may be obtained in several different ways.

(i) For small areas it is possible to measure the dbh of all trees, classify them and convert this tally to basal area using Table 64 (pages 202–241). (The basal area for any dbh is equivalent to the volume indicated for a length of 1 m, but expressed in square metres, eg a tree of 20 cm has a basal area of 0·031 sq m (page 204)).

(ii) It is more usual, however, to sample basal area. This can be done by laying down plots and assessing the dbh of all trees of 7 cm and above within the plot, converting these values to basal area, summing the values for the plots assessed, and converting this value to a per hectare basis by multiplying by the factor: 1 ha ÷ total area of sample plots. Plots should be of sufficient size as to include some 7–20 reckonable trees. In most cases plots of 0·01 ha will be suitable but for older stands (fewer trees per hectare) larger plots will be more appropriate. The number of plots will depend largely on the stand area and the variation within the stand, but also on the size of plots used. Using plots of 0·01 ha in reasonably uniform stands, about 5 plots will be required in stands of up to 2·0 ha, 8 plots in stands of 2·0–10·0 ha and about 12 in stands of over 10·0 ha. For more variable stands the number should be increased.

(iii) Easily the most convenient way of estimating basal area for the purpose intended here is by point sampling using a relascope. The use of relascopes is outlined in Part V (3), page 135.

10. Using the established top height and basal area per hectare data, the volume per hectare can be determined from Stand Volume Charts Nos. 20–37 given on pages 90–107. The appropriate values should be joined with a straight edge and the volume per hectare read from the right hand scale. Alternatively the basal area should be multiplied by the appropriate form height taken from Table 8. Where, in conifers, volume estimates are required of trees marked for thinnings, better estimates will be obtained by using the form heights given in Table 9. This assumes a predominantly low or 'intermediate' type of thinning.

11. The final step is to multiply the volume per hectare figure by the net area of the crop being assessed.

12. Where crop variation, particularly in height, is not random but follows a detectable geographical distribution, then it is better to calculate the volume for each plot using top height and basal area figures for the plot, presuming the plots are proportionately distributed; calculate an average volume per plot, and hence for the whole area.

13. Worked examples are shown on pages 83-84. Example (1) illustrates the calculation of a main crop volume where a relascope is used to assess basal area. Example (2) shows the calculation of a main crop volume where plots are used to assess basal area. Both methods of calculating basal area are of course acceptable in each case, though the relascope is generally more convenient.

Worked Example (1)

Species — *Scots pine*
Area — *8·0 ha*
Relascope Factor — *2*
Main Crop

Sampling Point	*Relascope Count*	*Top Ht. in Sample*
1	*13*	*15·3*
2	*11*	*15·1*
3	*16*	
4	*14*	*14·9*
5	*14*	*15·6*
6	*13*	
7	*14*	*14·4*
8	*12*	*14·9*
9	*16*	
10	*14*	*15·2*
11	*17*	*14·9*
12	*14*	
Total	*168*	*120·3*
Mean	*14·0*	*15·0*

Top Height — *15·0 m*

Basal Area — *28·0 m^2/ha*

Volume/ha — *178·0 m^3 (from chart No. 20)*

Volume of stand — *1424 m^3*

Worked Example (2)

Species—Scots pine *Plot Size 0·01 ha*

Area 8·0 ha

dbh cm	*Plot number*								*Total*	*Total Basal Area m²*
	1	2	3	4	5	6	7	8		
10	*I*	*I*							*2*	*0·016*
11			*I*	*I*	*I*				*3*	*0·029*
12	*II*	*II*	*II*		*I*		*I*	*I*	*9*	*0·102*
13	*I*	*I*		*II*	*II*	*II*	*II*	*I*	*11*	*0·15*
14	*II*	*II*	*III*	*IIII*	*I*	*I*	*III*	*II*	*18*	*0·28*
15	*II*	*I*	*I*	*II*	*III*	*III*	*II*		*14*	*0·25*
16	*I*	*I*		*I*			*III*	*II*	*8*	*0·161*
17			*I*	*I*	*I*				*3*	*0·068*
18	*I*	*I*	*I*			*I*	*I*	*I*	*6*	*0·153*
19	*I*			*I*	*I*	*I*			*4*	*0·113*
20		*I*	*I*	*I*					*3*	*0·094*
21							*I*	*I*	*2*	*0·069*
Total									*83*	*1·485*

Basal Area per ha = *1·485/0·08*

= *18·563 m²*

Top Ht. = *15·0 m*

Form Ht. = *6·36 (Top ht. 15·0 m, table 8)*

Volume per ha = *118·1 m³*

Main crop volume for stand—944·8 m³

MAIN CROP FORM HEIGHT

Top Ht in Metres	S P	C P	L P	S S	N S	E L	JL/HL	Top Ht in Metres
8.0	3.08	3.30	2.99	3.24	2.97	2.53	2.85	8.0
8.5	3.32	3.55	3.25	3.47	3.20	2.79	3.12	8.5
9.0	3.55	3.81	3.52	3.69	3.43	3.05	3.39	9.0
9.5	3.79	4.06	3.78	3.91	3.67	3.31	3.66	9.5
10.0	4.02	4.31	4.04	4.13	3.90	3.57	3.93	10.0
10.5	4.25	4.56	4.30	4.36	4.13	3.83	4.20	10.5
11.0	4.49	4.82	4.56	4.58	4.37	4.09	4.47	11.0
11.5	4.72	5.07	4.82	4.80	4.60	4.35	4.74	11.5
12.0	4.96	5.32	5.08	5.02	4.84	4.61	5.01	12.0
12.5	5.19	5.57	5.34	5.25	5.07	4.87	5.27	12.5
13.0	5.43	5.83	5.61	5.47	5.30	5.13	5.54	13.0
13.5	5.66	6.08	5.87	5.69	5.54	5.39	5.81	13.5
14.0	5.89	6.33	6.13	5.91	5.77	5.65	6.08	14.0
14.5	6.13	6.58	6.39	6.14	6.00	5.91	6.35	14.5
15.0	6.36	6.84	6.65	6.36	6.24	6.17	6.62	15.0
15.5	6.60	7.09	6.91	6.58	6.47	6.43	6.89	15.5
16.0	6.83	7.34	7.17	6.80	6.70	6.69	7.16	16.0
16.5	7.06	7.59	7.44	7.03	6.94	6.95	7.43	16.5
17.0	7.30	7.85	7.70	7.25	7.17	7.21	7.70	17.0
17.5	7.53	8.10	7.96	7.47	7.40	7.48	7.97	17.5
18.0	7.77	8.35	8.22	7.69	7.64	7.74	8.24	18.0
18.5	8.00	8.60	8.48	7.91	7.87	8.00	8.51	18.5
19.0	8.23	8.86	8.74	8.14	8.10	8.26	8.78	19.0
19.5	8.47	9.11	9.00	8.36	8.34	8.52	9.04	19.5
20.0	8.70	9.36	9.27	8.58	8.57	8.78	9.31	20.0
20.5	8.94	9.61	9.53	8.80	8.81	9.04	9.58	20.5
21.0	9.17	9.87	9.79	9.03	9.04	9.30	9.85	21.0
21.5	9.41	10.12	10.05	9.25	9.27	9.56	10.12	21.5
22.0	9.64	10.37	10.31	9.47	9.51	9.82	10.39	22.0
22.5	9.87	10.62	10.57	9.69	9.74	10.08	10.66	22.5
23.0	10.11	10.88	10.83	9.92	9.97	10.34	10.93	23.0
23.5	10.34	11.13	11.10	10.14	10.21	10.60	11.20	23.5
24.0	10.58	11.38	11.36	10.36	10.44	10.86	11.47	24.0
24.5	10.81	11.63	11.62	10.58	10.67	11.12	11.74	24.5
25.0	11.04	11.89	11.88	10.81	10.91	11.38	12.01	25.0
25.5	11.28	12.14	12.14	11.03	11.14	11.64	12.28	25.5
26.0	11.51	12.39	12.40	11.25	11.37	11.90	12.55	26.0
26.5	11.75	12.65	12.66	11.47	11.61	12.16	12.81	26.5
27.0	11.98	12.90	12.92	11.70	11.84	12.42	13.08	27.0
27.5	12.22	13.15	13.19	11.92	12.07	12.68	13.35	27.5
28.0	12.45	13.40	13.45	12.14	12.31	12.94	13.62	28.0
28.5	12.68	13.66	13.71	12.36	12.54	13.20	13.89	28.5
29.0	12.92	13.91	13.97	12.58	12.78	13.46	14.16	29.0
29.5	13.15	14.16	14.23	12.81	13.01	13.72	14.43	29.5
30.0	13.39	14.41	14.49	13.03	13.24	13.98	14.70	30.0

MAIN CROP FORM HEIGHT

Top Ht in Metres	Species							Top Ht in Metres
	D F	W H	R C	L C	G F	N F	OMS	
8.0	2.90	3.64	2.95	2.44	2.93	3.37	3.06	8.0
8.5	3.12	3.86	3.14	2.83	3.17	3.60	3.35	8.5
9.0	3.33	4.09	3.34	3.21	3.41	3.83	3.65	9.0
9.5	3.54	4.31	3.53	3.59	3.64	4.05	3.95	9.5
10.0	3.76	4.53	3.72	3.97	3.88	4.28	4.24	10.0
10.5	3.97	4.75	3.92	4.34	4.12	4.51	4.54	10.5
11.0	4.18	4.97	4.11	4.71	4.35	4.74	4.84	11.0
11.5	4.40	5.19	4.31	5.07	4.59	4.97	5.13	11.5
12.0	4.61	5.42	4.50	5.43	4.83	5.20	5.43	12.0
12.5	4.82	5.64	4.70	5.78	5.06	5.43	5.73	12.5
13.0	5.04	5.86	4.89	6.13	5.30	5.66	6.02	13.0
13.5	5.25	6.08	5.08	6.48	5.54	5.89	6.32	13.5
14.0	5.46	6.30	5.28	6.82	5.77	6.12	6.61	14.0
14.5	5.68	6.52	5.47	7.15	6.01	6.35	6.91	14.5
15.0	5.89	6.75	5.67	7.48	6.25	6.58	7.21	15.0
15.5	6.10	6.97	5.86	7.80	6.48	6.80	7.50	15.5
16.0	6.32	7.19	6.06	8.13	6.72	7.03	7.80	16.0
16.5	6.53	7.41	6.25	8.44	6.96	7.26	8.10	16.5
17.0	6.74	7.63	6.45	8.75	7.19	7.49	8.39	17.0
17.5	6.96	7.85	6.64	9.06	7.43	7.72	8.69	17.5
18.0	7.17	8.07	6.83	9.36	7.67	7.95	8.99	18.0
18.5	7.38	8.30	7.03	9.66	7.90	8.18	9.28	18.5
19.0	7.60	8.52	7.22	9.95	8.14	8.41	9.58	19.0
19.5	7.81	8.74	7.42	10.24	8.38	8.64	9.87	19.5
20.0	8.02	8.96	7.61	10.52	8.61	8.87	10.17	20.0
20.5	8.24	9.18	7.81	10.80	8.85	9.10	10.47	20.5
21.0	8.45	9.40	8.00	11.07	9.09	9.32	10.76	21.0
21.5	8.66	9.63	8.19	11.34	9.32	9.55	11.06	21.5
22.0	8.88	9.85	8.39	11.61	9.56	9.78	11.36	22.0
22.5	9.09	10.07	8.58	11.86	9.80	10.01	11.65	22.5
23.0	9.30	10.29	8.78	12.12	10.03	10.24	11.95	23.0
23.5	9.52	10.51	8.97	12.37	10.27	10.47	12.25	23.5
24.0	9.73	10.73	9.17	12.62	10.51	10.70	12.54	24.0
24.5	9.94	10.95	9.36	12.86	10.74	10.93	12.84	24.5
25.0	10.16	11.18	9.55	13.09	10.98	11.16	13.13	25.0
25.5	10.37	11.40	9.75		11.22	11.39		25.5
26.0	10.58	11.62	9.94		11.45	11.62		26.0
26.5	10.80	11.84	10.14		11.69	11.85		26.5
27.0	11.01	12.06	10.33		11.93	12.07		27.0
27.5	11.22	12.28	10.53		12.16	12.30		27.5
28.0	11.44	12.51	10.72		12.40	12.53		28.0
28.5	11.65	12.73	10.92		12.64	12.76		28.5
29.0	11.86	12.95	11.11		12.87	12.99		29.0
29.5	12.08	13.17	11.30		13.11	13.22		29.5
30.0	12.29	13.39	11.50		13.35	13.45		30.0

 Table 8 (contd)

MAIN CROP FORM HEIGHT

Top Ht in Metres	OAK	BEECH	S.A.B	POP	Top Ht in Metres
8.0	2.40	1.32	0.95	2.60	8.0
8.5	2.71	1.64	1.45	2.83	8.5
9.0	3.02	1.95	1.91	3.06	9.0
9.5	3.32	2.27	2.35	3.28	9.5
10.0	3.61	2.58	2.76	3.51	10.0
10.5	3.91	2.88	3.15	3.73	10.5
11.0	4.19	3.19	3.52	3.94	11.0
11.5	4.48	3.48	3.87	4.16	11.5
12.0	4.76	3.78	4.21	4.37	12.0
12.5	5.04	4.07	4.53	4.58	12.5
13.0	5.31	4.36	4.83	4.79	13.0
13.5	5.58	4.65	5.13	4.99	13.5
14.0	5.85	4.93	5.41	5.20	14.0
14.5	6.11	5.21	5.68	5.40	14.5
15.0	6.36	5.48	5.95	5.59	15.0
15.5	6.62	5.75	6.20	5.79	15.5
16.0	6.87	6.02	6.44	5.98	16.0
16.5	7.11	6.29	6.68	6.17	16.5
17.0	7.35	6.55	6.90	6.35	17.0
17.5	7.59	6.81	7.12	6.54	17.5
18.0	7.82	7.06	7.34	6.72	18.0
18.5	8.05	7.31	7.55	6.90	18.5
19.0	8.28	7.56	7.75	7.07	19.0
19.5	8.50	7.80	7.94	7.25	19.5
20.0	8.72	8.04	8.13	7.42	20.0
20.5	8.93	8.28	8.32	7.58	20.5
21.0	9.14	8.52	8.50	7.75	21.0
21.5	9.35	8.75	8.67	7.91	21.5
22.0	9.55	8.97	8.84	8.07	22.0
22.5	9.75	9.20	9.01	8.23	22.5
23.0	9.94	9.42	9.17	8.38	23.0
23.5	10.13	9.63	9.33	8.53	23.5
24.0	10.32	9.85	9.49	8.68	24.0
24.5	10.50	10.06	9.64	8.83	24.5
25.0	10.68	10.26	9.79	8.97	25.0
25.5	10.85	10.46	9.93	9.12	25.5
26.0	11.02	10.66	10.07	9.25	26.0
26.5	11.19	10.86	10.21	9.39	26.5
27.0	11.35	11.05	10.35	9.52	27.0
27.5	11.51	11.24	10.48	9.65	27.5
28.0	11.67	11.43	10.61	9.78	28.0
28.5	11.82	11.61	10.74	9.91	28.5
29.0	11.96	11.79	10.87	10.03	29.0
29.5	12.11	11.96	10.99	10.15	29.5
30.0	12.25	12.13	11.11	10.27	30.0

THINNING FORM HEIGHT

Top Ht in Metres	Species S P	C P	L P	S S	N S	E L	JL/HL	Top Ht in Metres
8.0	2.26	2.52	2.72	2.83	2.52	1.70	2.35	8.0
8.5	2.50	2.77	2.94	3.04	2.74	1.97	2.63	8.5
9.0	2.75	3.03	3.17	3.26	2.97	2.25	2.91	9.0
9.5	2.99	3.28	3.40	3.48	3.19	2.52	3.19	9.5
10.0	3.23	3.53	3.63	3.69	3.42	2.79	3.47	10.0
10.5	3.47	3.78	3.85	3.91	3.64	3.07	3.75	10.5
11.0	3.71	4.03	4.08	4.13	3.87	3.34	4.03	11.0
11.5	3.95	4.28	4.31	4.34	4.09	3.61	4.31	11.5
12.0	4.19	4.54	4.53	4.56	4.32	3.89	4.59	12.0
12.5	4.43	4.79	4.76	4.78	4.54	4.16	4.87	12.5
13.0	4.67	5.04	4.99	5.00	4.77	4.43	5.15	13.0
13.5	4.91	5.29	5.21	5.21	5.00	4.70	5.43	13.5
14.0	5.15	5.54	5.44	5.43	5.22	4.98	5.71	14.0
14.5	5.40	5.80	5.67	5.65	5.45	5.25	5.99	14.5
15.0	5.64	6.05	5.89	5.86	5.67	5.52	6.27	15.0
15.5	5.88	6.30	6.12	6.08	5.90	5.80	6.55	15.5
16.0	6.12	6.55	6.35	6.30	6.12	6.07	6.83	16.0
16.5	6.36	6.80	6.57	6.52	6.35	6.34	7.11	16.5
17.0	6.60	7.05	6.80	6.73	6.57	6.62	7.39	17.0
17.5	6.84	7.31	7.03	6.95	6.80	6.89	7.67	17.5
18.0	7.08	7.56	7.26	7.17	7.02	7.16	7.95	18.0
18.5	7.32	7.81	7.48	7.38	7.25	7.44	8.23	18.5
19.0	7.56	8.06	7.71	7.60	7.48	7.71	8.52	19.0
19.5	7.80	8.31	7.94	7.82	7.70	7.98	8.80	19.5
20.0	8.05	8.57	8.16	8.03	7.93	8.26	9.08	20.0
20.5	8.29	8.82	8.39	8.25	8.15	8.53	9.36	20.5
21.0	8.53	9.07	8.62	8.47	8.38	8.80	9.64	21.0
21.5	8.77	9.32	8.84	8.69	8.60	9.08	9.92	21.5
22.0	9.01	9.57	9.07	8.90	8.83	9.35	10.20	22.0
22.5	9.25	9.83	9.30	9.12	9.05	9.62	10.48	22.5
23.0	9.49	10.08	9.52	9.34	9.28	9.89	10.76	23.0
23.5	9.73	10.33	9.75	9.55	9.50	10.17	11.04	23.5
24.0	9.97	10.58	9.98	9.77	9.73	10.44	11.32	24.0
24.5	10.21	10.83	10.20	9.99	9.96	10.71	11.60	24.5
25.0	10.45	11.08	10.43	10.21	10.18	10.99	11.88	25.0
25.5	10.70	11.34	10.66	10.42	10.41	11.26	12.16	25.5
26.0	10.94	11.59	10.89	10.64	10.63	11.53	12.44	26.0
26.5	11.18	11.84	11.11	10.86	10.86	11.81	12.72	26.5
27.0	11.42	12.09	11.34	11.07	11.08	12.08	13.00	27.0
27.5	11.66	12.34	11.57	11.29	11.31	12.35	13.28	27.5
28.0	11.90	12.60	11.79	11.51	11.53	12.63	13.56	28.0
28.5	12.14	12.85	12.02	11.72	11.76	12.90	13.84	28.5
29.0	12.38	13.10	12.25	11.94	11.98	13.17	14.12	29.0
29.5	12.62	13.35	12.47	12.16	12.21	13.45	14.40	29.5
30.0	12.86	13.60	12.70	12.38	12.44	13.72	14.68	30.0

T H I N N I N G   F O R M   H E I G H T

Top Ht in Metres	Species							Top Ht in Metres
	D F	W H	R C	L C	G F	N F	O M S	
8.0	2.22	2.90	2.35	1.47	2.21	3.16	2.78	8.0
8.5	2.43	3.13	2.56	1.90	2.46	3.37	3.07	8.5
9.0	2.64	3.36	2.77	2.34	2.70	3.58	3.36	9.0
9.5	2.85	3.59	2.97	2.76	2.95	3.79	3.65	9.5
10.0	3.06	3.82	3.18	3.18	3.20	4.00	3.94	10.0
10.5	3.28	4.06	3.39	3.60	3.44	4.21	4.23	10.5
11.0	3.49	4.29	3.59	4.01	3.69	4.42	4.52	11.0
11.5	3.70	4.52	3.80	4.41	3.94	4.63	4.81	11.5
12.0	3.91	4.75	4.01	4.81	4.18	4.84	5.10	12.0
12.5	4.12	4.99	4.21	5.20	4.43	5.04	5.39	12.5
13.0	4.33	5.22	4.42	5.59	4.67	5.25	5.68	13.0
13.5	4.54	5.45	4.63	5.97	4.92	5.46	5.97	13.5
14.0	4.75	5.68	4.83	6.34	5.17	5.67	6.26	14.0
14.5	4.96	5.91	5.04	6.71	5.41	5.88	6.55	14.5
15.0	5.18	6.15	5.25	7.08	5.66	6.09	6.84	15.0
15.5	5.39	6.38	5.45	7.43	5.91	6.30	7.13	15.5
16.0	5.60	6.61	5.66	7.79	6.15	6.51	7.42	16.0
16.5	5.81	6.84	5.87	8.13	6.40	6.72	7.71	16.5
17.0	6.02	7.07	6.07	8.47	6.65	6.93	8.00	17.0
17.5	6.23	7.31	6.28	8.81	6.89	7.14	8.29	17.5
18.0	6.44	7.54	6.49	9.14	7.14	7.35	8.58	18.0
18.5	6.65	7.77	6.69	9.46	7.38	7.55	8.87	18.5
19.0	6.86	8.00	6.90	9.78	7.63	7.76	9.16	19.0
19.5	7.07	8.24	7.11	10.09	7.88	7.97	9.45	19.5
20.0	7.29	8.47	7.31	10.40	8.12	8.18	9.74	20.0
20.5	7.50	8.70	7.52	10.70	8.37	8.39	10.03	20.5
21.0	7.71	8.93	7.73	10.99	8.62	8.60	10.32	21.0
21.5	7.92	9.16	7.93	11.28	8.86	8.81	10.61	21.5
22.0	8.13	9.40	8.14	11.56	9.11	9.02	10.90	22.0
22.5	8.34	9.63	8.35	11.84	9.36	9.23	11.19	22.5
23.0	8.55	9.86	8.55	12.11	9.60	9.44	11.48	23.0
23.5	8.76	10.09	8.76	12.38	9.85	9.65	11.77	23.5
24.0	8.97	10.33	8.97	12.64	10.10	9.85	12.06	24.0
24.5	9.19	10.56	9.17	12.89	10.34	10.06	12.35	24.5
25.0	9.40	10.79	9.38	13.14	10.59	10.27	12.64	25.0
25.5	9.61	11.02	9.59		10.83	10.48		25.5
26.0	9.82	11.25	9.79		11.08	10.69		26.0
26.5	10.03	11.49	10.00		11.33	10.90		26.5
27.0	10.24	11.72	10.21		11.57	11.11		27.0
27.5	10.45	11.95	10.41		11.82	11.32		27.5
28.0	10.66	12.18	10.62		12.07	11.53		28.0
28.5	10.87	12.41	10.83		12.31	11.74		28.5
29.0	11.08	12.65	11.03		12.56	11.95		29.0
29.5	11.30	12.88	11.24		12.81	12.16		29.5
30.0	11.51	13.11	11.45		13.05	12.36		30.0

Stand Volume Chart

SCOTS PINE

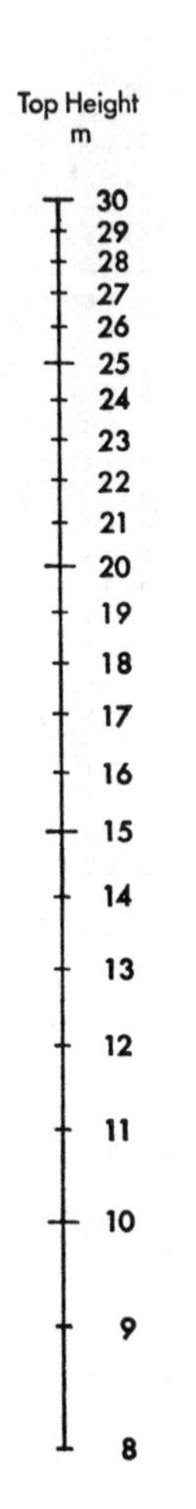
Top Height
m
30
29
28
27
26
25
24
23
22
21
20
19
18
17
16
15
14
13
12
11
10
9
8

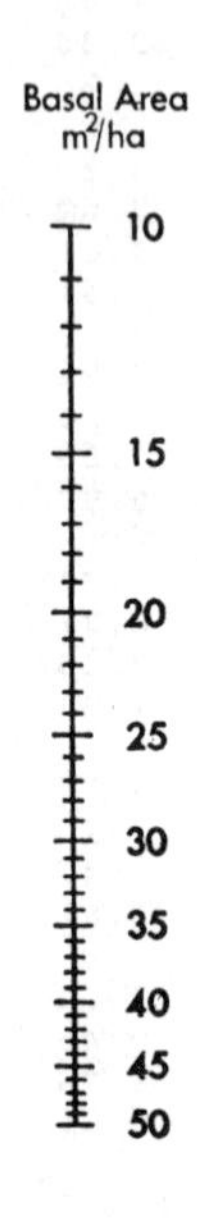
Basal Area
m²/ha
10
15
20
25
30
35
40
45
50

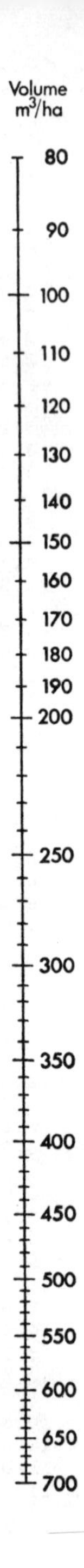
Volume
m³/ha
80
90
100
110
120
130
140
150
160
170
180
190
200
250
300
350
400
450
500
550
600
650
700

Stand Volume Chart

CORSICAN PINE

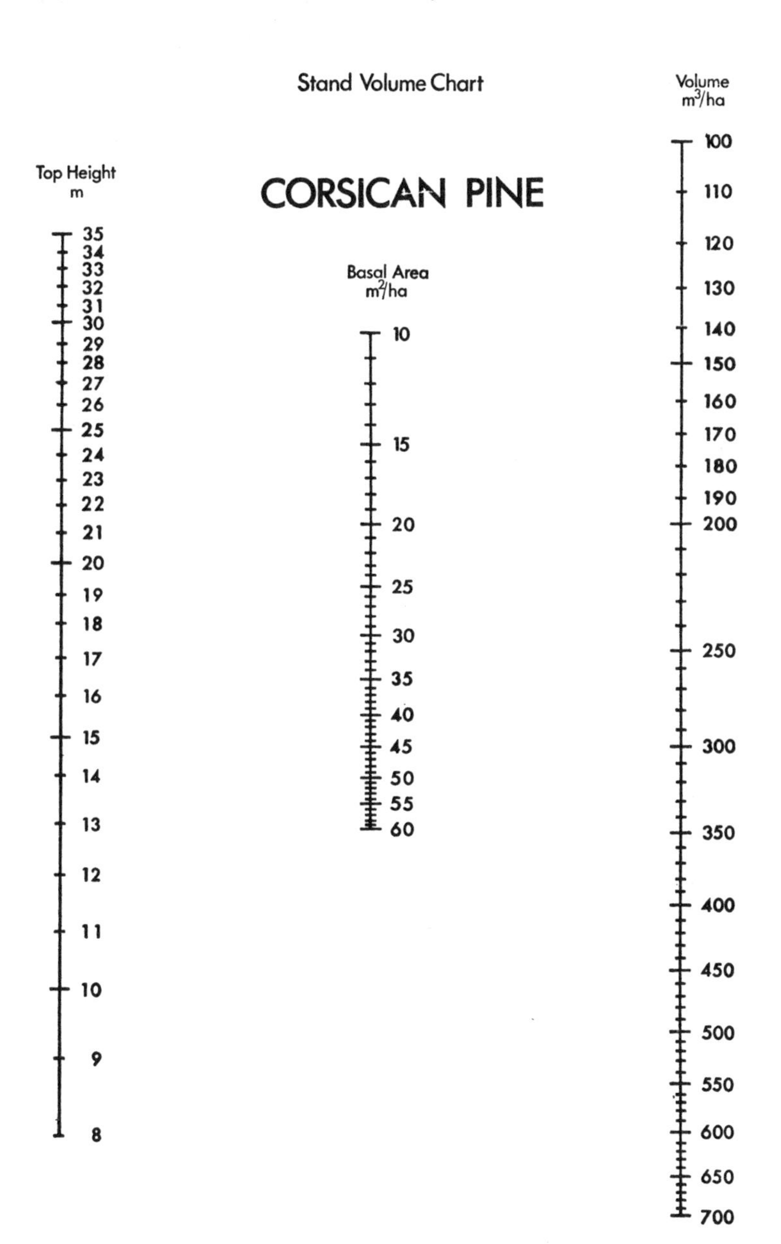

Stand Volume Chart

LODGEPOLE PINE

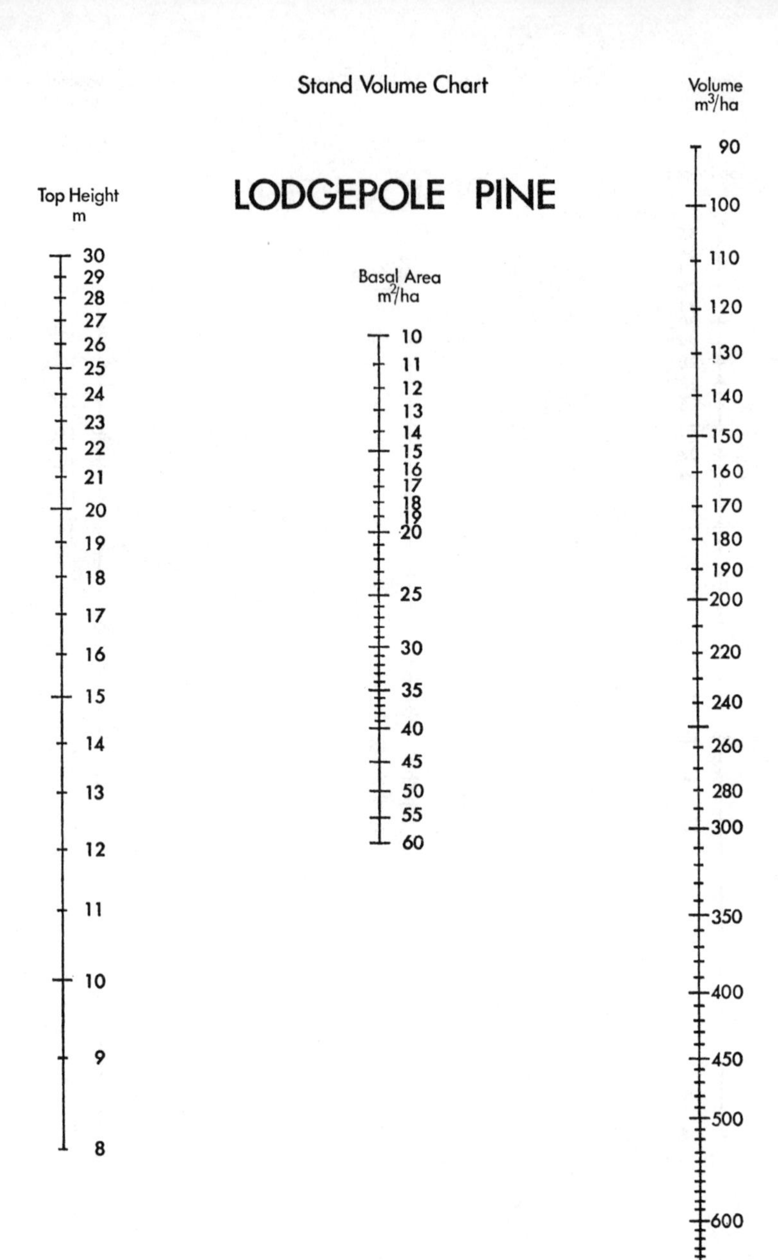

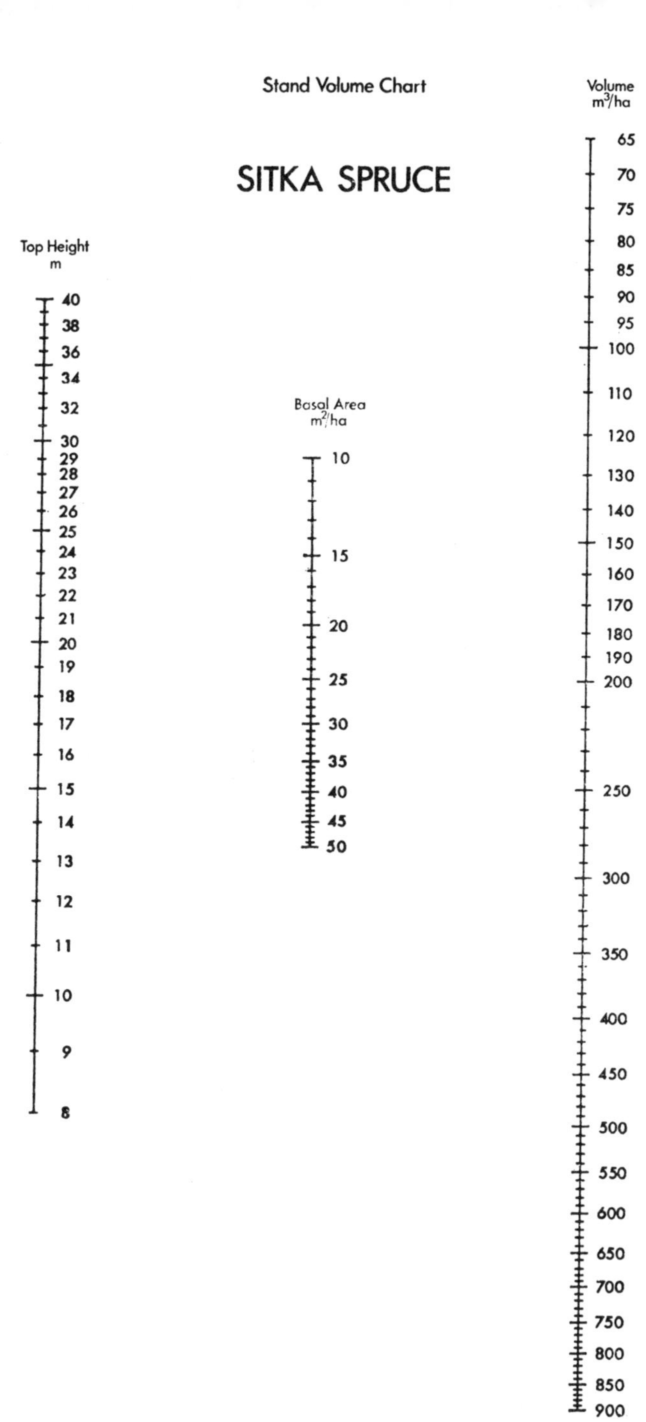
Stand Volume Chart
SITKA SPRUCE
Top Height
m
40
38
36
34
32
30
29
28
27
26
25
24
23
22
21
20
19
18
17
16
15
14
13
12
11
10
9
8
Basal Area
m²/ha
10
15
20
25
30
35
40
45
50
Volume
m³/ha
65
70
75
80
85
90
95
100
110
120
130
140
150
160
170
180
190
200
250
300
350
400
450
500
550
600
650
700
750
800
850
900

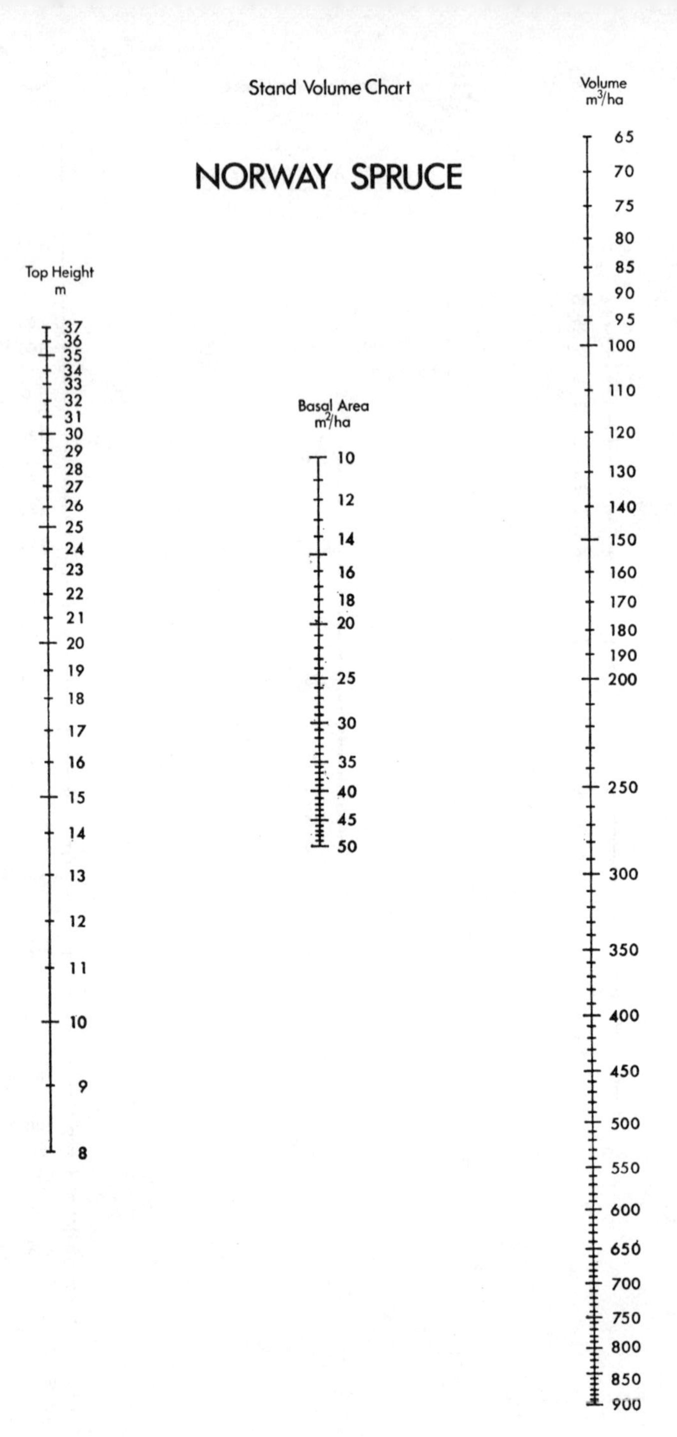
Stand Volume Chart
NORWAY SPRUCE
Top Height
m
37
36
35
34
33
32
31
30
29
28
27
26
25
24
23
22
21
20
19
18
17
16
15
14
13
12
11
10
9
8
Basal Area
m²/ha
10
12
14
16
18
20
25
30
35
40
45
50
Volume
m³/ha
65
70
75
80
85
90
95
100
110
120
130
140
150
160
170
180
190
200
250
300
350
400
450
500
550
600
650
700
750
800
850
900

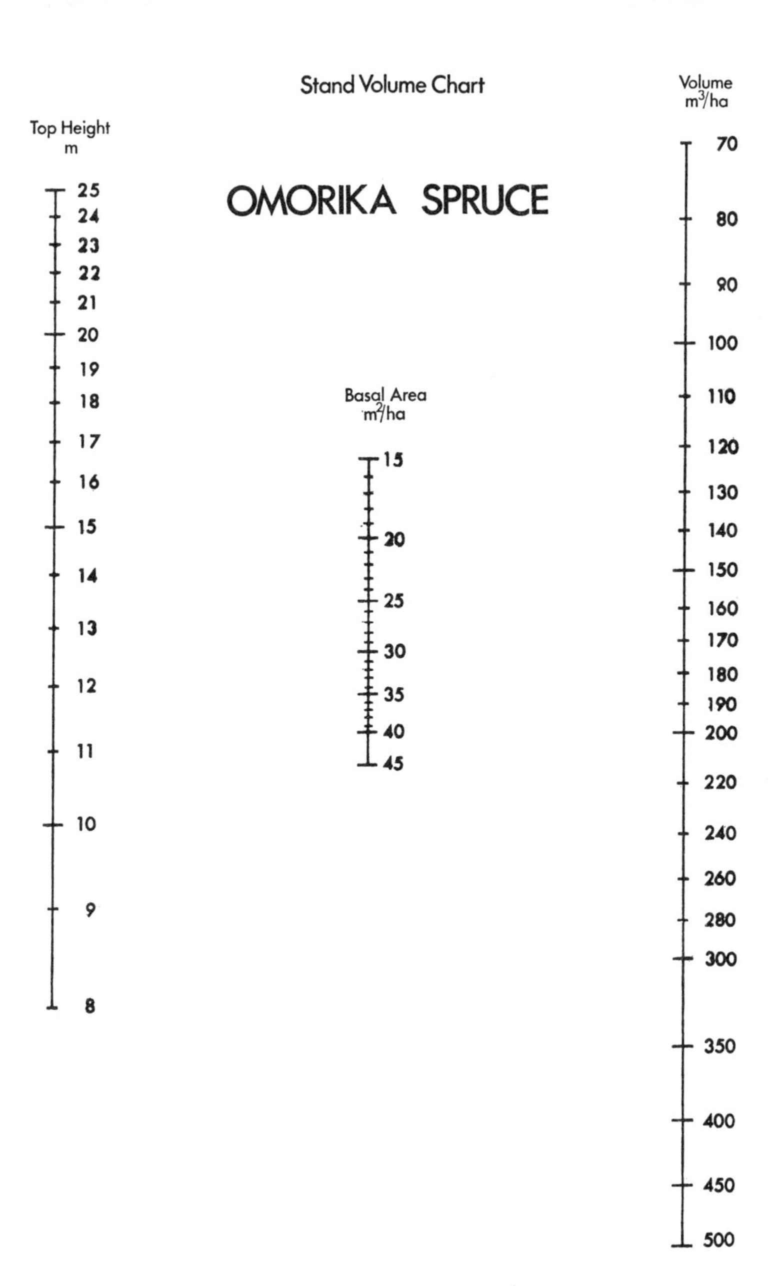
Stand Volume Chart
OMORIKA SPRUCE
Top Height
m
25
24
23
22
21
20
19
18
17
16
15
14
13
12
11
10
9
8
Basal Area
m2/ha
15
20
25
30
35
40
45
Volume
m3/ha
70
80
90
100
110
120
130
140
150
160
170
180
190
200
220
240
260
280
300
350
400
450
500

Stand Volume Chart

EUROPEAN LARCH

Volume
m^3/ha

50
55
60
65
70
75
80
85
90
95
100
110
120
130
140
150
160
170
180
190
200
250
300
350
400
450
500

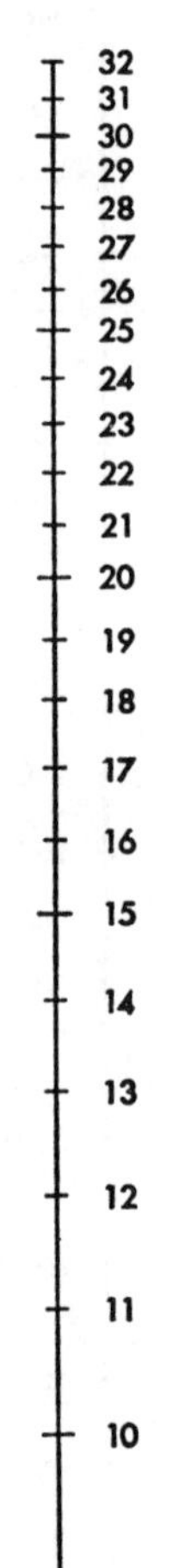

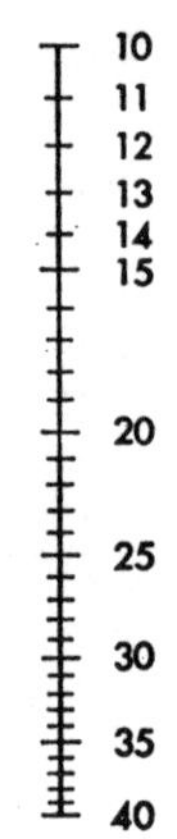

Basal Area
m^2/ha

Stand Volume Chart

JAPANESE AND HYBRID LARCH

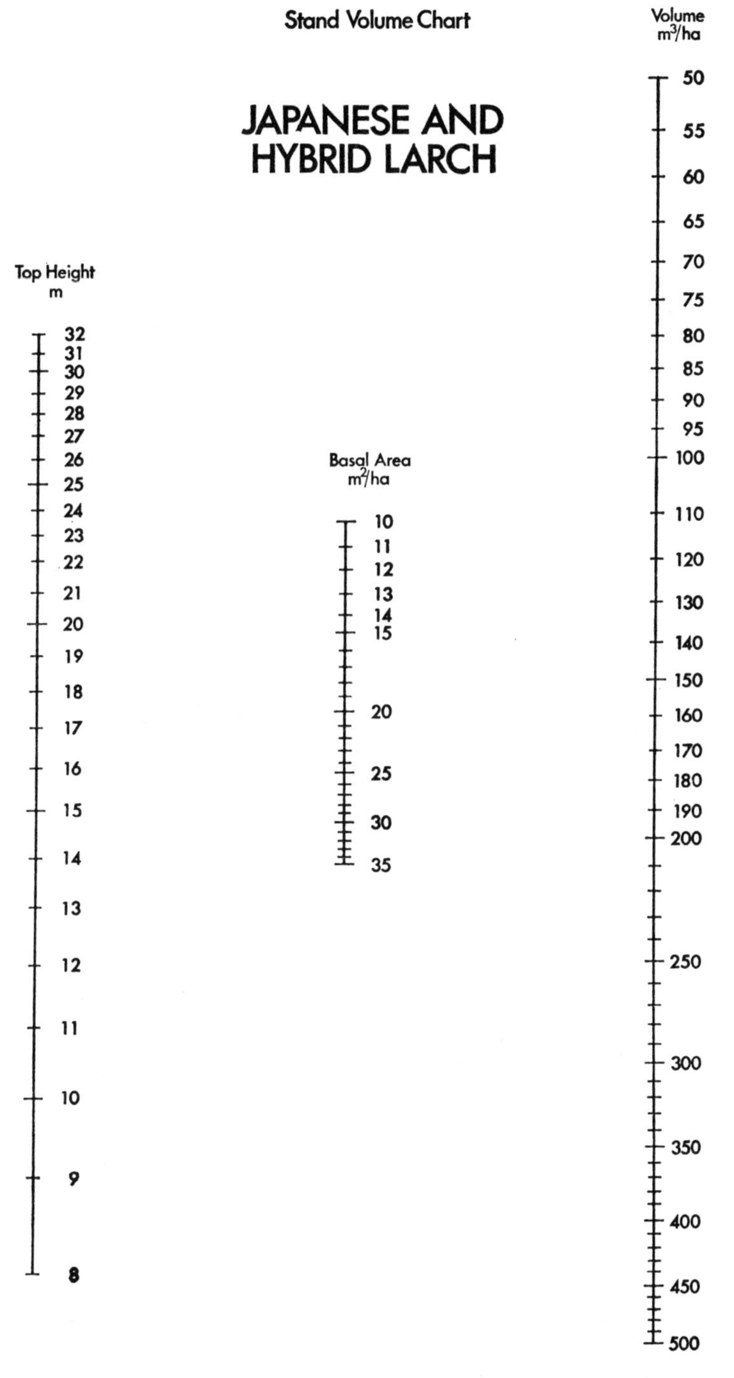

DOUGLAS FIR

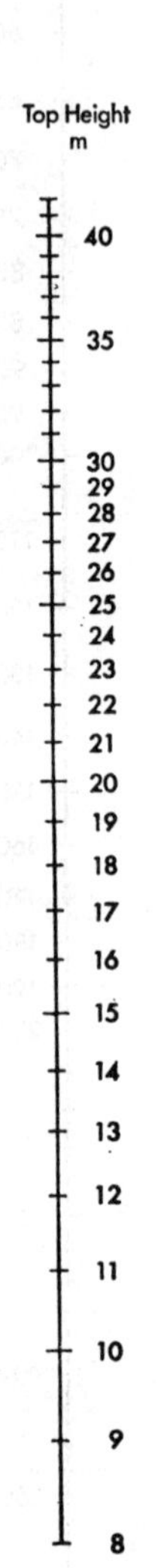
Top Height
m
40
35
30
29
28
27
26
25
24
23
22
21
20
19
18
17
16
15
14
13
12
11
10
9
8

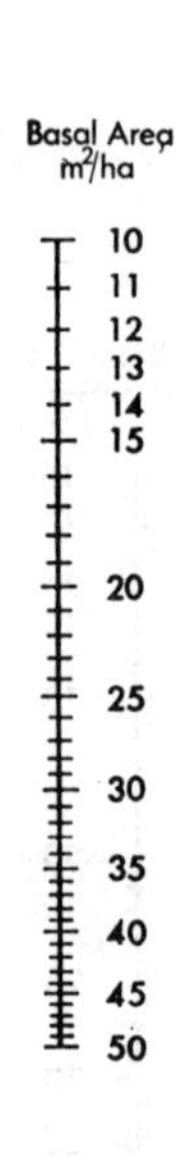
Basal Area
m²/ha
10
11
12
13
14
15
20
25
30
35
40
45
50

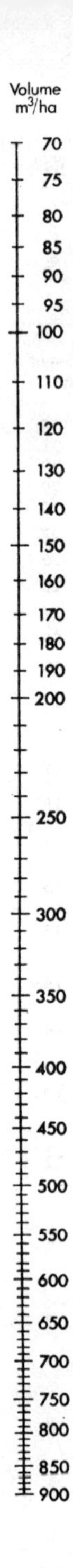
Volume
m³/ha
70
75
80
85
90
95
100
110
120
130
140
150
160
170
180
190
200
250
300
350
400
450
500
550
600
650
700
750
800
850
900

Stand Volume Chart

WESTERN HEMLOCK

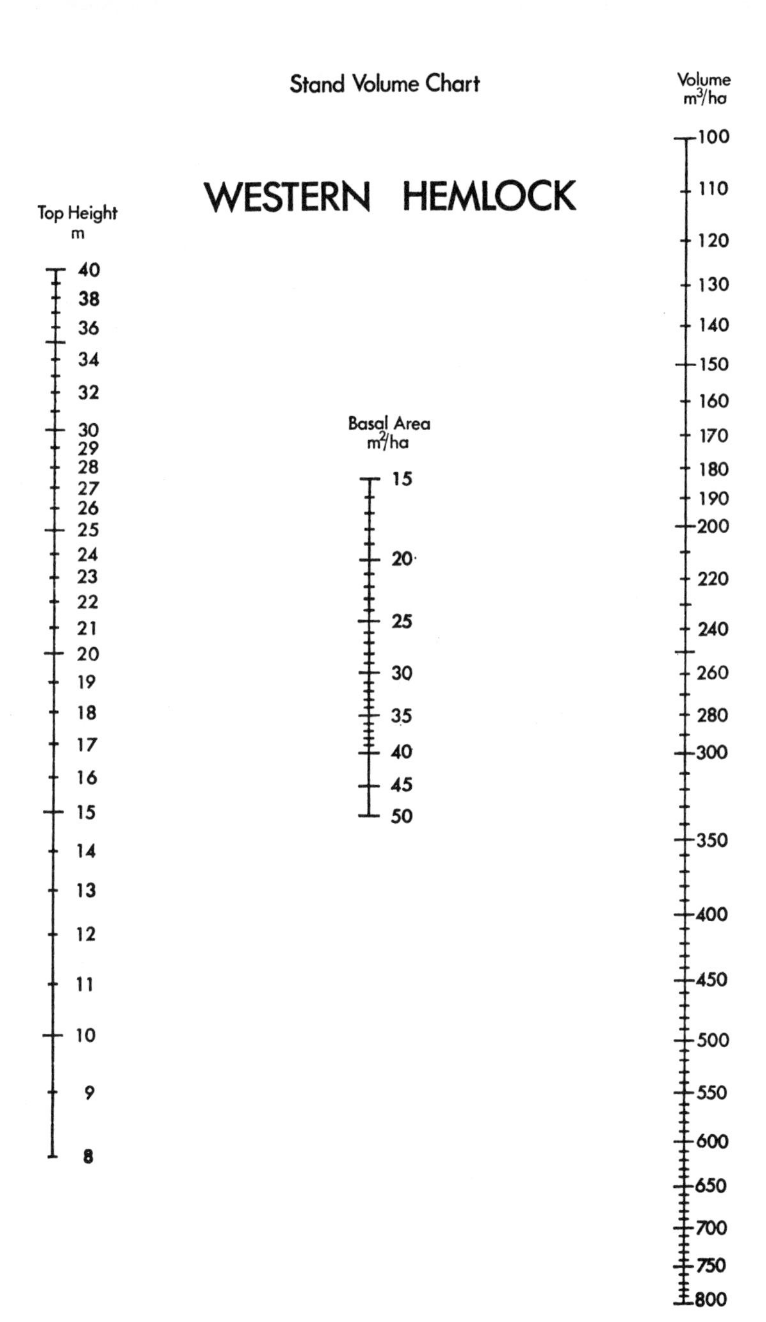

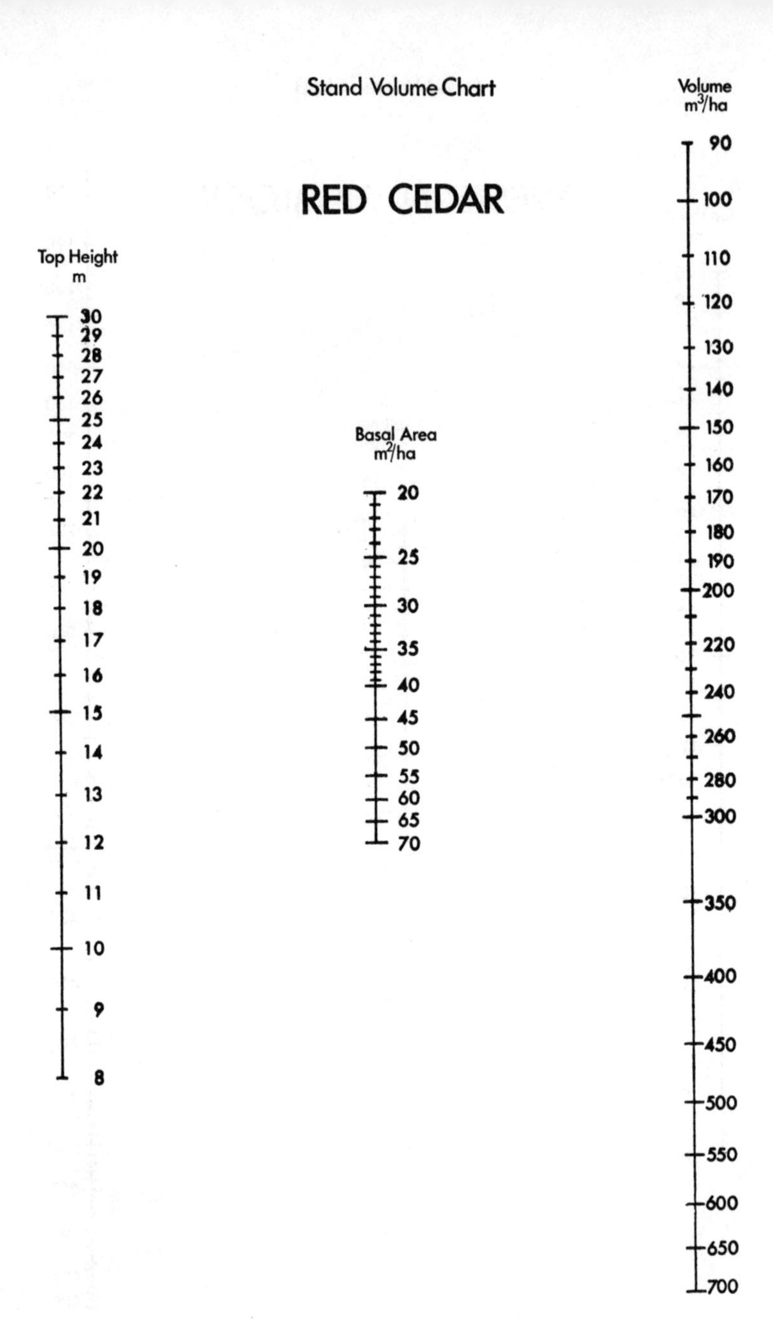
Stand Volume Chart
RED CEDAR
Top Height
m
30
29
28
27
26
25
24
23
22
21
20
19
18
17
16
15
14
13
12
11
10
9
8
Basal Area
m²/ha
20
25
30
35
40
45
50
55
60
65
70
Volume
m³/ha
90
100
110
120
130
140
150
160
170
180
190
200
220
240
260
280
300
350
400
450
500
550
600
650
700

Stand Volume Chart

LAWSON CYPRESS

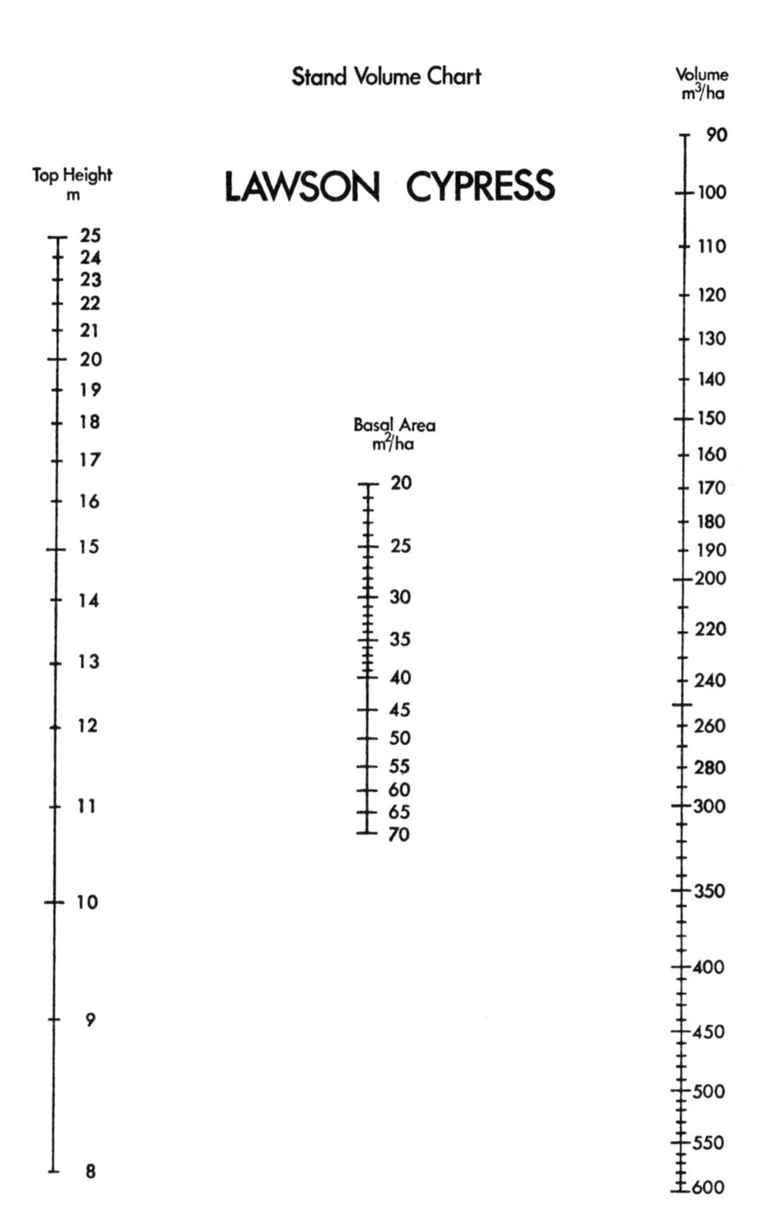

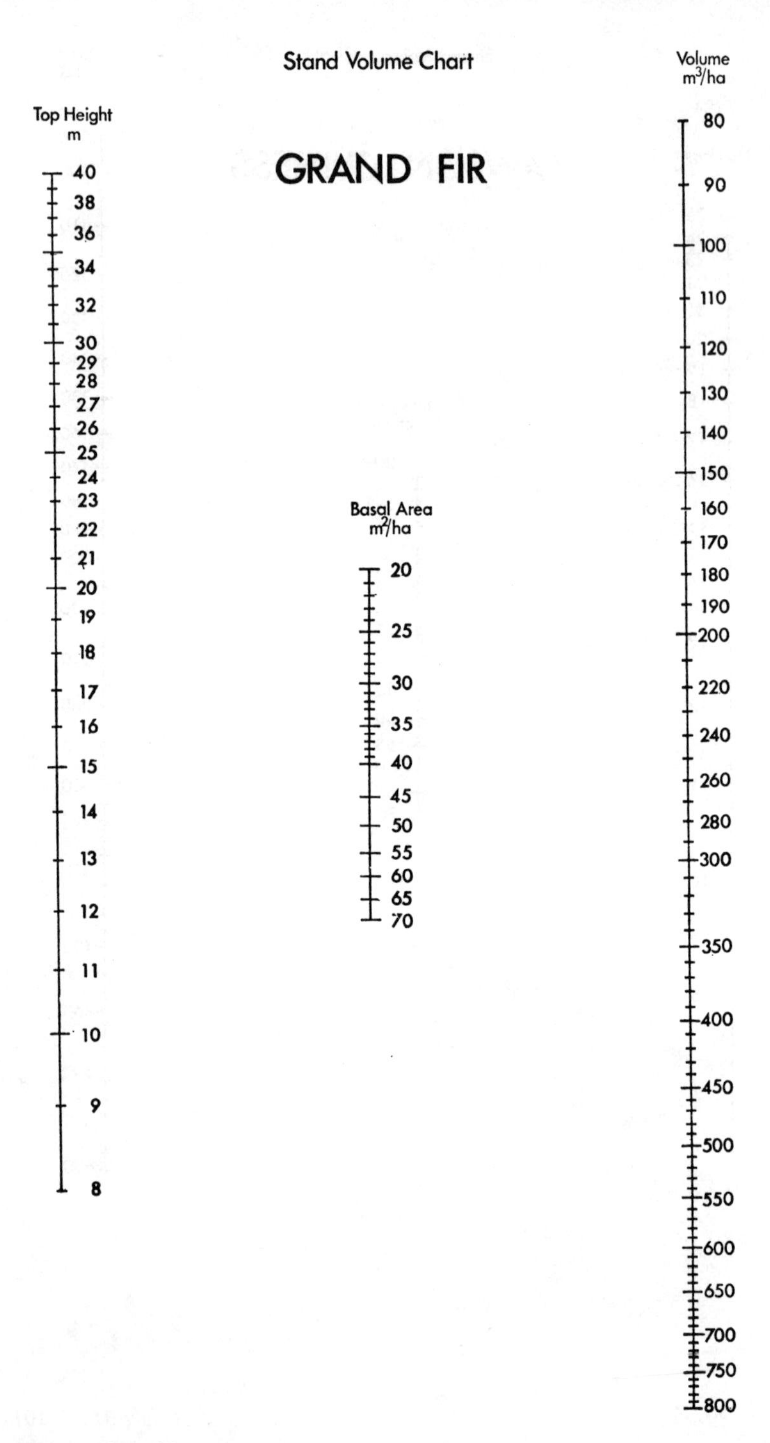
Stand Volume Chart
GRAND FIR
Top Height
m
40
38
36
34
32
30
29
28
27
26
25
24
23
22
21
20
19
18
17
16
15
14
13
12
11
10
9
8
Basal Area
m²/ha
20
25
30
35
40
45
50
55
60
65
70
Volume
m³/ha
80
90
100
110
120
130
140
150
160
170
180
190
200
220
240
260
280
300
350
400
450
500
550
600
650
700
750
800

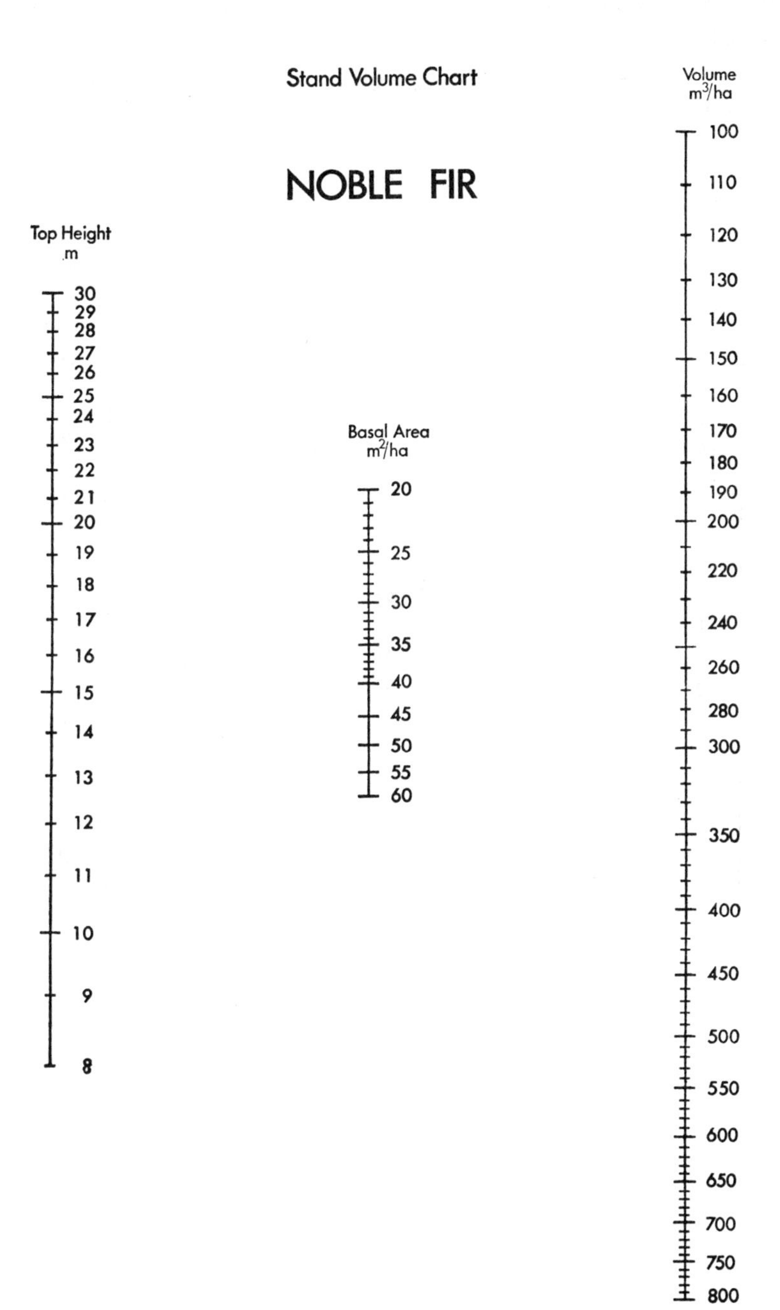
Stand Volume Chart
NOBLE FIR
Top Height m
30
29
28
27
26
25
24
23
22
21
20
19
18
17
16
15
14
13
12
11
10
9
8
Basal Area m²/ha
20
25
30
35
40
45
50
55
60
Volume m³/ha
100
110
120
130
140
150
160
170
180
190
200
220
240
260
280
300
350
400
450
500
550
600
650
700
750
800

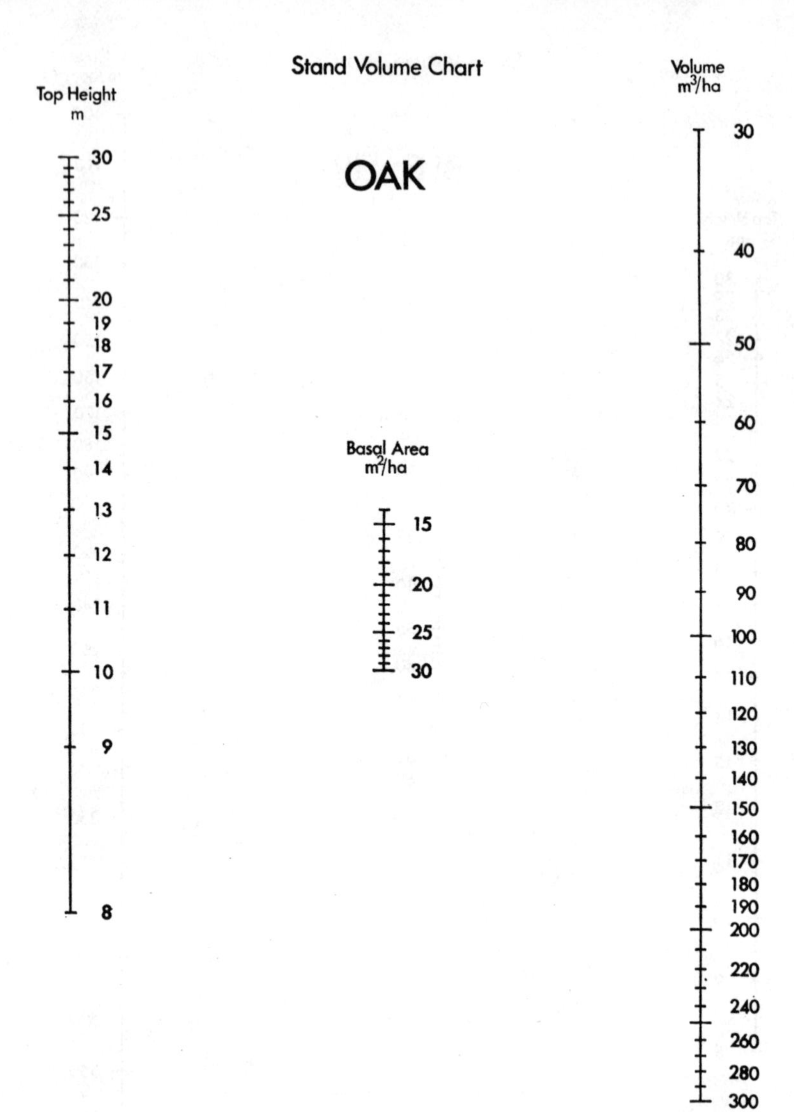
Stand Volume Chart
OAK
Top Height
m
30
25
20
19
18
17
16
15
14
13
12
11
10
9
8
Basal Area
m2/ha
15
20
25
30
Volume
m3/ha
30
40
50
60
70
80
90
100
110
120
130
140
150
160
170
180
190
200
220
240
260
280
300

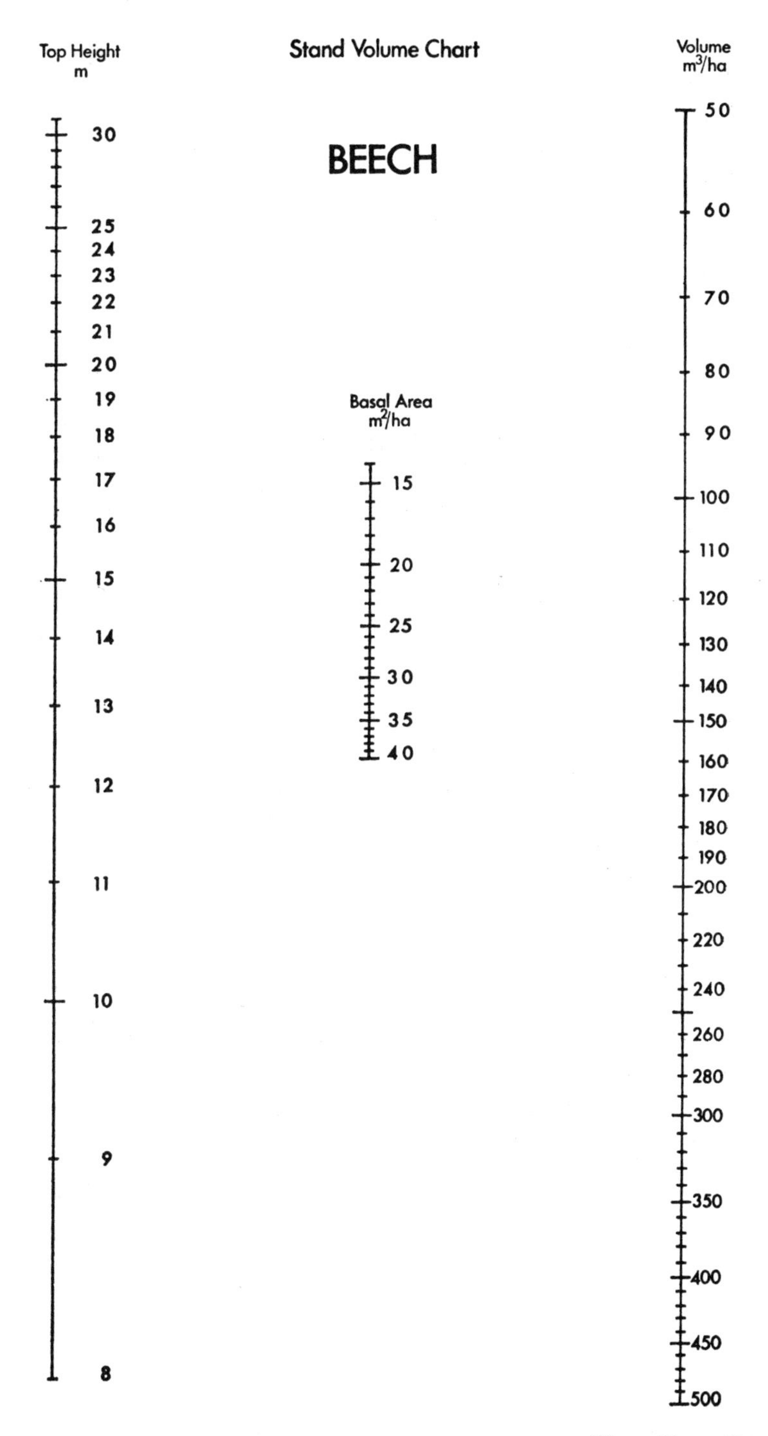
Top Height
m
30
25
24
23
22
21
20
19
18
17
16
15
14
13
12
11
10
9
8
Stand Volume Chart
BEECH
Basal Area
m²/ha
15
20
25
30
35
40
Volume
m³/ha
50
60
70
80
90
100
110
120
130
140
150
160
170
180
190
200
220
240
260
280
300
350
400
450
500

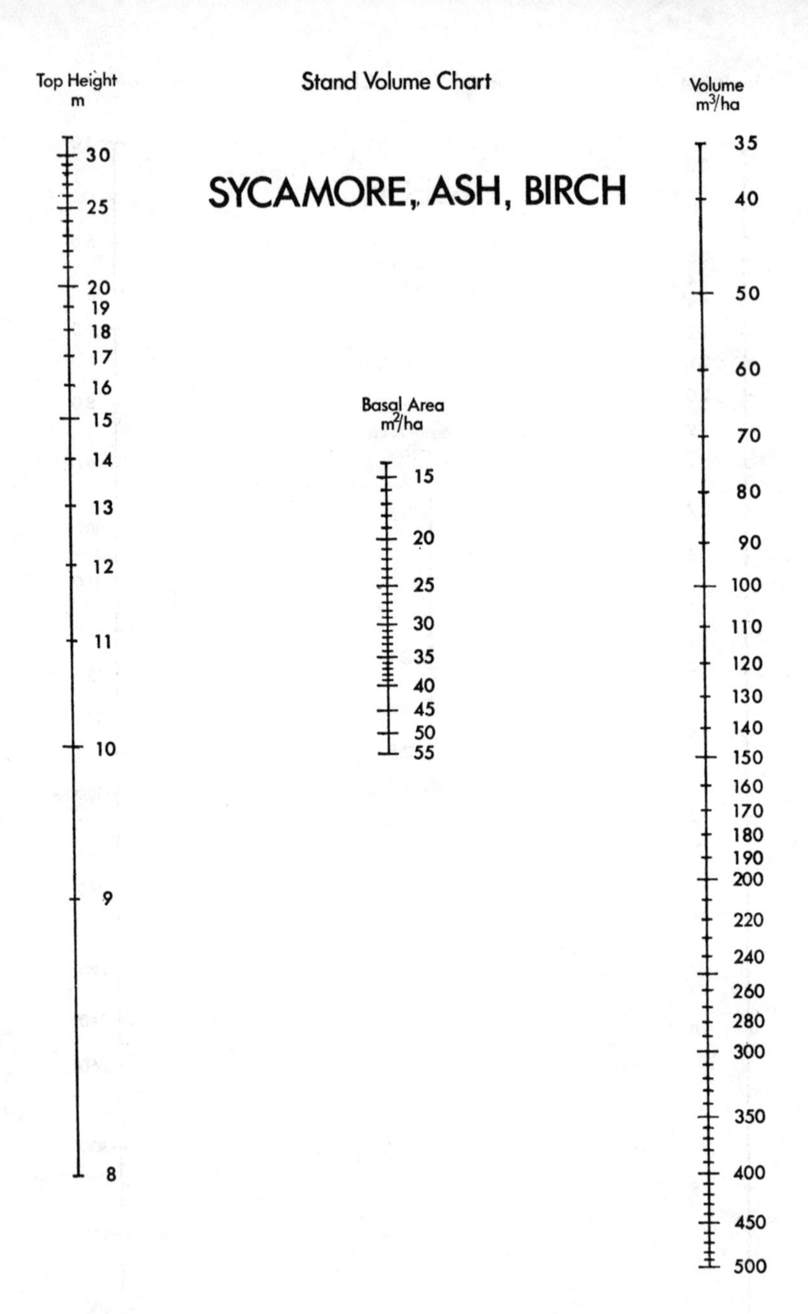

Top Height
m
Stand Volume Chart
Volume
m3/ha
SYCAMORE, ASH, BIRCH
30
25
20
19
18
17
16
15
14
13
12
11
10
9
8
Basal Area
m2/ha
15
20
25
30
35
40
45
50
55
35
40
50
60
70
80
90
100
110
120
130
140
150
160
170
180
190
200
220
240
260
280
300
350
400
450
500

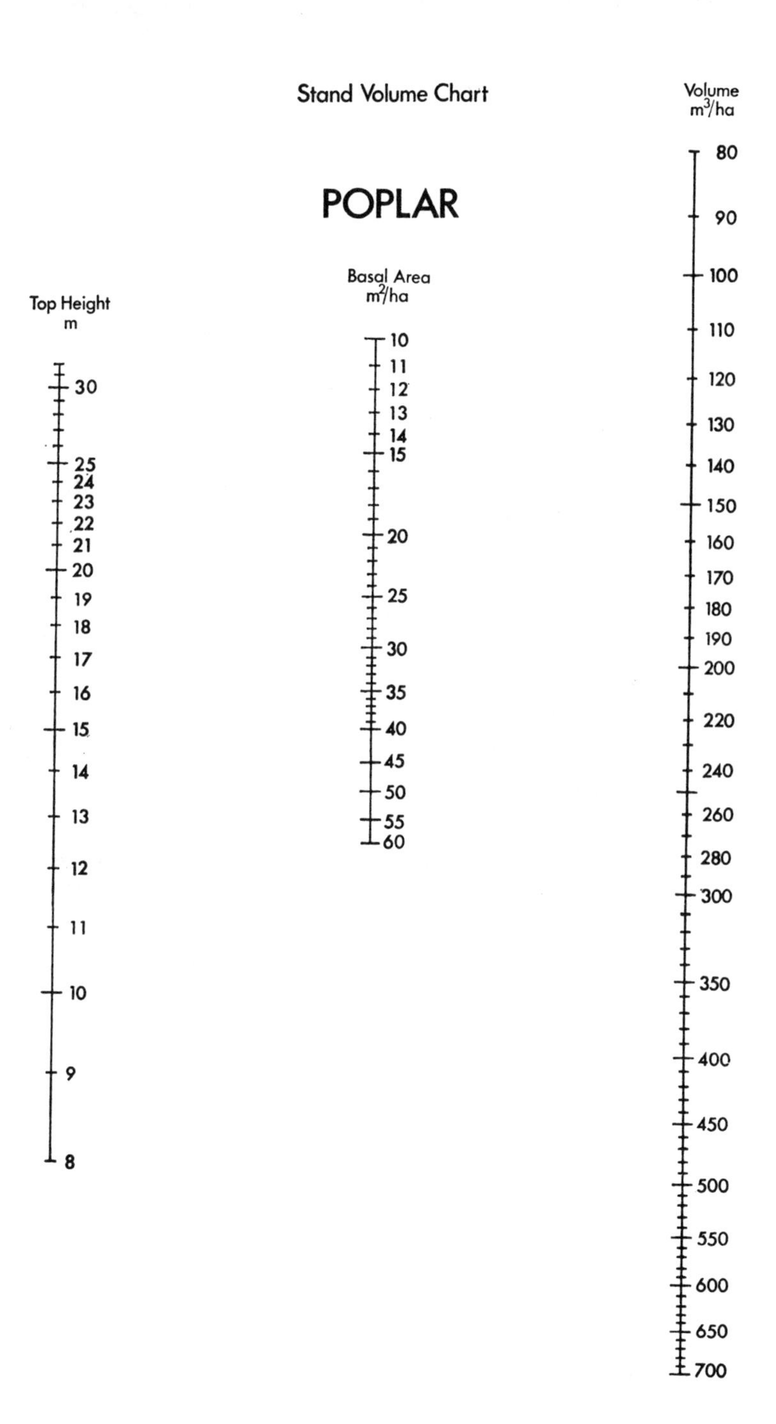
Stand Volume Chart
POPLAR
Top Height
m
30
25
24
23
22
21
20
19
18
17
16
15
14
13
12
11
10
9
8
Basal Area
m²/ha
10
11
12
13
14
15
20
25
30
35
40
45
50
55
60
Volume
m³/ha
80
90
100
110
120
130
140
150
160
170
180
190
200
220
240
260
280
300
350
400
450
500
550
600
650
700

PROCEDURE 10

THE ASSESSMENT OF VOLUME FOR PIECE-WORK PAYMENT

General

1. In harvesting operations, workers engaged in felling, cross-cutting and extraction are frequently paid on a piece-work basis.

2. Ideally, the basis for piece-work payment should be the measurement of the end product, which is invariably required for sale purposes.

3. In many cases, however, this is not feasible and a separate basis for payment is required. In these situations the methods outlined below are applicable.

4. Mean tree volume has been found to be one of the most reliable indicators of the work content in felling, extraction and to some extent in cross-cutting. Consequently, the assessment of this parameter is a major part of the procedure.

5. The method of assessing mean tree volume involves the use of tariff tables. (The tariff system is described on page 65). The tariff number of either thinnings or fellings may be estimated by one of two methods.

(i) Because tariff number is fairly closely related to the top height of the stand, it is possible to estimate tariff number from an assessment of the stand's top height. Top height/tariff number relationships are given in Table 11.

(ii) A rather more precise but more time consuming method of estimating tariff number is to use measurements of height and dbh of a sample of trees, and to derive their tariff numbers from Charts 1–19 (pages 46–64) according to the species. This method is more appropriate when dealing with rather variable stands, or stands which have a history of abnormal thinning, eg are markedly underthinned or overthinned.

Practice

Method (1)

6. The top height should be assessed following the procedure outlined in Part V (4) page 144.

7. For maincrops, or line thinnings, the appropriate tariff number can be obtained directly from Table 11, page 112. In the case of selective, predominantly low thinnings the tariff number used should be *one less* than indicated in Table 11.

8. The method adopted in sampling dbh depends on whether or not the stand has to be selectively marked, ie whether every tree has to be visited in any case in order to blaze it or mark it in some other way.

(i) In the case of normal selective thinnings, sampling of dbh is best done at the time of marking. The dbh of every 'n'th tree should be measured. The value of n can be determined from Table 10 below, according to the number of marked trees in the parcel. A count of the number of marked trees will be obtained in the process.

(ii) In the case of clear fellings or of line thinnings, where each tree to be felled is *not* marked, a different approach to sampling dbh can be adopted. Points should be located systematically throughout the area such that adequate representation of the stand is obtained. The dbh of the six trees (to be felled) nearest to the selected point should be measured. The number of sampling points again is dependent on the total number of trees in the parcel and column 3 of Table 10 below shows the number of such points required for different numbers of trees (column 1). (In line thinnings six consecutive trees in a line can be measured). The dbh tallies of each sample of six should then be combined. Note that in this case the total number of trees being removed is not obtained at this stage.

9. Convert the total tally of girth sample trees to volumes using the appropriate tariff table (pages 261–271).

10. Calculate the total volume of the girth sample trees by adding together the volumes of each dbh class, by dividing this figure by the total number of sample trees the mean volume can be deduced.

Table 10

Sampling Fractions and Numbers of Sampling Points

NO. OF MARKED TREES	SAMPLING FRACTION	NUMBER OF SAMPLING POINTS
(1)	(2)	(3)
200— 300	1 : 3	12
300— 400	1 : 4	14
400— 600	1 : 5	16
600— 800	1 : 6	18
800—1000	1 : 8	18
1000—1300	1 : 10	18
1300—1600	1 : 12	20
1600—2200	1 : 15	20
2200—3000	1 : 20	20
3000—4000	1 : 25	22
4000+	1 : 30	24+

11. A worked example showing the sampling method outlined in 8 (ii) is given below.

Worked Example

Species — *Scots pine*

Area — *2·0 ha*

Top Height — *15·0 m*

Tariff No. — *24* (*From Table 11*)

Mean volume— *0·114m*^{3}

Line Thinning

dbh cm	Sampling Point 1	2	3	4	5	6	7	8	9	10	11	12	Total	Volume per tree m^3	Volume per class m^3
9											I		1	0·024	0·02
10					I			I		I			3	0·035	0·11
11		I	I						I				3	0·048	0·14
12	I			II	I	I	I			I	I		8	0·061	0·49
13	I			I				I	I			I	5	0·076	0·38
14	I	I	I	I			I	I	I	I	I	I	10	0·092	0·92
15	II		I	II	I	II	I		I	I	I	I	13	0·109	1·42
16	I		I		I	I	I	II	I	I		I	10	0·127	1·27
17		I	I		I				I		I	I	6	0·147	0·88
18		I	I				I				I		4	0·167	0·67
19		I			I	I						I	4	0·189	0·76
20		I						I					2	0·212	0·42
21										I			1	0·24	0·24
22						I	I						2	0·26	0·52
													72		8·24

12. The total volume of the thinning or felling is derived from the product of the mean tree volume and the total number of trees. The latter is known where the first alternative sampling has been used, but must be independently assessed, usually as felling proceeds, with the second alternative sampling method.

13. Where variation in height or in stocking is particularly marked it is advisable to stratify the stands into more homogeneous parts, and to assess each part separately.

Method (2)

14. The procedure here is exactly the same as that described under Method (1) except that tariff number is derived, not from top height, but from height and dbh measurements of 10% of the trees sampled for dbh.

15. In addition to measuring dbh, the height of every 10th girth sample tree should be measured.

16. Using Charts 1–19, depending on the species, the tariff number of each sample tree can be assessed. For example, assuming the species is Sitka spruce, a sample tree of 30 cm dbh and of 21 m height will have a tariff number of 33, Chart 4, page 49.

17. The mean tariff number of the stand is taken simply as the average tariff number of the trees sampled for height and dbh.

T A R I F F   N U M B E R S

Top Ht in Metres	Species							Top Ht in Metres
	S P	C P	L P	S S	N S	E L	JL/HL	
8.0	17	16	15	16	16	14	16	8.0
8.5	17	16	16	16	17	15	16	8.5
9.0	18	17	16	17	18	15	17	9.0
9.5	18	18	17	18	18	16	18	9.5
10.0	19	18	18	18	19	17	18	10.0
10.5	19	19	19	19	19	18	19	10.5
11.0	20	20	19	19	20	18	20	11.0
11.5	20	20	20	20	20	19	20	11.5
12.0	21	21	21	21	21	20	21	12.0
12.5	21	22	21	21	22	20	22	12.5
13.0	22	23	22	22	22	21	22	13.0
13.5	22	23	23	23	23	22	23	13.5
14.0	23	24	24	23	23	22	24	14.0
14.5	24	25	24	24	24	23	24	14.5
15.0	24	25	25	24	24	24	25	15.0
15.5	25	26	26	25	25	25	26	15.5
16.0	25	27	26	26	26	25	26	16.0
16.5	26	27	27	26	26	26	27	16.5
17.0	26	28	28	27	27	27	28	17.0
17.5	27	29	28	27	27	27	29	17.5
18.0	27	30	29	28	28	28	29	18.0
18.5	28	30	30	29	29	29	30	18.5
19.0	28	31	31	29	29	29	31	19.0
19.5	29	32	31	30	30	30	31	19.5
20.0	29	32	32	30	30	31	32	20.0
20.5	30	33	33	31	31	31	33	20.5
21.0	30	34	33	32	31	32	33	21.0
21.5	31	34	34	32	32	33	34	21.5
22.0	31	35	35	33	33	34	35	22.0
22.5	32	36	36	33	33	34	35	22.5
23.0	32	37	36	34	34	35	36	23.0
23.5	33	37	37	35	34	36	37	23.5
24.0	33	38	38	35	35	36	37	24.0
24.5	34	39	38	36	35	37	38	24.5
25.0	34	39	39	36	36	38	39	25.0
25.5	35	40	40	37	37	38	39	25.5
26.0	35	41	40	38	37	39	40	26.0
26.5	36	41	41	38	38	40	41	26.5
27.0	36	42	42	39	38	40	42	27.0
27.5	37	43	43	39	39	41	42	27.5
28.0	37	43	43	40	40	42	43	28.0
28.5	38	44	44	41	40	43	44	28.5
29.0	38	45	45	41	41	43	44	29.0
29.5	39	46	45	42	41	44	45	29.5
30.0	39	46	46	42	42	45	46	30.0

TARIFF NUMBERS

Top Ht in Metres	DF	WH	RC	GF	NF	OAK	BIRCH	Top Ht in Metres
8.0	15	17	14	14	14	16	14	8.0
8.5	16	17	14	15	15	17	14	8.5
9.0	16	18	15	16	16	17	15	9.0
9.5	17	19	15	16	16	18	15	9.5
10.0	17	19	16	17	17	18	16	10.0
10.5	18	20	16	18	18	19	16	10.5
11.0	18	20	17	18	18	19	17	11.0
11.5	19	21	17	19	19	20	17	11.5
12.0	20	22	18	20	20	20	17	12.0
12.5	20	22	18	20	21	21	18	12.5
13.0	21	23	19	21	21	21	18	13.0
13.5	21	24	19	22	22	22	19	13.5
14.0	22	24	20	23	23	22	19	14.0
14.5	22	25	21	23	23	23	20	14.5
15.0	23	25	21	24	24	23	20	15.0
15.5	24	26	22	25	25	24	21	15.5
16.0	24	27	22	25	25	24	21	16.0
16.5	25	27	23	26	26	25	22	16.5
17.0	25	28	23	27	27	25	22	17.0
17.5	26	28	24	27	27	25	22	17.5
18.0	26	29	24	28	28	26	23	18.0
18.5	27	30	25	29	29	26	23	18.5
19.0	28	30	25	29	29	27	24	19.0
19.5	28	31	26	30	30	27	24	19.5
20.0	29	31	26	31	31	28	25	20.0
20.5	29	32	27	31	31	28	25	20.5
21.0	30	33	27	32	32	28	25	21.0
21.5	30	33	28	33	33	29	26	21.5
22.0	31	34	29	34	33	29	26	22.0
22.5	31	35	29	34	34	30	27	22.5
23.0	32	35	30	35	35	30	27	23.0
23.5	33	36	30	36	35	30	27	23.5
24.0	33	36	31	36	36	31	28	24.0
24.5	34	37	31	37	37	31	28	24.5
25.0	34	38	32	38	37	31	28	25.0
25.5	35	38	32	38	38	32	29	25.5
26.0	35	39	33	39	39	32	29	26.0
26.5	36	39	33	40	39	32	29	26.5
27.0	37	40	34	40	40	33	30	27.0
27.5	37	41	34	41	41	33	30	27.5
28.0	38	41	35	42	41	34	30	28.0
28.5	38	42	36	42	42	34	31	28.5
29.0	39	43	36	43	43	34	31	29.0
29.5	39	43	37	44	43	35	31	29.5
30.0	40	44	37	44	44	35	32	30.0

OAK. Use also for Beech, Ash, Elm, Alder and Sweet Chestnut

BIRCH. Use also for Sycamore and Poplar

PROCEDURE 11

THE ASSESSMENT OF VOLUME FOR PURPOSES OF THINNING CONTROL

GENERAL

1. In order to exercise control over the volume marked in thinning, the marker requires some quick and convenient way of assessing this volume.

2. Control may be exercised through basal area or volume. The principles and procedures of control by volume are considered in greater detail in FC Booklet 54 (*Thinning Control*). It is intended, therefore, to outline only the essential features of establishing the volume marked, using tables contained in this booklet.

3. The principle of the method is similar to that of Procedure 10. It involves the use of tariff tables, tariff numbers being derived from top height/tariff number relationships. In addition to top height the assessment of dbh of marked trees within sample plots of known area is required.

PRACTICE

4. The top height of the stand being thinned should be assessed by the procedure outlined in Part V (4), page 144.

5. The appropriate tariff number of the thinning is indicated in Table 11 by the top height of the stand, but in the case of predominantly low selective thinnings a tariff number one less than the value indicated should be used.

6. Lay down plots at intervals, during the marking, of sufficient size to include at least 5 marked trees per plot (Plot sizes are given in Part V (2), on page 132).

7. Measure the dbh of each marked tree in the plot and convert this to volume using the appropriate tariff table.

8. Add up the volumes of the marked trees and find the corresponding volume per hectare by multiplying by the factor: $\dfrac{1}{\text{area of plot (ha)}}$.

9. By repeating this procedure with successive plots, a reasonable estimate of the volume per hectare marked can be obtained, and the marking adjusted if required, depending on its comparison with the target figure. (This will normally be obtained from the above mentioned publication). As experience is gained subsequent checks will usually be less frequent.

Example:

Species—Norway spruce
Top height—14 m
Tariff number (from Table 11)—23 less 1 = 22
Plot area—0·01 ha

Marked trees

dbh *cm*	*Volume* *(tariff No. 22)* m^3
14	*0·085*
16	*0·117*
10	*0·033*
11	*0·044*
15	*0·100*
14	*0·085*
	0·464 m^3*/0·01 ha*

ie volume marked in sample plot is 46·4 m^3*/ha*

PART V MISCELLANEOUS

1. SAMPLING

1. In considering the cost/benefit aspects of measurement in Part 1 (page 9) the influence of sampling techniques on both costs and precision of measurement is briefly mentioned. The purpose of this section is to consider the subject of sampling in more detail and in particular to explore the connection between sampling and precision. In the first part (paras 2–13) the essential principles of sampling are discussed in general terms and without reference to statistical notation. The second part (paras 14–20) is intended mainly for reference purposes, and considers the more formal statistical concepts and their application.

GENERAL

2. A sample is a portion of anything which may be presented as evidence of the larger whole from which it is taken. Consider the measurement of a parcel of, say, 500 sawlogs. The volume of the whole parcel may be assessed by measuring the volume of each log and adding together their individual volumes. Alternatively the volume of the parcel could be deduced from a *sample* of the logs taken at random. If the sample was, say, 20%—ie 100 logs—the volume of the parcel would be estimated as the total volume of the sample, multiplied by five.

3. In comparing these two alternatives the first important point of difference concerns the *cost of measurement*. It is obviously less time consuming to measure the individual volumes of 100 logs than 500 and hence the cost of measurement is much less. It would be even cheaper, of course, to measure a sample of only 50 and calculate the volume of the whole parcel by multiplying the volume of the sample by ten. The most important reason for sampling is in fact to save time and money and, in general, the smaller the sample the cheaper the measurement.

4. The second major point of difference between the alternatives outlined in para 2 above concerns the *precision* of measurement. Excluding the possibility of measurement errors, caused for example by faulty, or incorrect use of, measuring tapes, the volume derived from the individual measurement of all 500 logs can be regarded as being absolutely accurate. This, however, is not the case where the estimate is based on the measurement of a sample. Given that the sample logs have been selected at random, one cannot know exactly how truly representative these are of the whole parcel. Consequently one cannot be absolutely confident of the accuracy of the estimate of total volume in the parcel. The *precision* of the estimate essentially reflects the confidence in the accuracy of the volume estimate. In general the smaller the sample, the less precise is the estimate of the whole parcel.

5. Whilst it is not possible to determine exactly how close an estimated value based on a sample may be to the true value, it is nonetheless possible to quantify precision in terms of *probabilities*. A common expression of precision is the concept of confidence limits. For example, it might be stated that an estimate of the volume of a parcel of logs—based on a sample measurement—was 200 cubic metres and that the confidence limits at the 95% probability level were 190 and 210 cubic metres respectively. To state that the true volume lies within the range covered by the confidence limits, in this particular case 190–210 cubic metres, would be true 95 times in 100 if the parcel of logs was repeatedly sampled in this way an infinite number of times (paras 14–19).

6. The benefits of increased precision are discussed in Part I (page 9). It is also demonstrated that the intensity of sampling adopted in practice should be the best compromise between the cost of measurement and the benefits derived from greater precision.

7. One factor which affects the level of precision obtained from a given sampling intensity, and hence the optimum intensity of sampling, is the *inherent variation* in the population being sampled. For example, the parcel of sawlogs considered above could, on the one hand, be composed of logs of a wide range of diameters and lengths, and hence rather variable volumes, or on the other hand be of constant length and of restricted diameter range, and hence have less variation in volume. Just as an individual log selected at random from the less variable parcel is likely to be closer to the average volume of the whole parcel than one selected at random from the more variable parcel, so the average of a sample of 20 from the more uniform parcel is likely to be closer to the true average of the parcel than is the average of a sample of 20 taken from the more variable parcel. In other words, for samples of a given size, a more precise estimate of the average of the whole population will be obtained in uniform populations compared with populations composed of relatively variable elements. Alternatively, in order to achieve a given degree of precision, a larger sample is required from the more variable population.

8. Two methods of sampling are commonly recognised, although alternatives exist which embrace elements of both methods. The first is termed *random* sampling. By this method all individuals and all groups of a given number of individuals in a population have an equal chance of being selected. Random sampling is typified by the lottery principle in which, for example, the individual members are allocated a different number and each number written on an individual slip of paper. The slips are then placed in a drum, thoroughly mixed and a number of slips drawn from the drum. The sample would then be selected according to the numbers on the drawn slips.

9. The second method of sampling is known as *systematic* sampling. By this method samples are selected according to a pre-determined system. For example, to take a 10% sample by selecting every 10th individual encountered in a population is a typical example of systematic sampling. If the number of individuals in the population is a multiple of 10 and if the first individual

is sampled at random from the first 10, all *individuals* have the same chance of being chosen, but all *groups* do not, because the composition of the whole sample is completely determined by the choice of the first member.

10. The statistical theory of sampling outlined in paras 14–19 below relates to random sampling only. In fact there is no available comparable theory for systematic sampling. It follows, therefore, that the advantages of being able to quantify precision, or to determine sampling intensities required to produce a given degree of precision are in theory available only with random sampling.

11. Unfortunately, random sampling is just not a practical proposition in many applications in forest measurement. Consider, for example, the practical implications of estimating the mean dbh of a stand by random sampling. This would require allocating a number to every tree in the stand, selecting the sample from numbered slips drawn from a drum, *revisiting* the appropriate trees and measuring their dbh. It would obviously be much quicker (and cheaper) to measure the dbh of every 'n'th tree visitied.

12. The main disadvantage of systematic sampling is that for a single systematic sample there is no guarantee that the estimate of precision is unbiased as there is for a random sample. This means that there is a greater chance of obtaining a misleading estimate. On the other hand, circumstances exist where a systematic sample may produce more precise estimates than a random sample. In practice one often knows too little about the population to be able to predict whether systematic sampling will be more or less reliable than random sampling. The most hazardous situations are those where a trend exists in the population. If the trend is such as to produce significant variation between different parts of the population, it may be possible to stratify the population into more homogeneous parts and to sample systematically within each part. Where the gradient of the trend is clearly detectable it is always best to aim at sampling according to the proportion of the population occurring in each section of the gradient. For example, in sampling a stand where a site-induced trend is apparent in the crop, it is best to traverse the stand at right angles to the direction of the gradient of the trend. Particular situations are discussed elsewhere in this booklet.

Where a trend occurs in regular cycles such that systematic sampling might repeatedly coincide with the peak, or alternatively the trough of the cycle, the resultant sample could prove misleading. The solution here might be to use a sampling system that is 'out of step' with the cycle. These situations are less common in forest measurement situations. Elsewhere the use of systematic sampling is not likely to result in levels of precision significantly lower than those obtained by random sampling, and for that reason the theory of sampling outlined in the succeeding paragraphs (paras 14–19) has been freely applied in examples relating to systematic sampling.

13. A final point to be considered here is the size of the sampling unit. For example, to sample the basal area of a stand, one could lay out at random, one sample plot of 1 ha. Alternatively, one could lay out 10 plots of 0·1 ha or 100 plots of 0·01 ha to obtain the same overall size of sample. From the

point of view of convenience, the single large plot would be the most favourable and the 100 smaller plots would be least favourable. From the point of view of precision, the reverse is true. The size of sampling unit should bear some reasonable relationship to the measured components comprising the sample. It would be awkward in the extreme to have in the above example, plots containing on average less than one whole tree. Some guidance on the appropriate size of sampling units is contained in the detailed procedures elsewhere in this publication. Dimensions of plots of various sizes and shapes are given in Part V (2) page 132.

Statistical Concepts and Their Application

14. The following paragraphs are directed ultimately at two problems which frequently arise in forest mensuration. These are:

a. the problem of attaching a degree of precision (sampling error) to an estimate of a particular parameter of a population, derived from a known sample.

b. the problem of selecting a sampling intensity to provide a desired degree of precision in estimating a particular parameter.

Inevitably, statistical concepts and formulae are involved in solving these problems. In this book the explanation of these concepts and formulae is rather restricted. The reader who is unfamiliar with statistics is advised to consult a suitable textbook on the subject for a more detailed explanation of these and other related concepts.

15. Frequency distributions

The *frequency distribution* describes the relative frequency with which different values of a variable occur in a population. The concept is also applied to the frequency with which sample statistics occur in repeated random sampling from the same population (the term *sampling distribution* is used in this case). Of the various forms of distribution the familiar *normal distribution* is the most commonly used in forest mensuration. It usually fits the distribution of heights, diameters etc, reasonably well but even more important, fits more closely the distribution of sample means from virtually any population, the more so as the sample size increases. The normal distribution is shown diagramatically in Fig 12.

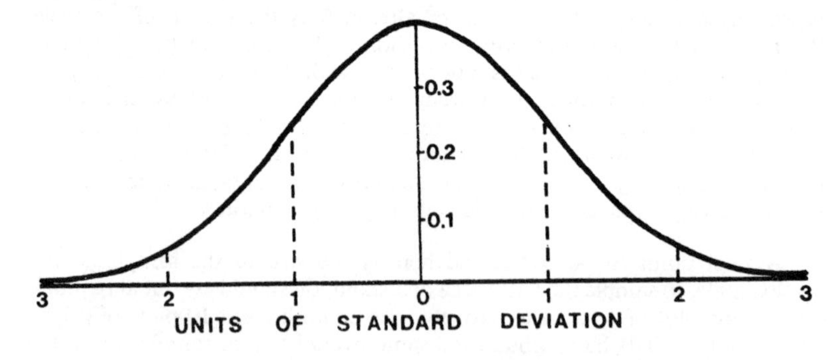

Figure 12

16. The Mean and Standard Deviation

These parameters completely specify the normal distribution. The *population mean* is simply the arithmetic average of the whole set of values in a population and is expressed thus:

$$\mu = \frac{\Sigma x}{N}$$

where μ = mean of the population
x = value of an individual member of the population
Σx = sum of all members of the population
N = the number of members

The sample mean is expressed conventionally as:

$$\bar{x} = \frac{\Sigma x}{n}$$

where Σx = sum of the members of the sample
$\bar{x}$ = sample mean
n = number of observations in the sample

The *standard deviation* is a measure of the dispersion of the values of individual members of the population about their mean. In a normally distributed population 68% of individual values will be within ±1 standard deviation of the mean, 95% will be within ±1·96 standard deviations and approximately 99% will be within ±2·58 standard deviations. Thus in a stand where the dbh is distributed normally, and where the mean dbh is 20 cm and the standard deviation is 4, then 68% of the trees in the stand will be expected to have a dbh within the range 16–24 cm.

The standard deviation of a *population* (σ) is calculated by the formula:

$$\sigma = \sqrt{\frac{\Sigma (x - \mu)^2}{N}} = \sqrt{\frac{\Sigma x^2 - (\Sigma x)^2/N}{N}}$$

The standard deviation of a *sample* (s) is calculated by the formula:

$$s = \sqrt{\frac{\Sigma (x - \bar{x})^2}{n - 1}} = \sqrt{\frac{\Sigma x^2 - (\Sigma x)^2/n}{n - 1}}$$

The *range* (r) of a sample is the difference between the highest and lowest observed value in the sample. For random samples of a given size taken from a normally distributed population the average range is in a fixed ratio to the population standard deviation. Therefore the range may be used to provide an approximation for the standard deviation given the appropriate ratios. Standard deviation/range ratios are given in the table below for samples of up to 6 observations. For larger samples the range, as defined above, is a less efficient estimator of the standard deviation of the population. Better estimates can be obtained from a modified range obtained by using the difference between the *sum of the two largest* observed values and the *sum of the two smallest* observed values. This method works well for samples of up to 10, but for even larger samples still more observations should be used as indicated in Table 12.

This method of calculation is almost as good as the formula given above by which the standard deviation is defined. For larger samples the sample may be divided at random into two or more groups, the above method applied to each group and the results averaged over groups, but it may be simpler to use the exact formulae.

Table 12

Range /standard deviation ratios

Sample size	Range or Modified Range (Observations numbered in order of magnitude)	Ratio
2	1—2	1·13
3	1—3	1·69
4	1—4	2·06
5	1—5	2·33
6	1—6	2·53
7	(1+2)—(6+7)	4·22
8	(1+2)—(7+8)	4·55
9	(1+2)—(8+9)	4·83
10	(1+2)—(9+10)	5·08
11	(1+2+4)—(8+10+11)	6·22
12	(1+2+4)—(9+11+12)	6·56
13	(1+2+4)—(10+12+13)	6·87
14	(1+2+4)—(11+13+14)	7·15
15	(1+2+4)—(12+14+15)	7·40
16	(1+2+4)—(13+15+16)	7·63
17	(1+2+3+5)—(13+15+16+17)	9·52
18	(1+2+3+5)—(14+16+17+18)	9·80
19	(1+2+3+5)—(15+17+18+19)	10·06
20	(1+2+4+6)—(15+17+19+20)	9·57

Examples:

(i) In a sample of 5, the highest observed value is 19, and the lowest is 14. From the table above the range is $x_1 - x_5 = 19 - 14 = 5$.

The ratio of range/standard deviation = 2·33

$$\therefore \text{ The standard deviation is } \frac{5}{2{\cdot}33} = 2{\cdot}146 \quad \text{(approx)}$$

(ii) With a sample of 15, the samples would be arranged in order of magnitude and the modified range calculated as the sum of the 1st, 2nd and 4th highest values, less the sum of the 12th, 14th and 15th highest values. This value would then be divided by the ratio indicated—7·40—to provide the estimate of standard deviation.

17. The Standard Error of the Mean

Whereas the standard deviation is a measure of the variation of *individuals*, the standard error of the mean is a measure of the variation of *sample means* calculated from samples of the population. It can be regarded as a standard deviation of the sampling distribution of sample means.

The formula for the calculation of the standard error of the mean ($s_{\bar{x}}$) is given as:

$$s_{\bar{x}} = \sqrt{\frac{s^2}{n}\left(1 - \frac{n}{N}\right)}$$

Where N is very large compared with n the formula reduces to:

$$s_{\bar{x}} = \sqrt{\frac{s^2}{n}}$$

18. Confidence Limits

The reliability which may be attached to a mean derived from a sample can be expressed by *confidence limits*. If for example we describe the confidence limits of a sample mean value of 20 as being 24 and 16, at the 95% probability level, then this means that in repeated independent samples of this kind, the true mean would lie within the range covered by the confidence limits 95 times out of 100. Confidence limits for the mean of random samples taken from approximately normally distributed populations are calculated from the standard error of the mean and a table of 't' values given below. (Table 13). The calculation is formulated thus:

$$\text{Confidence limits} = \text{mean} \pm t.\ (\text{standard error}),\ \text{or:}$$

$$\text{Upper limit } (F_1) = \bar{x} + t.\ s_{\bar{x}}$$

$$\text{Lower limit } (F_2) = \bar{x} - t.\ s_{\bar{x}}$$

The appropriate value of 't' is determined from the Table 13 according to a value one less than the number of observations in the sample (n) and the desired level of probability. The 95% level is most commonly used in practice. Thus for a sample where the number of observations is 19, $n - 1 = 18$. The appropriate value of 't' for a probability of 95% is therefore 2·101.

Example:

To calculate the confidence limits which can be attached to a volume estimate for a parcel of sawlogs.

Consider a parcel of 200 sawlogs where 10% of the logs (20) have been selected at random and the volume of each assessed. The volumes of the 20 logs are:

0·29, 0·48, 0·36, 0·51, 0·30, 0·46, 0·45, 0·56, 0·63, 0·55, 0·38, 0·53, 0·51, 0·32, 0·47, 0·42, 0·51, 0·40, 0·59, 0·31.

The mean volume of the logs ($\bar{x}$) is:

$$\frac{\Sigma x}{n} = \frac{9{\cdot}03}{20} = 0{\cdot}45 \text{ m}^3$$

Table 13

Distribution of "t"

n − 1	Probability 0·10 (90%)	0·05 (95%)	0·01 (99%)
1	6·314	12·706	63·657
2	2·920	4·303	9·925
3	2·353	3·182	5·841
4	2·132	2·776	4·604
5	2·015	2·571	4·032
6	1·943	2·447	3·707
7	1·895	2·365	3·499
8	1·860	2·306	3·355
9	1·833	2·262	3·250
10	1·812	2·228	3·169
11	1·796	2·201	3·106
12	1·782	2·179	3·055
13	1·771	2·160	3·012
14	1·761	2·145	2·977
15	1·753	2·131	2·947
16	1·746	2·120	2·921
17	1·740	2·110	2·898
18	1·734	2·101	2·878
19	1·729	2·093	2·861
20	1·725	2·086	2·845
21	1·721	2·080	2·831
22	1·717	2·074	2·819
23	1·714	2·069	2·807
24	1·711	2·064	2·797
25	1·708	2·060	2·787
26	1·706	2·056	2·779
27	1·703	2·052	2·771
28	1·701	2·048	2·763
29	1·699	2·045	2·756
30	1·697	2·042	2·750
40	1·684	2·021	2·704
60	1·671	2·000	2·669
120	1·658	1·980	2·617
∞	1·645	1·960	2·576

Table 13 is taken from Table III of Fisher and Yates: *Statistical Tables for Biological, Agricultural and Medical Research,* published by Longman Group Ltd., London (previously published by Oliver and Boyd, Edinburgh), and by permission of the authors and publishers.

The standard deviation is calculated thus:

$$s = \sqrt{\frac{\Sigma x^2 - (\Sigma x)^2/n}{n-1}}$$

$$= \sqrt{\frac{4{\cdot}2707 - (9{\cdot}03)^2/20}{20-1}}$$

$$= 0{\cdot}101 \text{ m}^3$$

(ie 68% of logs can be expected to have volumes within $\pm 0{\cdot}101$ m^3 of the mean volume).

The standard error of the mean is calculated thus:

$$s_{\bar{x}} = \sqrt{\frac{s^2}{n}\left(1 - \frac{n}{N}\right)}$$

$$= \sqrt{\frac{0{\cdot}0102}{20}\left(1 - \frac{20}{200}\right)}$$

$$= 0{\cdot}0214 \text{ m}^3$$

(ie with repeated samples of this kind, the true mean could be expected to be within $\pm$ the standard error of the sample mean, in this case within $\pm 0{\cdot}0214$ m^3 of the sample mean, 68 times out of 100).

The confidence limits attached to the sample mean are:

$$F_1 = \bar{x} + t.\, s_{\bar{x}}$$
$$F_2 = \bar{x} - t.\, s_{\bar{x}}$$

Since: the sample mean, $\bar{x}$ $= 0{\cdot}45$

the standard error of the mean $s_{\bar{x}}$ $= 0{\cdot}0214$

the appropriate value of 't' for a probability of 95% (where n–1=19) $= 2{\cdot}093$

then: $F_1 = 0{\cdot}45 + 2{\cdot}093 \times 0{\cdot}0214 = 0{\cdot}4948 \text{m}^3$

$F_2 = 0{\cdot}45 - 2{\cdot}093 \times 0{\cdot}0214 = 0{\cdot}4052 \text{m}^3$

Now the volume estimate (U) of the whole parcel is derived as the total number (N) multiplied by the mean value. The confidence limits attached to the volume estimate are proportional to the confidence limits attached to the mean.

Therefore the volume estimate $U = 200 \times 0{\cdot}45$

$= 90 \text{ m}^3$

and the associated confidence limits are:

$$F_1 \times 200 = 0{\cdot}4948 \times 200 = 98{\cdot}96 \text{ m}^3$$

and $F_2 \times 200 = 0{\cdot}4052 \times 200 = 81{\cdot}04 \text{ m}^3$

The conclusion is drawn that with indefinitely repeated samples of this kind, 95 times in 100 the true volume of the 200 logs would lie within the range covered by the confidence limits, which for this sample is 81·04 – 98·96 m^3.

19. Combining Errors

Estimates of some parameters may involve drawing two or more independent samples. This situation is common in forest mensuration and it is therefore useful to know the procedure for calculating the combined error attached to the estimate.

The situation where the estimate is derived as the *product* of two parameters, sampled independently, is particularly common. For example, the volume of a stand per hectare may be computed from the product of mean height and mean basal area per hectare (form being assumed). Both height and basal area may be sampled independently, and attract sampling errors independently. The formula for combining standard errors (SE) of two estimated means y_1 and y_2 is:

$$SE(y_1 \times y_2) = \sqrt{y_1^2 (SEy_2)^2 + y_2^2 (SEy_1)^2}$$

where SEy_1 and SEy_2 are the standard errors of y_1 and y_2

The formula is valid only where y_1 and y_2 are strictly independent of each other.

The standard error of the *sum* of a number of independent estimates is given by the formula

$$SE(y_1 + y_2 + y_3 \ldots\ldots) = \sqrt{(SEy_1)^2 + (SEy_2)^2 + (SEy_3)^2}$$

and the standard error of the *difference* of two independent estimates is given as

$$SE(y_1 - y_2) = \sqrt{(SEy_1)^2 + (SEy_2)^2}$$

Example (1):

To find the standard error attached to an estimate of mean volume per hectare derived from height, basal area, and an assumed form factor.

The volume estimate is derived as:

$$U = ba.h.ff$$

where U is the volume estimate in cubic metres per hectare

ba ,, ,, mean basal area in square metres per hectare

h ,, ,, mean height of the stand in metres

and ff ,, ,, form factor assumed.

Assume that from independent samples of both height and basal area the means and their standard errors are

ba = 35 m^2, standard error, 3

h = 15 m, ,, ,, 1

According to the formula above, the combined standard errors for the product of the means will be:

$$SE = \sqrt{(35)^2 \times (1)^2 + (15)^2 \times (3)^2}$$
$$= 57 \text{ m}^3$$

Thus the volume estimate will be given as:

$$U = 35 \times 15 \times ff \pm 57 \times ff \text{ m}^3/\text{ha}$$

If the form factor is assumed to be 0·45 then:

$$U = 236{\cdot}25 \pm 25{\cdot}65 \text{ m}^3/\text{ha}$$

Appropriate confidence limits could be calculated according to the probability level required and the smaller of the two samples used to find appropriate value of 't' from Table 13.

Example (2):

To calculate confidence limits for an estimate of volume of standing timber assessed by the tariff system.

The method of estimating timber volume is outlined in Procedure 8 (page 65). There are essentially two independent sources of sampling error to be considered. First the mean tariff number, being estimated from a sample, is subject to a sampling error. The volume estimate is directly proportional to the tariff number, so the resultant errors in the volume estimate from this source will also be directly proportional to errors in the estimate of the mean tariff number. (Additionally the practice of rounding down the average tariff number to the nearest whole number has to be considered as a source of error). The second source of error is that associated with the dbh distribution which is generally derived from a sample. The error attached to the volume estimate arising from the second source can be taken as being proportional to the error of the mean volume of the girth sample trees. The volumes are assigned by applying the appropriate tariff table to the dbh distribution of the girth sample trees.

Using the worked example given on pages 78–80 as a source of data, the various steps in the calculation of confidence limits are outlined below.

a. *The error attached to the volume estimate by reason of rounding down the mean tariff number.*

On account of the conventional practice of rounding down the calculated mean tariff number to the nearest whole number, the volume estimate (E) which is given in Part A of the assessment form U15 (see page 78) usually embraces an error from this practice which is not related to sampling. In order to calculate the sampling error it is necessary to eliminate this source of error and consider the volume estimate (U) which would be calculated if this practice was omitted.

The error in the specified volume estimate (E) due to the rounding down of the mean tariff number is directly proportional to the error involved in rounding down the mean tariff number. If the actual mean tariff number is t_m and the rounded down tariff number is t_r then the error is given as:

$$p = \frac{t_m - t_r}{t_r}$$

The error due to this factor in the volume estimate will be pE. If we consider the volume estimate which would have resulted without rounding down the tariff number as U, then its value can be expressed as:

$$U = E + pE$$

In the worked example $t_r = 29$

$t_m = 29{\cdot}1$

thus: $p = \frac{29{\cdot}1 - 29}{29} = 0{\cdot}003448$

since: $E = 437{\cdot}8$

then: $U = 437{\cdot}8 + (437{\cdot}8 \times 0{\cdot}003448)$

$= 439{\cdot}3\text{m}^3$

b. The standard error of the mean tariff number

The standard deviation $= \sqrt{\frac{\Sigma x^2 - (\Sigma x)^2/n}{n - 1}}$

(where x is the tariff number of each volume sample tree)

$$= \sqrt{\frac{19644{\cdot}0 - (670)^2/23}{23 - 1}}$$

$$= 2{\cdot}3989$$

The standard error of the mean $= \sqrt{\frac{s^2}{n}\left(1 - \frac{n}{N}\right)}$

(where n is the number of volume sample trees and N is the number of trees in the parcel)

$$= \sqrt{\frac{(2{\cdot}3989)^2}{23}\left(1 - \frac{23}{2171}\right)}$$

$$= 0{\cdot}4975$$

c. The standard error of the mean volume

The volume per tree given in column 5 of Part C (page 80) is used in conjunction with the frequency given in column 3 to calculate the error in volume resulting from the sample of dbh.

The mean volume is 0·202 m³ (Part A).

The standard deviation $= \sqrt{\dfrac{\Sigma x^2 - (\Sigma x)^2/n}{n - 1}}$

(Where x is the volume of each girth sample tree)

$$= \sqrt{\frac{12{\cdot}349644 - (48{\cdot}648)^2/241}{241 - 1}}$$

$$= 0{\cdot}102665 m^3$$

The standard error of the mean $= \sqrt{\dfrac{s^2}{n}\left(1 - \dfrac{n}{N}\right)}$

(Where n is the number of girth sample trees and N is the number of trees in the parcel)

$$= \sqrt{\left(\frac{(0{\cdot}102665)^2}{241}\right)\left(1 - \frac{241}{2171}\right)}$$

$$= 0{\cdot}00623538 m^3$$

d. Standard error of the total volume

The standard error of the total volume (SE_u) is derived by combining the errors of the mean tariff number and mean volume.

The error in the volume estimate arising from the error in the mean tariff number is directly proportional to the latter error. Given that the standard error of the mean tariff number (29·1) is ±0·4975, then the percentage error is:

$$\pm \frac{0{\cdot}4975 \times 100}{29{\cdot}1}\% = \pm 1{\cdot}710\%$$

Consequently the standard error of the volume estimate from this source, expressed as a percentage of the volume estimate U, is given as:

$$SE_{u_t} = \pm 1{\cdot}710\%$$

Similarly the standard error of the volume estimate arising from the standard error of the mean volume is derived as:

$$SE_{u_v} = \pm \frac{0{\cdot}00623538 \times 100}{0{\cdot}202}\% = \pm 3{\cdot}087\%$$

Since SE_{u_v} and SE_{u_t} are derived from entirely independent samples, the errors can be combined as follows:

$$\begin{aligned} SE_u &= \sqrt{(SE_{u_t})^2 + (SE_{u_v})^2} \\ &= \sqrt{(1{\cdot}710)^2 + (3{\cdot}087)^2} \\ &= 3{\cdot}529\% \end{aligned}$$

ie the standard error of the volume estimate U

$$\begin{aligned} &= \pm 3{\cdot}529\% \text{ of U} \\ &= \frac{3{\cdot}529}{100} \times 439{\cdot}3 \\ &= 15{\cdot}502 \end{aligned}$$

e. Confidence limits

The value of 't' from Table 13 is selected according to the probability level required, in this case 95%, and to the smaller sample of the two components, in this case 23, so that n− 1 is 22 and 't' is 2·074. The confidence limits for the volume estimate are therefore

$$F_1 = U + t.SE_u$$
$$F_2 = U - t.SE_u$$

ie $F_1 = 439{\cdot}3 + 2{\cdot}074 \times 15{\cdot}502$
$F_2 = 439{\cdot}3 - 2{\cdot}074 \times 15{\cdot}502$

$F_1 = 471{\cdot}5$ *or* $U + 7{\cdot}3\%$ *or* $E + 7{\cdot}7\%$
$F_2 = 407{\cdot}1$ *or* $U - 7{\cdot}3\%$ *or* $E - 7{\cdot}0\%$

Example (3):

To find the confidence limits of a combined estimate of volume from several independently assessed areas.

Three stands A, B and C have been independently measured and have volume estimates and associated standard errors as follows:

$$A = 332 \pm 13 \text{ m}^3$$
$$B = 179 \pm 3{\cdot}2 \text{ m}^3$$
$$C = 674 \pm 16{\cdot}8 \text{ m}^3$$

The standard errors are in common units and may be combined thus:

$$\begin{aligned} SE(A+B+C) &\pm \sqrt{(SE_A)^2 + (SE_B)^2 + (SE_C)^2} \\ &= \sqrt{(13)^2 + (3{\cdot}2)^2 + (16{\cdot}8)^2} \\ &= 21{\cdot}5 \text{ m}^3 \end{aligned}$$

Thus the total estimate and standard error is: $1185 \pm 21{\cdot}5$ m³

The appropriate confidence limits at the 95% probability level, and using a value of 't' (from Table 13) of 2·06 (assuming the smallest sample size is 25) are:

$$F_1 = 1185 + 2{\cdot}06 \times 21{\cdot}5 = 1229 \text{ m}^3$$

$$F_2 = 1185 - 2{\cdot}06 \times 21{\cdot}5 = 1141 \text{ m}^3$$

20. Choosing a Sampling Intensity to Achieve a Desired Level of Precision

The following formula can be used to calculate the number of samples required to achieve a specified level of precision in estimating the mean of the total population.

$$n = \frac{(\text{Coefficient of variation in percent})^2}{(\text{Desired standard error of mean in percent})^2}$$

where n = required number of samples, and

$$\text{coefficient of variation} = \frac{\text{standard deviation}}{\text{mean}} \%$$

The calculation of the coefficient of variation clearly implies some advance knowledge of the nature of the population. This can be obtained

(a) by conducting a preliminary sample of the population.

(b) by experience gained from sampling similar populations.

a. Preliminary sampling should not be aimed at anything other than a rough estimate of the mean and standard deviation. The use of the range/standard deviation ratio (Table 12 above) will often provide suitable estimates of standard deviation. The sampling unit used in the preliminary sample should be the same as that used in the main sampling.

b. Experience of the coefficient of variation from similar populations can be an invaluable aid to establishing the required sampling intensity. Here too, however, it is important that the experience relates to the same or a similar size of sampling unit. In Procedures 5 and 6, dealing respectively with stacked timber measurement and weight measurement, some typical average values of coefficients of variation are given for solid/stacked conversion factors and for volume/weight ratios. Values for most other parameters which are the subject of sampling exercises vary so much from one situation to another that to provide average coefficients of variation is not considered worthwhile.

Example:

To find the number of relascope sweeps required to produce a standard error of ±5% in the mean basal area per hectare of a stand.

Assume that from experience, the coefficient of variation in this particular situation is 15%. The number of samples required would be:

$$n = \frac{(15)^2}{(5)^2} = 9$$

2. PLOT SIZES

1. The choice of a suitable size of plot depends on its purpose and also frequently on the nature of the tree crop, notably in terms of stem numbers per hectare. Larger plots are generally required for situations where there are fewer trees per hectare. Recommendations on plot sizes for particular purposes are given in the appropriate part of the booklet. Plots can be square, rectangular or circular but different situations call for different shapes of plots. When the rows are still clearly visible it pays to use a rectangular plot. In stands where the rows are not distinct, but where there are enough trees to use small plots, circular plots will usually be most convenient; but where the plot size is 0·05 ha or larger, square plots will probably take less time to lay out.

Table 14

2. **Circular and Square Plot Sizes**

	Length in metres for plot sizes (ha)							
Shape	0·005	0·01	0·02	0·05	0·10	0·20	0·50	1·00
Circular (radius)	4·0	5·6	8·0	12·6	17·8	25·2	39·9	56·4
Square (sides)	7·1	10·0	14·1	22·4	31·6	44·7	70·7	100·0

Table 15

3. **Rectangular Plot Sizes in Plantations Where Rows Are Clearly Visible**

Average Spacing Between Rows	3 rows wide		4 rows wide	6 rows wide	9 rows wide
	Distance in metres along the row for plot size				
metres	0·005 ha	0·01 ha	0·02 ha	0·05 ha	0·10 ha
1·2	13·9	27·8	41·7	69·4	92·6
1·3	12·8	25·6	38·5	64·1	85·5
1·4	11·9	23·8	35·7	59·5	79·4
1·5	11·1	22·2	33·3	55·6	74·1
1·6	10·4	20·8	31·25	52·1	69·4
1·7	9·8	19·6	29·4	49·0	65·4
1·8	9·3	18·5	27·8	46·3	61·7
1·9	8·8	17·5	26·3	43·9	58·5
2·0	8·3	16·7	25·0	41·7	55·6
2·1	7·9	15·9	23·8	39·7	52·9
2·2	7·6	15·2	22·7	37·9	50·5
2·3	7·25	14·5	21·7	36·2	48·3
2·4	6·9	13·9	20·8	34·7	46·3

Note:

Doubling the number of rows doubles the plot area, and similarly halving the distance halves the plot area.

4. **Correction for slope**

a. **To convert a known horizontal distance to the equivalent length along a uniform slope.**

Table 16

Angle of slope	Factor (secant)	Correction for 20 metres
(1) degrees	(2)	(3) metres
5	1·0038	0·08
7½	1·0086	0·17
10	1·0154	0·31
12½	1·0243	0·49
15	1·0353	0·71
17½	1·0485	0·97
20	1·0642	1·28
22½	1·0824	1·65
25	1·1034	2·07
30	1·1547	3·09
35	1·2208	4·42
45	1·4142	8·28
60	2·0000	20·00

Example

If the horizontal distance is 36 metres, and the slope is 10°, the distance required to be measured up or down the slope and in the direction of the slope is 36 × 1·0154

= 36·5544

For convenience, the length to be *added* to a standard 20 m measuring tape is given in column 3.

b. **To convert a known distance measured on a uniform slope to its horizontal equivalent.**

Table 17

Angle of slope	Factor (cosine)	Correction for 20 metres
(1) degrees	(2)	(3) metres
5	0·99619	0·08
7½	0·99144	0·17
10	0·98481	0·30
12½	0·97630	0·47
15	0·96593	0·68
17½	0·95372	0·93
20	0·93969	1·21
22½	0·92388	1·52
25	0·90631	1·87
30	0·86603	2·68
35	0·81915	3·62
45	0·70711	5·86
60	0·50000	10·00

Example

If the distance measured up or down a 10° slope, and in the direction of the slope, is 36 metres, the equivalent horizontal distance is 36 × 0·98481

= 35·45316

For convenience, the length to be *subtracted* from a standard 20 m tape is given in column 3.

c. Plot areas

The above tables may also be used for plot area correction, and apply irrespective of the shape of the plot.

Example (1):

If the horizontal area of a plot is 0·3 ha, then the equivalent area on a slope of 7½ degrees is 0·3 × 1·0086 (Table 16).

= 0·30258 ha

Example (2):

If the area of a plot measured on a 7½° slope is 0·3 ha, the equivalent horizontal area is 0·3 × 0·99144 (Table 17).

= 0·297432 ha

3. THE RELASCOPE

General

1. A *relascope* is a simple instrument which can be used to estimate the basal area of stands without the need for laying down plots. This instrument is alternatively described as an *angle-gauge*.

2. Commonly associated with relascopes are the terms *plotless survey* and *point-sampling*.

Point Sampling

3. A plan of a forest stand representing a horizontal plane at breast height (1·3 m from ground level) could be depicted as in Figure 13. The basal area of the stand is evidently a very small proportion of the total area of the stand. In fact in fully stocked stands this proportion is normally in the region of 0·2% to 0·7%.

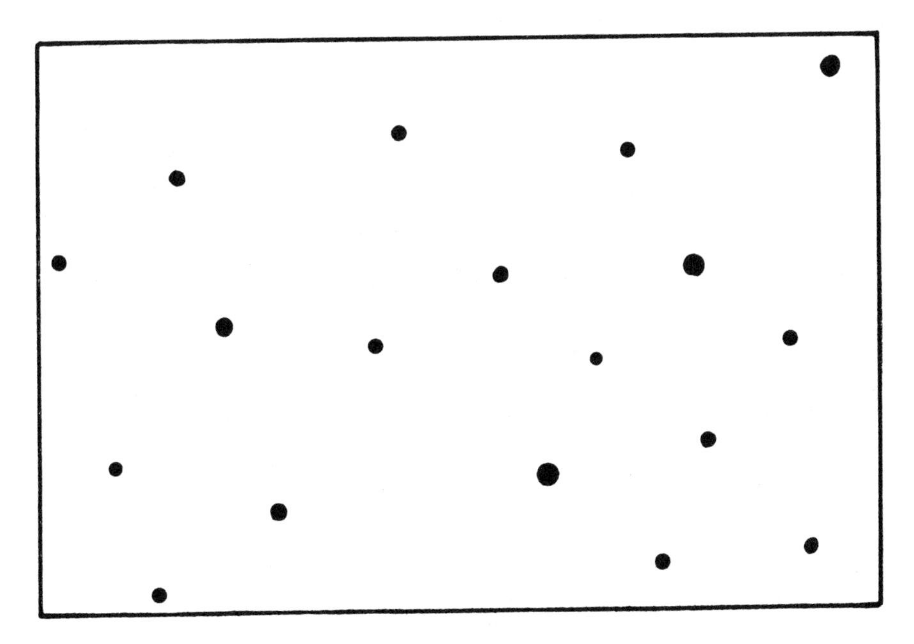

Figure 13

4. If a number of points were selected at random in this plan, the number falling on area occupied by (the stems of) trees, relative to the total number of points selected, would provide an estimate of the basal area of the stand. For example, if 0·5% of points fell on areas occupied by trees, then the basal area per hectare (10 000 m^2) would be:

$$10\,000 \times \frac{0{\cdot}5}{100} = 50 \text{ m}^2.$$

5. Now clearly, the number of random points required to provide adequate estimates of basal area in this situation would be exceedingly high, and consequently any sampling scheme on these lines would be so inefficient as to be wholly impractical.

6. If, however, one considered an imaginary circular zone around each tree, the diameter of which was f (a constant factor) times the actual diameter of the tree, the plan of the horizontal plane would look rather like Fig 14. The zones are seen to overlap many times.

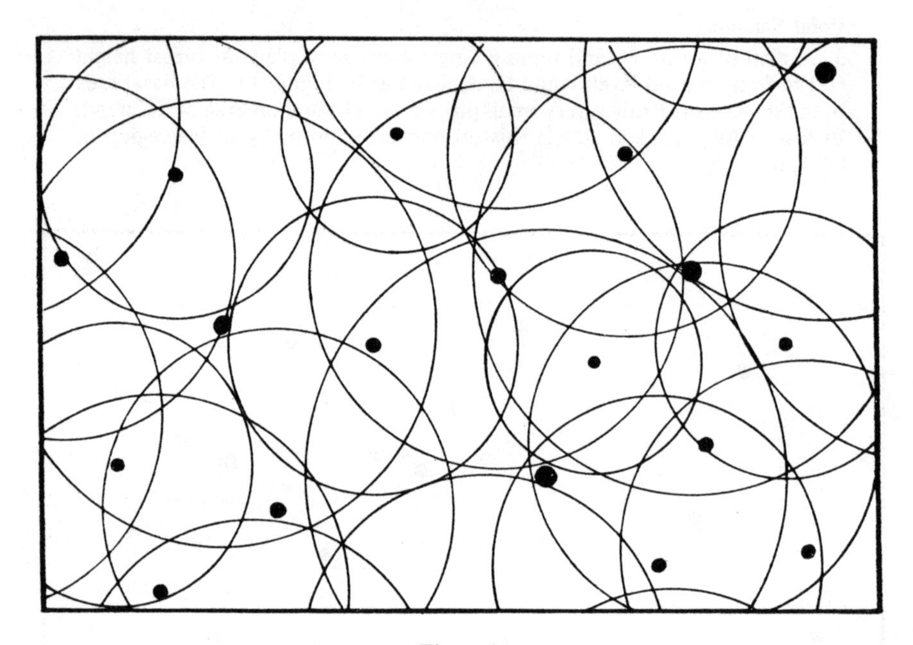

Figure 14

7. The ratio of the total area of zones to the total basal area will be f^2:1.

8. If one now selects points at random on this plan, the relevant question is not about the proportion of points falling on trees, but rather the average number of zones each point falls on.

9. The average number of zones within which one point falls indicates the ratio of the total area of zones per unit area of the stand. For example, if the average number of zones counted is 8, then the total area of zones will be 8 m^2/m^2 of the stand, or 8 ha/ha of the stand.

10. Since the ratio of zone area to basal area is f^2: 1 (para 7) the basal area per hectare must equal the average number of zones counted per sample point multiplied by $\frac{10\,000}{f^2}$.

11. The efficiency of sampling is thus greatly increased and in this situation a few sample points can provide a degree of precision which would require hundreds of sample points in the original situation (para 4).

12. The technique described here can be used directly in the forest as well as on the notional plan. In this case points are selected at random throughout the stand and the number of zones assessed at each point. What is yet to be explained is how these zones may be determined and counted in the real situation. It is for this purpose a relascope is used.

The Relascope

13. Consider Figure 15 which depicts the position of the perimeter of the expanded zone relative to the tree. Clearly since 'f' is common to all trees the angle Ø subtended at the perimeter by the tree profile at breast height must also be common. The angle subtended by the tree at a point inside the zone will be greater than Ø, whilst that of a point outside the zone will be smaller than Ø.

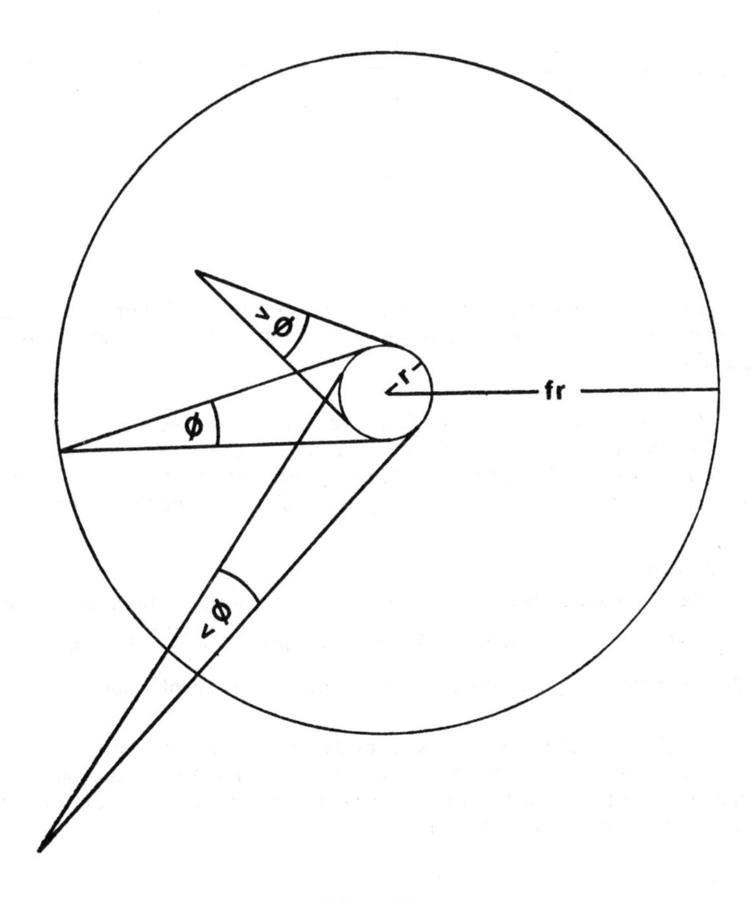

Figure 15

14. A relascope is simply a device incorporating the fixed angle Ø. By comparing the angles subtended at the sampling point by neighbouring trees with this fixed angle it is possible to determine the number of zones within which the point is situated.

15. In practice it is necessary to assess in this way all neighbouring trees in a 360° 'sweep' at the selected point.

Types of Relascopes

16. The simplest type of relascope consists of a distance piece (d) and a cross piece (c) fixed at right angles at one end of the distance piece as shown in Figure 16. The ends of the cross piece form the angle Ø at the opposite end of the distance piece, which is held close to the eye of the observer.

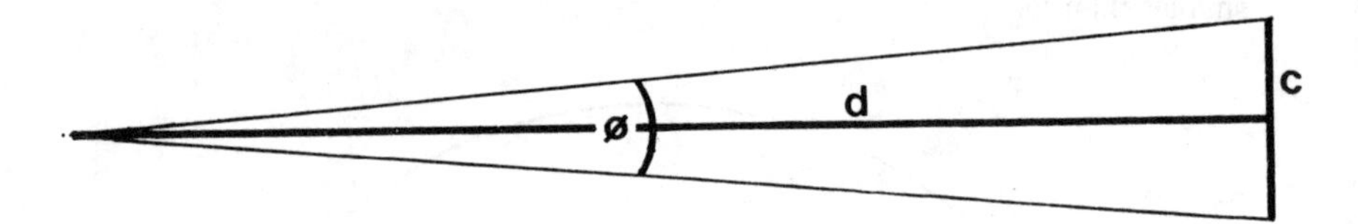

Figure 16

17. The distance piece may in practice consist of a piece of chain, a cardboard tube etc and the cross piece likewise may alternatively be a metal blade or metal tubing etc.

18. Another commonly used angle gauge is a glass wedge prism. The angle Ø is in this case formed by the displacement of the image of an object at right angles to the line of sight (effectively the cross piece) and the distance between the prism and the object displaced (effectively the distance piece).

Calibration

19. Basal area per hectare is estimated as the average number of zones counted per sample point multiplied by a factor $F = \frac{10\,000}{f^2}$. It clearly makes the procedure simple if this multiplier F has a convenient value.

20. In this connection one must consider the number of zones which are counted at each sampling point. Too many makes the assessment rather tedious whilst too few leads to relatively low precision. An ideal number is about 10–15 per sampling point.

21. In British conditions basal area stocking per hectare of fully stocked stands is frequently in the range 20–50 m^2/ha suggesting F values of 2–5. For thinnings and very young or poorly stocked crops basal areas may be in the order of 5–15 suggesting F values of ½–1.

22. The following formulae will assist in relating the factor F to the physical properties of the relascope:

$$\text{(i) } F = 2\,500 \left(\frac{c}{d}\right)^2$$

where F = basal area factor (m^2/ha)
c = width of cross piece
d = length of distance piece

$$\text{or (ii) } F = 10\,000 \left(\tan \frac{Ø}{2}\right)^2$$

where Ø = angle of relascope

23. Table 18 following gives the relative dimensions of commonly used relascope factors.

Table 18

Basal Area Factor (F)	Ratio of width of cross piece(c) to length of distance piece (d)	Angle (ø)
0·25	1 : 100·0	0° 34′ 23″
0·5	1 : 70·7	0° 48′ 37″
1	1 : 50·0	1° 8′ 46″
2	1 : 35·3	1° 37′ 12″
3	1 : 28·9	1° 59′ 2″
4	1 : 25·0	2° 17′ 27″
5	1 : 22·4	2° 33′ 37″
6	1 : 20·4	2° 48′ 17″

PRACTICE

24. A number of points should be selected, preferably systematically, or with a point-sampling grid on a map, throughout the area being assessed. As a rough guide Table 19 following can be used to determine the appropriate number of sampling points in reasonably uniform stand conditions.

Table 19

Area (ha)	No. of sampling points
0·5—2·0	8
2·0—10·0	12
Over 10·0	16

Where the crop is more variable the number of sampling points should be increased.

25. Viewed from the sampling point, neighbouring trees are counted or not counted as the case may be, as follows. Using the more conventional type of relascope, the end of the instrument opposite the cross piece is held close to the eye of the observer. Sighting along the distance piece the apparent width of the cross piece is compared with the apparent width of the tree at breast height. If the tree appears wider than the cross piece it is counted (see Figure 17). With wedge prism relascopes the prism is held as close to the eye as is convenient such that the breast height point on the tree is viewed in line with the top horizontal edge of the prism. The image of the tree at breast height is displaced laterally and according to the degree of displacement the tree is or is not counted (see Figure 18). It is important to view the trees *at breast height* (1·3 m) and this should be periodically checked.

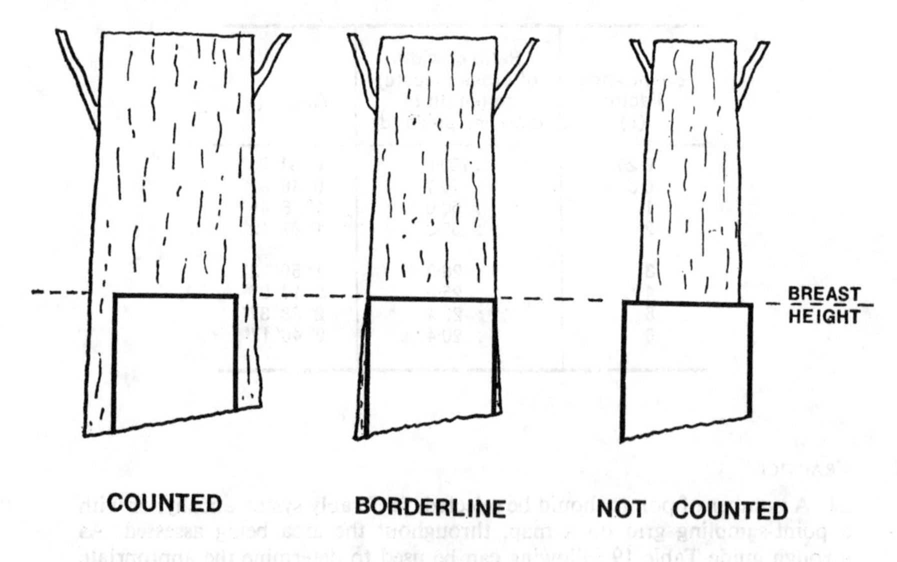

Figure 17

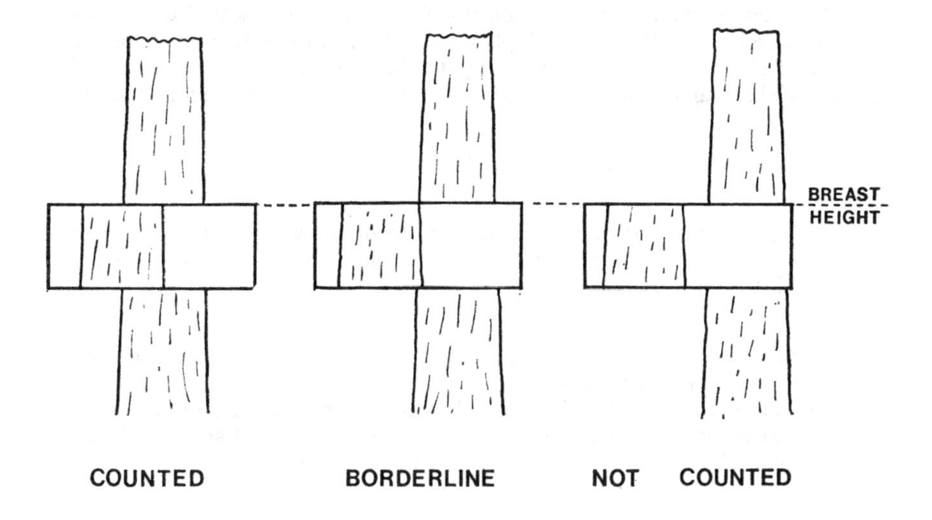

Figure 18

26. Starting from an easily identified direction, all trees in a 360° sweep are viewed and counted, or not as the case may be. (It soon becomes apparent that more distant trees are not 'counted').

27. Where trees are borderline (Figures 17 and 18) they may be alternatively counted as ½ or every second borderline tree (at successive points) counted as 1.

28. Trees which are obscured by others can be viewed by temporarily moving the sampling point a sufficient distance at right angles to the direction of sighting.

29. Where, as in most cases, the object is to assess *measurable* basal area ie for measurable volume, trees of less than 7 cm dbh are excluded. (These can easily be checked in practice, since they will normally only be reckonable when very close to the observer.)

30. Basal area per hectare is the product of the factor of the relascope and the number of trees counted in a 360° sweep. For example, if the number of trees counted is 13, and the factor of the relascope is 2, the basal area estimate will be 26 m^2 ha. The average basal area of the stand is simply the average of the estimates made at each selected sampling point.

31. Where sampling points fall on sloping ground it is essential to increase the basal area estimates by multiplying by the factor (secant) given in column 2 of Table 16 (page 133) appropriate to the angle of slope. For example, given a basal area estimate of 26 m²/ha assessed on a slope of 10°, the corrected value will be:

$$26 \times 1{\cdot}0154 \text{ (Table 16)} = 26{\cdot}4 \text{ m}^2/\text{ha}.$$

32. Note that in assessing the basal area of thinnings by this method it is usually necessary to mark the tree on three sides so that at least one mark is visible to the observer.

33. Accurate use of the relascope requires practice. In particular, when using relascopes with small factors, eg a factor of 0·5, there is a tendency to underestimate basal area. It is useful to cross check relascope estimates of basal area against estimates derived by measuring the basal area of all trees in a plot of known size, in order to assess personal bias.

4. HEIGHT MEASUREMENT

Height Measurement of Individual Trees

1. There are two expressions of tree height normally encountered in practice. The first is *total height* which is the vertical distance from the base of the tree to the uppermost point (tip). The second is *timber height* which concerns conventionally merchantable material only and is the distance from the base to the highest point on the main stem where the diameter is not less than 7 cms overbark. In hardwoods and occasionally in conifers this point may alternatively be the 'spring of the crown', ie the lowest point at which no main stem is distinguishable.

2. Apart from young crops where height can be measured with graduated poles, it is assumed here that a modern hypsometer or clinometer will be used to assess height. Examples of these are: *Haga, Blumę-Leiss, Suunto.* These instruments are supplied with full instructions which it is not proposed to reproduce here. All of these instruments, however, are based on trigonometrical principles which are briefly outlined in the following paragraph.

3. In Figure 19, the observer positioned at 0 views the top of the tree (or timber height if required) and, effectively, records the angle a_1 formed with the horizontal. The base of the tree is then sighted with the instrument and the angle a_2 recorded. The distance OB is assessed either by measuring tape or with the aid of a rangefinder incorporated in the instrument. The height of the tree is then assessed using the formulae shown in Figure 19.

N.B. With a rangefinder it is usually more convenient to assess the distance between the observer and a point on the tree other than the base. Irrespective

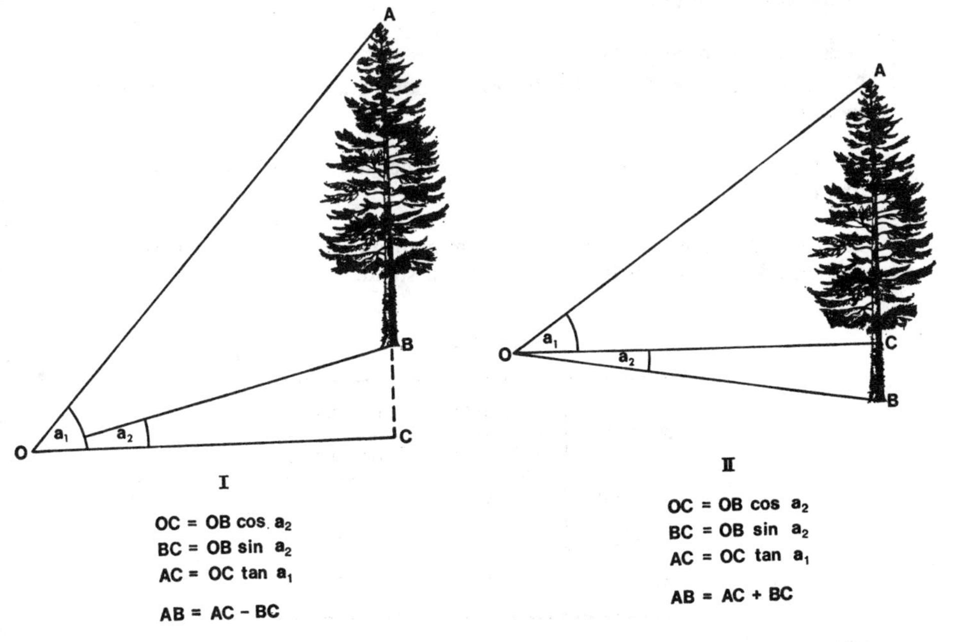

Figure 19

of the point chosen, OC can be calculated as the product of the distance and the cosine of the angle which is formed with the horizontal by the line joining the chosen point on the tree and the eye of the observer. The other calculations remain as in Fig 19.

4. Each of the instruments mentioned above incorporates a device for establishing the horizontal plane. Some are calibrated to read AC and BC directly in metres, for a range of fixed values of OB (or its alternative—see note under Para 3), although where this line deviates from the horizontal plane appropriate corrections should be made to the readings obtained as given with the instruments instructions. Apart from purpose-designed instruments, any angle measuring device which has the facility for establishing the horizontal plane, such as an Abney level, can be used to assess height using the above-mentioned principles.

5. The distance of the observation point from the tree should be in the region of 1–1½ times the height of the tree. Errors can prove to be sizeable where the observer is too close to the tree. The main difficulty in achieving the ideal position is that of being able to view the tops of trees in dense stands.

6. The height of the tree is always the *vertical* distance between the top and the base. On sloping ground the base of the tree is taken as ground level on the upper side of the tree.

7. It is advisable to take two or three measurements of each point viewed and to use the average of the readings.

8. The precision of the measurement is inevitably related to the capability of the instrument used.

Height measurement of stands

9. Two expressions of stand height are commonly encountered, *top height* and *mean height*.

10. *Top height* is defined as the average total height of the 100 trees of largest dbh per hectare.

11. Table 20 below gives the likely minimum number of trees required to give an adequate top height estimate for a stand.

Table 20

Area (ha)	No of top-height trees	
	Uniform crop	Variable crop
0·5– 2·0	6	8
2·0–10·0	8	12
Over 10·0	10	16

12. In pure stands, each top height tree must be selected from a plot of 0·01 hectares. A series of points which will be equal in number to the desired number of sample trees should be located at random throughout the stand. The height of the tree of largest dbh within a radius of 5·6 m (six paces) from each point is measured and the arithmetic mean of the heights of trees thus selected gives the top height of the stand.

13. Where the top height of each species in a mixed stand is required larger sample plots are necessary. For two species, plots of 0·02 ha (radius 8 m) are used. Where there are three or four species use 0·05 ha (radius 12·6 m), measuring in each plot the height of the tree of largest dbh of each species.

14. *Mean height* refers to the mean total height of the stand. Where timber height is the parameter sought, *mean timber height* is the expression used. In practice mean height in either form is rarely used, but can be assessed by taking heights of trees randomly selected, irrespective of dbh, throughout the stand.

15. Mean height is closely related to top height and Table 21 summarises these relationships for stands subject to conventional spacings and intermediate thinning.

STAND MEAN HEIGHT AT SPECIFIED TOP HEIGHT

Top Ht in Metres	Species						Top Ht in Metres
	S P	C P	L P	S S	N S	E L	
8	6.6	6.9	7.0	6.3	5.9	6.3	8
10	8.7	9.0	9.0	8.3	8.0	8.4	10
12	10.8	11.1	11.1	10.4	10.2	10.6	12
14	12.9	13.1	13.1	12.5	12.3	12.7	14
16	15.0	15.2	15.1	14.6	14.4	14.8	16
18	17.1	17.2	17.2	16.7	16.6	17.0	18
20	19.1	19.3	19.2	18.8	18.7	19.1	20
22	21.2	21.4	21.3	20.8	20.8	21.2	22
24	23.3	23.4	23.3	22.9	22.9	23.4	24
26	25.4	25.5	25.4	25.0	25.1	25.5	26
28	27.5	27.6	27.4	27.1	27.2	27.6	28
30	29.6	29.6	29.5	29.2	29.3	29.8	30

Top Ht in Metres	J L	D F	W H	R C	G F	N F	Top Ht in Metres
8	7.0	6.3	6.7	6.4	6.0	6.0	8
10	9.1	8.4	8.7	8.5	8.1	8.1	10
12	11.2	10.5	10.8	10.5	10.2	10.1	12
14	13.3	12.5	12.8	12.5	12.3	12.1	14
16	15.3	14.6	14.9	14.5	14.4	14.2	16
18	17.4	16.7	16.9	16.5	16.5	16.2	18
20	19.5	18.7	19.0	18.6	18.6	18.3	20
22	21.5	20.8	21.0	20.6	20.7	20.3	22
24	23.6	22.9	23.1	22.6	22.8	22.4	24
26	25.7	24.9	25.1	24.6	24.9	24.4	26
28	27.7	27.0	27.2	26.7	26.9	26.4	28
30	29.8	29.1	29.2	28.7	29.0	28.5	30

5. BARK

1. Values of dbh, basal area and volume may be described in terms of *overbark* (outside bark) or *underbark* (inside bark). These descriptions generally follow the way in which their measurement has been carried out. Thus the volume of a log derived from the length and mid diameter measured overbark will be described as an overbark volume. A volume assessed from length and top diameter measured underbark will be regarded as an underbark volume.

2. Occasionally estimates of underbark volume may be required from measurements taken overbark, and vice versa. Only rarely are measurements of bark justifiable in practice. The alternative is to use previously assembled information on average bark thickness or bark volumes. The tables which follow are designed to meet this requirement.

3. In quantifying bark thickness and volume, the measurement conventions are of some importance. Bark configuration varies according to the species and the age of the tree. If an accurate assessment of the actual average bark thickness was required, the more irregular bark surfaces would present considerable problems. In practice, however, a *peripheral* bark thickness is measured, which in effect largely discounts the influence of furrows and similar irregularities in the bark surface. Bark thickness is the average distance between the plane traversed (overbark) by a girthing tape encircling a log or tree, and the corresponding plane of a tape held in the same position underbark. Bark thickness measured with a standard bark gauge (with adequate flange) will be approximately the same.

4. The volume of bark in timber is calculated from the product of the average cross-sectional area of bark, derived in turn from the average *peripheral* bark thickness, and the length.

5. The tables of bark thickness and bark volume percentages given below are derived from numerous measurements of bark thickness taken at different positions in the tree and made in permanent sample plots located throughout the country.

Bark Thickness

6. For most species, bark thickness is found to be closely related to the diameter of the tree at the same point, irrespective of the position in the tree. In some pines, however, different relationships are recognised in different parts of the tree.

7. Table 22 details the average *double* bark thickness corresponding to various overbark diameters. In the case of Scots pine and Corsican pine a distinction is drawn between the upper half and the lower half of the merchantable section (length to timber height) of standing trees.

8. In order to establish the underbark diameter the *double* bark thickness is subtracted from the overbark diameter.

DOUBLE BARK THICKNESS IN MILLIMETRES

Species	Diameter overbark in centimetres										
	10	15	20	25	30	35	40	45	50	55	60
S P											
Lower stem	11	13	15	18	22	28	34	41	48		
Upper stem	6	8	9	11	13	15					
C P											
Lower stem	13	17	21	25	29	34	39	44	50		
Upper stem	9	12	15	18	21	24					
L P											
Inland	6	9	12	15	19						
S Coastal	7	10	14	17	21						
S S	6	8	9	11	13	14	15	17	18		
N S	6	8	9	11	13	14	15	17	18		
E L	9	15	20	24	28	30	32	34	35		
J L/ H L	7	12	17	20	23	25	26	27	28		
D F	7	10	13	16	19	23	27	31	35		
W H	7	9	11	13	16	18	20	22	25		
R C/ L C	7	10	12	14	16	18	19	21	22		
G F	6	7	9	10	11	13	15	17	19		
N F	8	9	10	11	13	15	17	19	22		
Oak	12	15	18	20	21	22	23	24	25	27	28
Be	5	7	8	10	11	12	13	14	14	15	15
Syc	6	8	10	12	14	15	15	16	16	17	17
Ash	7	9	11	13	15	17	19	21	23	24	26
Bi	6	10	13	16	19	21	23				
Elm	10	13	16	18	20	22	24	26	27	28	29
Po	7	12	17	23	28	32	36	39	41	43	45

Bark Volumes

9. The bark volume of an individual tree of specified height and dbh can be found in Tables 23–43, depending on the species. Bark volumes are expressed as percentages of overbark volumes to 7 cm top diameter overbark. Heights are given in 3 m classes. For example, the 15 m height class covers the height range, 13·5 m–16·4 m. Similarly, 5 cm classes are given for dbh, such that, for example the 20 cm class covers the dbh range 18–22 cm inclusive.

Example:

Japanese larch 19·2 m height, 25 cm dbh
Enter Table 30 (page 153) 18 m height class, 25 cm dbh class

Bark % = 15%

10. A reasonable estimate of the bark volume of *stands* can be obtained by applying to the overbark volume of the whole stand, the percentage value indicated for an individual tree corresponding to the mean dbh and mean height of the stand.

11. To estimate the volume of bark in a *billet, or log, measured overbark*, an underbark diameter may be estimated using the double bark thickness table (Table 22) and an underbark volume calculated (by the same method used to calculate the overbark volume). Bark volume is the difference between the over and underbark estimates of volume.

12. In the case of *sawlogs measured underbark* by Procedure 2 (page 22), the overbark volume can be estimated using Table 44 which provides volumes expressed as a percent of the underbark volume. (See notes on page 161.)

Scots pine

dbh Class cm	9	12	15	18	21	24	27	30	dbh Class cm
	BARK AS A PERCENT OF OVERBARK VOLUME								
	Height Class in metres								
10	17	17							10
15	17	17	16	15					15
20	17	16	15	15	13				20
25		15	15	15	13	13			25
30			15	14	13	13	12		30
35			15	14	13	13	12		35
40					13	13	12		40
45							12		45
50									50

Corsican pine

dbh Class cm	9	12	15	18	21	24	27	30	dbh Class cm
	BARK AS A PERCENT OF OVERBARK VOLUME								
	Height Class in metres								
10	21	20							10
15	20	20	19	19					15
20	20	19	19	19	19	18			20
25	19	19	18	18	18	18	18		25
30		18	18	18	18	18	18	18	30
35				18	18	17	17	17	35
40				17	17	17	17	17	40
45							17	16	45
50								16	50

Table 23

 Table 24

Lodgepole pine – Inland

BARK AS A PERCENT OF OVERBARK VOLUME

dbh Class cm	Height Class in metres 9	12	15	18	21	24	27	30	dbh Class cm
10	12	11	11						10
15	12	11	11						15
20	11	10	10						20
25		10	10						25
30									30
35									35

Lodgepole pine – South Coastal

BARK AS A PERCENT OF OVERBARK VOLUME

dbh Class cm	Height Class in metres 9	12	15	18	21	24	27	30	dbh Class cm
10	15	14							10
15	14	14	13						15
20		13	12	12					20
25		13	12	12					25
30									30
35									35

Sitka spruce

dbh Class cm	BARK AS A PERCENT OF OVERBARK VOLUME — Height Class in metres 9	12	15	18	21	24	27	30	dbh Class cm
10	12	11	11						10
15	11	11	10	10	10				15
20	10	10	10	10	10	10			20
25		10	9	9	9	9	9		25
30			9	9	9	9	8	8	30
35					8	8	8	8	35
40						8	8	8	40
45						8	8	7	45
50							7	7	50

Norway spruce

dbh Class cm	BARK AS A PERCENT OF OVERBARK VOLUME — Height Class in metres 9	12	15	18	21	24	27	30	dbh Class cm
10	13	12							10
15	12	11	11	11					15
20	10	10	10	10	10				20
25		10	10	10	9	9			25
30			9	9	9	9	9		30
35			9	8	8	8	8	8	35
40					8	8	8	8	40
45					8	8	8	8	45
50									50

Table 27

 Table 28

European larch

BARK AS A PERCENT OF OVERBARK VOLUME

dbh Class cm	Height Class in metres 9	12	15	18	21	24	27	30	dbh Class cm
10	21	20	19						10
15	20	20	19	19	20				15
20		19	19	19	20				20
25		18	18	19	19	19	19		25
30				19	19	19	18		30
35					19	18	18	18	35
40					19	18	18	18	40
45							18	18	45
50								18	50

Japanese/Hybrid larch

BARK AS A PERCENT OF OVERBARK VOLUME

dbh Class cm	Height Class in metres 9	12	15	18	21	24	27	30	dbh Class cm
10	18	18	19						10
15	17	17	17	18					15
20	16	16	16	16	18	20			20
25		15	15	15	16	18			25
30			14	14	15	16	17		30
35				14	15	16	16		35
40					15	15	15		40
45									45
50									50

Douglas fir

dbh Class cm	BARK AS A PERCENT OF OVERBARK VOLUME								dbh Class cm
	Height Class in metres								
	9	12	15	18	21	24	27	30	
10	13	13	13						10
15	13	13	13	13	13				15
20	13	13	13	13	13	13	13		20
25		12	12	12	12	12	12	12	25
30			12	12	12	12	12	12	30
35				12	12	12	12	12	35
40						12	12	12	40
45							12	12	45
50								12	50

Western hemlock

dbh Class cm	BARK AS A PERCENT OF OVERBARK VOLUME								dbh Class cm
	Height Class in metres								
	9	12	15	18	21	24	27	30	
10	14	13	13						10
15	13	12	12	12	12				15
20	13	12	12	12	12				20
25			11	11	11	11			25
30					11	11	11		30
35					11	11	11		35
40					10	10	10	10	40
45						10	10	10	45
50									50

Table 31
Table 32

Red cedar

dbh Class cm	BARK AS A PERCENT OF OVERBARK VOLUME								dbh Class cm
	Height Class in metres								
	9	12	15	18	21	24	27	30	
10	15	15							10
15	15	14	14	14					15
20	13	12	12	12	12				20
25			12	12	12	12			25
30			11	11	11	11			30
35				11	11	11			35
40					11	10			40
45					10	10	9		45
50						9	9		50

Lawson cypress

dbh Class cm	BARK AS A PERCENT OF OVERBARK VOLUME								dbh Class cm
	Height Class in metres								
	9	12	15	18	21	24	27	30	
10	14	16							10
15	13	15	16						15
20	12	14	15	16					20
25			15	15					25
30				15	15				30
35				14	14				35
40					13	13			40
45					13	12			45
50									50

Grand fir

dbh Class cm	BARK AS A PERCENT OF OVERBARK VOLUME Height Class in metres 9	12	15	18	21	24	27	30	dbh Class cm
10	11	10	10						10
15	10	10	10	10	10	10			15
20		10	9	9	9	9			20
25		10	9	8	8	8			25
30					8	7			30
35					7	7			35
40									40
45									45
50									50

Noble fir

dbh Class cm	BARK AS A PERCENT OF OVERBARK VOLUME Height Class in metres 9	12	15	18	21	24	27	30	dbh Class cm
10	11	11							10
15	11	11	10						15
20		11	9	9					20
25		10	9	8	8				25
30			9	8	8				30
35			8	8	7				35
40				8	7				40
45									45
50									50

Table 35
Table 36

Oak

BARK AS A PERCENT OF OVERBARK VOLUME

dbh Class cm	Timber Height Class in metres 5	10	15	20	25	30	dbh Class cm
10	21	20	19				10
15	19	19	19	19			15
20	18	18	18	19			20
25	18	18	18	18			25
30	18	18	18	17	16		30
35	17	17	17	17	16		35
40	17	17	16	16	15		40
45	16	16	15	15	14		45
50	15	15	14	14	13		50
55	15	14	14	14	13		55
60	14	14	13	13	12		60

Beech

BARK AS A PERCENT OF OVERBARK VOLUME

dbh Class cm	Timber Height Class in metres 5	10	15	20	25	30	dbh Class cm
10	11	9					10
15	11	9	10	10			15
20	10	9	9	9	9		20
25	10	9	9	9	8	8	25
30	9	9	8	8	8	8	30
35	9	9	8	8	7	7	35
40	8	8	8	7	7	7	40
45	8	8	7	7	6	6	45
50	7	7	7	7	6	6	50
55	7	7	6	6	6	5	55
60	7	6	6	6	5	5	60

Table 37
Table 38

Sycamore

dbh Class cm	BARK AS A PERCENT OF OVERBARK VOLUME						dbh Class cm
	Timber Height Class in metres						
	5	10	15	20	25	30	
10	11	11					10
15	11	10	9				15
20	11	10	9				20
25	10	9	8				25
30	10	9	8				30
35	10	9	8				35
40	9	9	8				40
45	9	8	7				45
50	9	8	7				50
55	9	8	7				55
60	8	7	7				60

Ash

dbh Class cm	BARK AS A PERCENT OF OVERBARK VOLUME						dbh Class cm
	Timber Height Class in metres						
	5	10	15	20	25	30	
10	14	15					10
15	13	14	12				15
20	13	13	12	12			20
25	12	12	12	11	11		25
30	11	11	11	10	10		30
35	10	11	11	10	10		35
40	10	10	10	10	9		40
45	10	10	10	9	9		45
50	9	9	9	9	9		50
55	9	9	9	9	9		55
60	9	9	9	9	8		60

Table 39

Table 40

Birch

BARK AS A PERCENT OF OVERBARK VOLUME

dbh Class cm	Timber Height Class in metres 5	10	15	20	dbh Class cm
10-40	14	13	12	11	10-40

Although the bark percentage of Birch varies within very wide limits, it is approximately similar for all diameters within a timber height class.

Elm

BARK AS A PERCENT OF OVERBARK VOLUME

dbh Class cm	Timber Height Class in metres 5	10	15	20	25	30	dbh Class cm
10	22						10
15	19	21					15
20	16	18	20	20			20
25	14	16	18	19			25
30	13	15	17	18			30
35	12	14	16	17			35
40	12	13	15	16			40
45	12	13	15	16			45
50	11	12	14	15			50
55	11	12	14	15			55
60	11	12	13	14			60

Poplar

dbh Class cm	BARK AS A PERCENT OF OVERBARK VOLUME						dbh Class cm
	Timber Height Class in metres						
	5	10	15	20	25	30	
10	18						10
15	19	19	18				15
20	20	19	18				20
25		19	18	18			25
30		19	18	18			30
35		19	18	18			35
40		18	18	17			40
45		18	18	17			45
50		18	18	17			50
55		18	18	17			55
60		18	18	17			60

Top diameter under-bark cm	BARK AS A PERCENT OF UNDERBARK VOLUME						
	SPECIES						
	SP	CP	SS	NS	EL	JL	DF
10	16.5	25.5	13.5	10.0	25.0	20.5	16.5
15	14.0	22.0	11.0	10.0	22.0	18.0	14.0
20	14.0	20.5	10.0	9.5	20.5	16.5	13.0
25	15.5	20.5	9.0	9.0	20.0	16.0	13.0
30	17.5	21.0	8.5	8.5	20.5	16.0	13.5
35	19.5	21.5	8.0	8.0	21.0	16.0	13.5
40	21.5	22.5	7.5	7.5	21.5	16.5	14.0
45	23.0	23.5	7.5	7.0	22.0	17.0	14.0
50	24.0	24.5	7.0	6.5	22.5	17.5	14.5

Notes

(i) It is important to note that the above values are percentages of *underbark* volume. To convert underbark volume to overbark volume merely add the appropriate percentage (p) of the underbark volume—

$$\text{ie o.b. volume} = \text{u.b. volume} \times \frac{(100 + p)}{100}$$

(ii) The table is applicable only to the range of log lengths covered by the sawlog tables.

(iii) The values given for Scots pine and Corsican pine are, as a result of new information, slightly different from previously published values (FC Booklet 31). It should be noted that the part of the tree from which the sawlog is taken in these species has a marked influence on the bark percentage (see Table 22). The assumption made in calculating the values in the table is that sawlog material is taken predominantly from the lower half of the merchantable stem.

(iv) *Other Species*

For South Coastal Lodgepole pine use Scots pine bark percentages minus 2%. For other provenances of Lodgepole pine use Scots pine bark percentages minus 4%.

For: Western hemlock, Red cedar, Grand fir, Noble fir, Omorika spruce } use Sitka spruce bark percentages.

6. ASSORTMENTS

General

1. Forest managers frequently require quantitative information of forest produce other than simply gross volume. The actual dimensions of round timber often relate directly to the end-use of the produce and consequently attract different prices. The produce from a thinning or felling may usually be expected to furnish more than one specific product, eg, pulpwood and sawlogs, and it is of considerable advantage to the manager to know in advance the proportion of the produce which he might expect to supply to the different markets.

Size Assortments

2. Size assortments are various categories of timber, specified by length, or diameter, or both, which may be produced in cross-cutting a tree.

3. In any stand, individual trees differ in height, diameter, and form, so that the task of forecasting quantities of specific size assortments, given a few average stand parameters, appears forbidding. Without discounting the importance of this variation, there are certain stand features which are sufficiently predictable to enable such forecasts to be made with some confidence.

4. Individual coniferous trees have characteristic profiles such as shown in Fig 20. The profiles are shown as the relationship between diameter and height, with the diameter scale some twenty four times larger than the height scale. The profiles shown are of trees with a common height but of varying dbh.

5. Varying stand conditions induce differences in the relationship between height and dbh of individuals. Irrespective of the stand conditions, it is broadly true in British conditions that within a given height and dbh class, the profile remains basically the same.

6. Different coniferous species exhibit differences in profiles within a given height and dbh class, but these are not of any great practical significance.

7. Hardwood species are less predictable than conifers in terms of profiles. This follows from the branching habits of these species and the consequent difficulty in establishing average profiles in the upper regions of the stem.

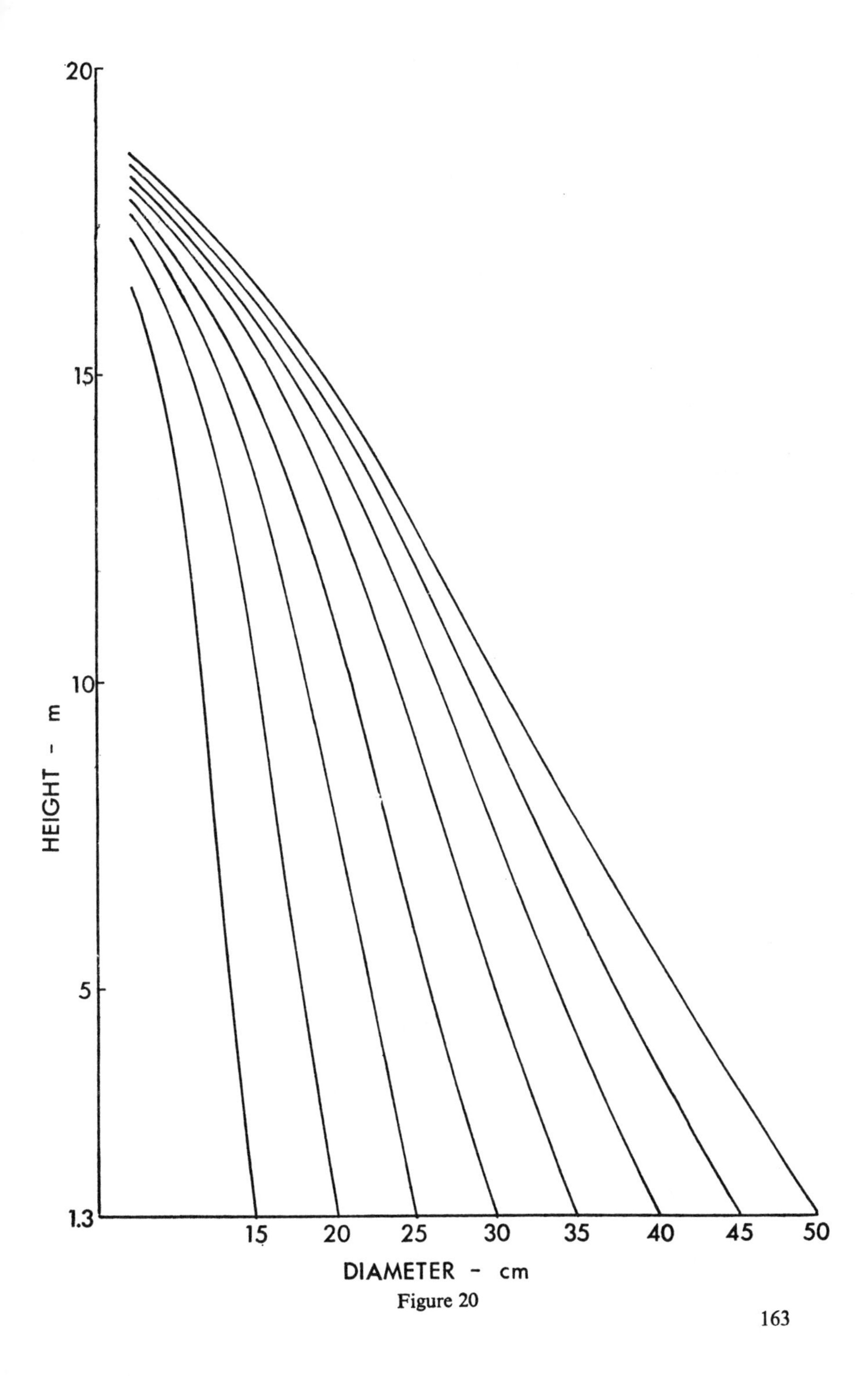

Figure 20

8. With the exception of hardwoods, however, it is relatively straightforward to predict size assortments in individual trees, given height and dbh. Tree profiles have been constructed for a wide range of diameter and height classes, using information obtained from measurements taken in permanent sample plots.

9. In dealing with stands, however, it is clearly not a practical proposition to assess the height and dbh of all trees individually. In practice, forecasts must be produced from relatively few average stand parameters, usually the total volume, average dbh, and sometimes top height.

10. The first assumption which must be made therefore concerns the dbh distribution. The distributions assumed here are those given in the stand table on page 184, and are broadly those resulting from the normal thinning regime outlined in FC Booklet 48 (ie, intermediate type, 'marginal intensity'). In practice it is only where the stand treatment has resulted in markedly unusual distributions, as for example by heavy crown thinnings, that differences between actual and assumed distributions have a significant impact on the resulting size assortments.

11. An assumption must also be made on the heights appropriate to each dbh class. Although within any class one can expect to encounter varied heights, adequate results are obtained by assuming a standard height for each dbh class. Generally, of course, diminished height accompanies smaller dbh.

Assortment Tables

12. Distinction has already been drawn between forecasting individual tree assortments and stand assortments. In order to meet the needs of these two situations *individual tree assortment tables* and *stand assortment tables* are provided.

13. Additionally, one recognises *volume assortment tables* and *length assortment tables*. Volume assortment tables provide percentage volumes to specified top diameters, whereas length assortment tables show the (average) length of billet obtainable to a given top diameter from individual trees.

14. In the case of volume assortment tables entry is by dbh (mean dbh in the case of stands). In the case of length assortment tables, factors such as taper become more critical and thus the dbh/height relationship must be taken into account. Both height and dbh are therefore required as entries

15. One further aspect has to be considered. Estimates of size assortments are frequently required in underbark terms from overbark measurements. Special tables are required for this purpose.

16. In order to clarify the provision, specification and use of the tables the Index opposite has been prepared. Small differences exist between Table 50 and previously published Volume Assortment Tables covering the same specification. Table 50 has been produced using revised methods of computation and employing more recent data.

Table	Description	Entry	Information Provided
	1. *VOLUME ASSORTMENT TABLES*		
45	Single tree overbark	dbh	% of o.b. volume to specified o.b. top diameter (no minimum length)
46	Single tree underbark (pines, larches, Douglas fir)	dbh	% of o.b. volume to specified u.b. top diameter (1·3 minimum length)
47	" " underbark (spruces, other conifers)	dbh	" " " " " " u.b. " " (" " ")
48	Stand overbark	mean dbh	% of o.b. volume to specified o.b. top diameter (1 m minimum length)
49	" "	" "	" " " " " " o.b. " " (2 m " ")
50	" "	" "	" " " " " " o.b. " " (3 m " ")
51	" "	" "	" " " " " " o.b. " " (4 m " ")
52	Stand underbark (pines, larches, Douglas fir)	mean dbh	% of o.b. volume to specified u.b. top diameter (3 m minimum length)
53	" " (spruces, other conifers)	" "	" " " " " " u.b. " " (3 m " ")
	2. *LENGTH ASSORTMENT TABLES*		
54	Single tree overbark	dbh, ht	Length from butt to specified o.b. top diameter (1·3 m minimum length)
55	" " underbark (pines, larches, Douglas fir)	" "	" " " " " u.b. " " (1·3 m " ")
56	" " underbark (spruces, other conifers)	" "	" " " " " u.b. " " (1·3 m " ")
	3. *STAND/STOCK TABLES*		
57	Stand table	mean dbh	Distribution of numbers of trees by dbh classes
58	Stock table	" "	" " stand volume by dbh classes

Notes: dbh = diameter at breast height. ht = height.

17. Assortment problems can be complex in nature. The use of assortment tables to solve these more complex problems is usually laborious and consequently better handled by computers. The use of the tables included here will usually be confined to the more straightforward problems, examples of which are given below. No allowance has been made for quality constraints or stem defects which may affect the actual out-turn of specific products.

Example 1

To find the proportion of volume of an individual tree:

(i) *greater than x cm diameter*

(ii) *less than x cm diameter*

(iii) *between x and y cm diameter*
—given dbh

Table 45 should be used.

In (i) the answer is given directly in the table, ie for a dbh of 20 cm, the proportion of volume greater than 16 cm is 66%.
The proportion less than 16 cm (ii) is clearly 100 − 66% = 34%. The proportion of volume between 16 cm and 10 cm (iii) is 94 − 66% = 28%.

Notes:

If, in conifers, the diameters specified are underbark then Tables 46 or 47 should be used depending on the species. Table 46 covers pines, Douglas fir and larches, whilst Table 47 covers spruces and other conifers. In Tables 46 and 47 the minimum length assumed is 1·3 m.

Example 2

To find the proportion of volume of a stand:

(i) *greater than x cm diameter*

(ii) *less than x cm diameter*

(iii) *between x and y cm diameter*
—given mean dbh of the stand

Tables 48, 49, 50 or 51 should be used depending on the minimum lengths desired. Consider a specification of 18 cm top diameter and a minimum length of 2 m. The appropriate table is Table 49. The answer to (i) is read directly from the table and for a stand mean diameter of 25 cm the percentage volume to 18 cm is 73%. Likewise the percentage volume less than 18 cm (ii) will be 100 − 73% = 27% and, (iii) the difference between 18 cm and, say, 10 cm diameter will be 97 − 73% = 24%.

Note:

Depending on the values of x and y, the minimum length specification will not necessarily apply to (ii) or (iii).

Example 3

To find the volume of a stand:

(i) *underbark to a top diameter of 16 cm underbark and of 3 m minimum length.*

(ii) *overbark to 7 cm top diameter overbark of the remaining volume after maximising (i).*

Consider a stand of Scots pine, mean dbh of 25 cm. The appropriate table required to answer (i) is Table 52. The percentage of the stand overbark volume is 65%. In order to answer (ii) this percentage has to be converted to an overbark volume percentage. Using the bark percent table on page 161 it is found that an appropriate additional percentage for an underbark top diameter of 16 cm is 14% of the underbark volume.

$$\text{Thus } 65 + \frac{14 \times 65}{100}$$

$= 74\%$, is the overbark volume percentage to 16 cm underbark and the remaining percentage overbark to 7 cm top diameter (ii) is:

$$100 - 74\%$$
$$= 26\%$$

Note:

Table 52 applies to pines, larches and Douglas fir; Table 53 to spruces and other conifers.

Example 4

To find (in an individual tree) the maximum length of log:

(i) *with a minimum diameter of x cm*

(ii) *with a maximum diameter of x cm*

(iii) *between x and y cm diameter*
—given dbh and height of the tree

Consider a tree of 30 cm dbh and 15 m height. Using Table 54, enter the table by height class 15 and dbh 30. The average length expected to a top diameter of 18 cm (i) is 8·5 m.

The length to a maximum diameter (ii) of 18 cm is the difference between the length to 18 cm and that to 7 cm top diameter, ie 12·3 − 8·5 = 3·8 m. Similarly the length between any other two specified diameters is the difference between the values tabulated against these diameters.

Notes:

The height classes are given in 3 m intervals, the specified value referring to the mean of the class. For estimates where actual heights are at the extremities of the classes, the accuracy may be improved by interpolation. The same is true, but obviously less critical, of diameter classes. Where diameters are specified underbark Table 55 or 56 should be used, depending on the species.

A minimum length of 1·3 m is assumed in Tables 54, 55, and 56.

Example 5

To find the proportion of the number of trees in a stand of given mean dbh which:

(i) *Occur in a given dbh class*

(ii) *Are greater than a given dbh*

(iii) *Are less than a given dbh*

(iv) *Occur between two specified diameter classes.*

Table 57 should be used. Note that proportions are for 5 cm classes which are specified by the average of the class. For example, the 25 cm dbh class includes dbh's of 23, 24, 25, 26 and 27 centimetres. Assume mean dbh of stand to be 35 cm.

(i) The proportion of the trees that occur in the 25 cm dbh class is 15%.

(ii) The proportion of trees that are greater than the 40 cm class (42 cm dbh) = 11%.
(the trees in the 45 cm class plus the trees in 50 cm class)

(iii) The proportion of trees less than 30 cm dbh class (32 cm dbh) = 19%

(iv) The proportion of trees between 25 and 35 cm classes = 68%.

Example 6

To find the proportion of the volume of a stand with a given mean diameter occurring:

(i) *In a given diameter class*

(ii) *In classes greater than a given diameter*

(iii) *In classes less than a given diameter*

(iv) *Between two classes, or class boundaries*

Table 58 is used in exactly the same way as for the stand tables. Assume mean dbh of stand to be 35 cm:

(i) The proportion of the stand volume in the 25 cm dbh class is 9%.

(ii) The proportion of the stand volume in the dbh classes greater than 40 cm = 19%.

(iii) The proportion of the stand volume in the dbh classes less than 30 cm dbh class = 10%.

(iv) The proportion of the stand volume between—and including—the dbh classes of 25 and 35 cm = 58%.

SINGLE TREE OVERBARK VOLUME ASSORTMENT TABLE

(NO MINIMUM LENGTH)

VOLUMES TO SPECIFIED TOP DIAMETERS O.B. AS A PERCENTAGE OF OVERBARK VOLUME

dbh cm	Top Diameter in centimetres: to tip	7*	8	10	12	14	16	18	20	22	24	26	28	30	32	34	36	38	40	dbh cm
7	130	100																		7
8	119	100	16																	8
9	115	100	68																	9
10	112	100	78	42																10
11	109	100	84	63																11
12	107	100	87	71	26															12
13	106	100	90	77	52															13
14	105	100	92	81	63	24														14
15	104	100	94	84	70	42														15
16	103	100	95	87	76	55	15													16
17	103	100	96	90	80	64	36													17
18	102	100	97	92	83	70	50	15												18
19	102	100	98	93	86	75	59	32												19
20	102	100	98	94	88	79	66	46	14											20
21	102	100	99	95	90	82	72	56	27	2										21
22	101	100	99	96	92	85	76	63	38	12										22
23	101	100	99	97	93	87	79	68	48	22	2									23
24	101	100	99	97	94	89	82	72	56	33	11									24
25	101	100	99	98	95	91	85	76	62	43	21	2								25
26	101	100	99	98	96	92	87	79	68	51	31	9								26
27	101	100	99	98	96	93	88	82	72	57	39	18	2							27
28	101	100	100	98	97	94	90	84	75	63	46	27	9							28
29	101	100	100	99	97	95	91	86	78	67	52	35	16	3						29
30	101	100	100	99	97	95	92	88	81	71	58	42	25	9						30
31	101	100	100	99	98	96	93	89	83	74	62	48	32	15	3					31
32	101	100	100	99	98	96	94	90	85	77	67	54	38	22	9					32
33	100	100	100	99	98	96	94	91	86	79	70	58	44	29	15	4				33
34	100	100	100	99	98	97	95	92	88	81	73	62	49	35	21	9				34
35	100	100	100	99	98	97	95	93	89	83	76	66	54	40	27	15	4			35
36	100	100	100	99	98	97	96	94	90	85	78	69	58	45	32	21	9			36
37	100	100	100	99	98	97	96	94	91	86	80	72	62	50	38	26	14	5		37
38	100	100	100	99	98	97	96	95	92	87	82	74	65	54	43	31	19	10		38
39	100	100	100	99	99	98	97	95	92	88	83	76	68	58	47	36	24	15	5	39
40	100	100	100	99	99	98	97	95	93	89	85	78	71	62	51	40	29	20	10	40
41	100	100	100	99	99	98	97	96	94	90	86	80	73	65	55	45	34	24	14	41
42	100	100	100	99	99	98	97	96	94	91	87	82	75	68	59	49	39	28	19	42
43	100	100	100	99	99	98	97	96	95	92	88	84	77	70	62	53	43	33	23	43
44	100	100	100	99	99	98	98	96	95	93	89	85	79	73	65	56	47	37	27	44
45	100	100	100	99	99	98	98	97	95	93	90	86	81	75	68	59	50	41	31	45
46	100	100	100	99	99	98	98	97	96	94	91	87	82	77	70	62	53	44	35	46
47	100	100	100	99	99	98	98	97	96	94	92	88	84	79	72	65	56	48	38	47
48	100	100	100	99	99	98	98	97	96	95	92	89	85	80	74	67	59	51	42	48
49	100	100	100	99	99	99	98	97	96	95	93	90	86	81	76	69	62	54	46	49
50	100	100	100	99	99	99	98	98	97	95	93	90	87	82	77	71	64	57	49	50

* The volume to 7cm top diameter assumes the conventional minimum length of 1.3m.

This table can be used for all conifers, but for broadleaved species its use should be restricted to trees with a dbh of 30cm or less.

For values shown to the left of the line in the body of the table, the lengths to specified top diameters, for a given dbh are at least 3m.

SINGLE TREE UNDERBARK VOLUME ASSORTMENT TABLE FOR PINES, LARCHES AND DOUGLAS FIR

(MINIMUM LENGTH 1·3m)

UNDERBARK VOLUME TO SPECIFIED TOP DIAMETERS U.B. AS A PERCENT OF OVERBARK VOLUME *

dbh cm	Top Diameter underbark in centimetres																		dbh cm
	7	8	10	12	14	16	18	20	22	24	26	28	30	32	34	36	38	40	
7	0																		7
8	42																		8
9	69																		9
10	75	63																	10
11	78	71																	11
12	80	75	54																12
13	81	77	63																13
14	82	79	68	41															14
15	83	80	71	52															15
16	84	81	74	59	35														16
17	84	82	75	64	45														17
18	84	82	77	67	52	29													18
19	84	83	78	70	58	39													19
20	84	83	79	72	62	48	25												20
21	84	83	80	74	65	53	35												21
22	84	83	80	76	68	58	43	23											22
23	84	83	81	77	70	62	49	31											23
24	84	83	81	78	72	65	54	39	16										24
25	84	83	82	79	74	67	57	44	26										25
26	84	84	82	79	75	69	60	49	33										26
27	85	84	82	80	76	71	63	52	39	23									27
28	85	84	83	81	77	72	65	56	44	29									28
29	85	84	83	81	78	74	67	59	48	35	19								29
30	85	84	83	82	79	75	69	62	52	40	26								30
31	85	84	83	82	80	76	71	64	55	44	31	17							31
32	85	84	83	82	80	77	72	66	58	48	36	23							32
33	85	84	84	83	81	78	74	68	60	51	40	28	14						33
34	85	84	84	83	81	79	75	69	63	54	44	33	20						34
35	85	84	84	83	82	79	76	71	65	57	47	37	25	12					35
36	85	84	84	83	82	80	77	72	67	59	51	40	30	18					36
37	85	84	84	84	82	80	78	73	68	61	53	44	34	23					37
38	85	84	84	84	83	81	78	75	70	64	56	47	38	27	16				38
39	85	84	84	84	83	81	79	76	71	65	58	50	41	31	20				39
40	85	84	84	84	83	82	80	76	72	67	60	53	45	35	25	14			40
41	85	84	84	84	83	82	80	77	73	69	62	56	48	39	29	19			41
42	85	85	84	84	83	82	81	78	75	70	64	58	50	42	32	23	13		42
43	85	85	84	84	84	83	81	79	76	71	66	60	53	45	36	27	17		43
44	85	85	84	84	84	83	81	79	76	73	67	62	55	48	39	30	21	11	44
45	85	85	84	84	84	83	82	80	77	74	69	64	57	50	42	33	24	15	45
46	85	85	84	84	84	83	82	80	78	75	70	65	59	52	45	36	28	19	46
47	85	85	84	84	84	83	82	81	79	75	71	67	61	54	47	39	31	22	47
48	85	85	84	84	84	84	83	81	79	76	72	68	63	56	49	42	34	25	48
49	85	85	85	84	84	84	83	82	80	77	73	69	64	58	51	44	36	29	49
50	85	85	85	84	84	84	83	82	80	78	74	70	65	60	53	46	39	31	50

* Volume overbark is measured to the normal conventions of 7 cm top diameter o.b. and 1.3 m minimum length.

SINGLE TREE UNDERBARK VOLUME ASSORTMENT TABLE FOR SPRUCES AND OTHER CONIFERS

(MINIMUM LENGTH 1·3m)

UNDERBARK VOLUME TO SPECIFIED TOP DIAMETERS U.B. AS A PERCENT OF OVERBARK VOLUME *

dbh cm	Top Diameter underbark in centimetres																		dbh cm
	7	8	10	12	14	16	18	20	22	24	26	28	30	32	34	36	38	40	
7	0																		7
8	83																		8
9	86	78																	9
10	88	81																	10
11	88	83	57																11
12	89	84	68																12
13	89	86	73	38															13
14	89	86	77	55															14
15	89	87	79	63	27														15
16	89	88	81	68	44														16
17	90	88	83	72	54	21													17
18	90	89	84	75	60	35													18
19	90	89	85	77	65	46	20												19
20	90	89	86	79	69	54	33												20
21	90	89	87	81	72	60	43	15											21
22	90	90	87	82	75	65	50	27											22
23	90	90	88	84	77	69	56	37	14										23
24	90	90	88	85	79	72	61	45	26										24
25	90	90	89	86	81	74	65	52	34	13									25
26	90	90	89	86	82	76	68	57	41	22									26
27	90	90	89	87	83	78	71	61	47	30									27
28	90	90	90	88	85	80	73	64	52	37	20								28
29	90	90	90	88	85	81	76	68	57	43	28								29
30	90	90	90	89	86	83	78	70	61	49	34	18							30
31	90	90	90	89	87	84	79	72	64	53	40	25							31
32	90	90	90	89	88	85	81	74	67	57	45	31	16						32
33	91	91	90	90	88	85	82	76	69	61	50	37	23						33
34	91	91	90	90	88	86	83	78	72	64	54	42	30	16					34
35	91	91	91	90	89	87	84	79	74	66	57	47	35	22					35
36	91	91	91	90	89	87	85	81	75	69	61	51	40	28	15				36
37	91	91	91	90	89	88	85	82	77	71	64	55	45	33	21				37
38	91	91	91	90	90	88	86	83	79	73	66	58	49	38	26	15			38
39	91	91	91	90	90	89	87	84	80	75	68	61	52	42	31	20			39
40	91	91	91	91	90	89	87	84	81	76	71	63	55	46	36	25	13		40
41	91	91	91	91	90	89	87	85	82	78	72	66	58	49	40	29	18		41
42	91	91	91	91	90	89	88	86	83	79	74	68	61	52	43	33	23	12	42
43	91	91	91	91	90	90	88	86	84	80	75	70	63	55	46	37	27	16	43
44	91	91	91	91	90	90	88	87	84	81	77	71	65	58	49	40	31	21	44
45	91	91	91	91	91	90	89	87	85	82	78	73	67	60	52	43	34	25	45
46	91	91	91	91	91	90	89	87	85	83	79	74	69	62	55	47	38	29	46
47	91	91	91	91	91	90	89	88	86	83	80	76	70	64	57	49	41	32	47
48	91	91	91	91	91	90	89	88	86	84	81	77	72	66	59	52	44	36	48
49	91	91	91	91	91	90	90	88	87	85	82	78	73	68	62	55	47	39	49
50	92	92	91	91	91	90	90	89	87	85	82	79	75	70	64	57	50	42	50

* Volume overbark is measured to the normal conventions of 7 cm top diameter o.b. and 1.3 m minimum length.

STAND OVERBARK VOLUME ASSORTMENT TABLE

(MINIMUM LENGTH 1m)

VOLUMES TO SPECIFIED TOP DIAMETERS O.B. AS A PERCENTAGE OF OVERBARK VOLUME

mean dbh cm	Top Diameter in centimetres																				mean dbh cm
	to tip	7*	8	10	12	14	16	18	20	22	24	26	28	30	32	34	36	38	40		
10	128	100	68	43	15	4															10
11	120	100	78	55	25	8	1														11
12	116	100	85	66	36	15	3	1													12
13	112	100	89	74	48	23	7	2													13
14	110	100	92	80	58	33	12	5	1												14
15	108	100	94	84	67	43	20	9	3												15
16	107	100	95	87	73	52	28	15	5	1											16
17	106	100	96	89	78	61	38	22	9	3	1										17
18	105	100	97	91	82	68	47	30	14	6	2										18
19	104	100	97	93	85	73	55	38	20	9	4	1									19
20	104	100	98	94	88	78	62	46	27	14	6	2	1								20
21	103	100	98	95	90	81	68	53	34	19	10	4	1								21
22	103	100	99	96	91	84	73	59	41	25	14	6	2	1							22
23	102	100	99	96	92	86	77	65	48	32	19	9	4	2	1						23
24	102	100	99	97	93	88	80	70	54	38	25	13	7	3	1	1					24
25	102	100	99	97	94	90	83	74	60	44	30	17	10	5	2	1					25
26	102	100	99	98	95	91	85	77	64	50	36	22	13	8	4	2	1				26
27	102	100	99	98	96	92	87	80	68	55	41	27	17	11	6	3	1				27
28	102	100	100	98	96	93	89	82	72	59	46	32	22	14	8	5	2	1			28
29	101	100	100	98	96	94	90	84	75	64	51	37	26	18	11	7	4	2	1		29
30	101	100	100	98	97	94	91	86	78	67	55	42	31	22	14	9	5	3	1		30
31	101	100	100	99	97	95	92	87	80	70	59	47	35	26	18	12	7	4	2		31
32	101	100	100	99	97	95	93	88	82	73	63	51	40	30	21	15	9	6	3		32
33	101	100	100	99	98	96	93	89	84	76	66	55	44	33	25	18	12	8	5		33
34	101	100	100	99	98	96	94	90	85	78	69	58	48	37	29	21	15	10	7		34
35	101	100	100	99	98	96	94	91	87	80	72	61	51	41	32	24	18	12	9		35
36	101	100	100	99	98	97	95	92	88	82	74	64	55	45	36	28	21	15	11		36
37	101	100	100	99	98	97	95	93	89	83	76	67	58	48	39	31	24	18	13		37
38	101	100	100	99	98	97	96	93	90	84	78	69	60	51	42	34	27	20	15		38
39	101	100	100	99	98	97	96	94	91	86	80	72	63	54	45	37	30	23	18		39
40	101	100	100	99	98	97	96	94	91	87	81	74	65	57	48	40	33	26	20		40
41	100	100	100	99	99	98	96	95	92	88	83	76	68	60	51	43	36	29	23		41
42	100	100	100	99	99	98	97	95	92	89	84	77	70	62	54	46	39	32	25		42
43	100	100	100	99	99	98	97	95	93	89	85	79	72	64	56	49	41	34	28		43
44	100	100	100	99	99	98	97	96	93	90	86	80	74	66	59	51	44	37	31		44
45	100	100	100	99	99	98	97	96	94	91	87	82	75	68	61	53	46	39	33		45
46	100	100	100	99	99	98	97	96	94	91	88	83	77	70	63	56	49	42	36		46
47	100	100	100	99	99	98	97	96	95	92	88	84	78	72	65	58	51	44	38		47
48	100	100	100	99	99	98	98	97	95	92	89	85	80	74	67	60	53	47	41		48
49	100	100	100	99	99	98	98	97	95	93	90	86	81	75	68	62	55	49	43		49
50	100	100	100	99	99	99	98	97	96	93	90	87	82	76	70	64	57	51	45		50

* The volume to 7cm top diameter assumes the conventional minimum length of 1.3m.

No minimum length has been assumed in calculating the 'to tip' percent -ages.

This table can be used for all conifers, but for broadleaved species its use should be restricted to stands with a mean dbh of 30cm or less.

STAND OVERBARK VOLUME ASSORTMENT TABLE

(MINIMUM LENGTH 2m)

VOLUMES TO SPECIFIED TOP DIAMETERS O.B. AS A PERCENTAGE OF OVERBARK VOLUME

mean dbh cm	Top Diameter in centimetres: to tip	7*	8	10	12	14	16	18	20	22	24	26	28	30	32	34	36	38	40	mean dbh cm
10	128	100	68	43	12	2														10
11	120	100	78	55	20	6	1													11
12	116	100	85	66	32	12	3													12
13	112	100	89	74	44	20	7	2												13
14	110	100	92	80	55	29	12	4	1											14
15	108	100	94	84	65	40	20	8	2											15
16	107	100	95	87	72	50	28	13	4	1										16
17	106	100	96	89	78	59	38	20	8	2										17
18	105	100	97	91	82	66	47	28	13	4	1									18
19	104	100	97	93	85	72	55	36	19	7	2	1								19
20	104	100	98	94	88	77	62	44	26	11	4	1								20
21	103	100	98	95	90	81	68	52	33	16	7	3	1							21
22	103	100	99	96	91	84	73	58	40	22	12	5	2							22
23	102	100	99	96	92	86	77	64	47	28	16	8	3	1						23
24	102	100	99	97	93	88	80	69	53	35	22	12	6	3	1					24
25	102	100	99	97	94	90	83	73	59	41	27	16	9	4	2	1				25
26	102	100	99	98	95	91	85	77	64	47	33	21	12	6	3	1				26
27	102	100	99	98	96	92	87	80	68	53	39	26	16	9	5	2	1			27
28	102	100	100	98	96	93	89	82	72	58	44	31	20	12	7	4	2	1		28
29	101	100	100	98	96	94	90	84	75	62	49	36	25	16	10	6	3	1		29
30	101	100	100	98	97	94	91	86	78	66	54	41	30	20	13	8	4	2	1	30
31	101	100	100	99	97	95	92	87	80	70	58	46	34	24	16	10	6	4	2	31
32	101	100	100	99	97	95	93	88	82	73	62	50	39	28	20	13	8	5	3	32
33	101	100	100	99	98	96	93	89	84	75	65	54	43	32	23	16	11	7	4	33
34	101	100	100	99	98	96	94	90	85	78	68	58	47	36	27	20	14	9	6	34
35	101	100	100	99	98	96	94	91	87	80	71	61	50	40	31	23	17	11	8	35
36	101	100	100	99	98	97	95	92	88	82	74	64	54	44	35	27	20	14	10	36
37	101	100	100	99	98	97	95	93	89	83	76	67	57	47	38	30	22	17	12	37
38	101	100	100	99	98	97	96	93	90	84	77	69	60	50	41	33	26	19	14	38
39	101	100	100	99	98	97	96	94	91	86	79	71	63	53	44	36	29	22	17	39
40	101	100	100	99	98	97	96	94	91	87	81	73	65	56	47	39	32	25	19	40
41	100	100	100	99	99	98	96	95	92	88	82	75	67	59	50	42	35	28	22	41
42	100	100	100	99	99	98	97	95	92	89	84	77	69	61	53	45	38	31	24	42
43	100	100	100	99	99	98	97	95	93	89	85	79	71	64	56	48	40	34	27	43
44	100	100	100	99	99	98	97	96	93	90	86	80	73	66	58	50	43	36	30	44
45	100	100	100	99	99	98	97	96	94	91	87	82	75	68	60	53	46	39	32	45
46	100	100	100	99	99	98	97	96	94	91	88	83	76	69	62	55	48	41	35	46
47	100	100	100	99	99	98	97	96	95	92	88	84	78	71	64	57	50	43	37	47
48	100	100	100	99	99	98	98	97	95	92	89	85	80	73	66	59	53	46	40	48
49	100	100	100	99	99	98	98	97	95	93	90	86	81	74	68	61	55	48	42	49
50	100	100	100	99	99	99	98	97	96	93	90	87	82	76	70	63	57	50	44	50

* The volume to 7cm top diameter assumes the conventional minimum length of 1.3m.

No minimum length has been assumed in calculating the 'to tip' percent -ages.

This table can be used for all conifers,but for broadleaved species its use should be restricted to stands with a mean dbh of 30cm or less.

STAND OVERBARK VOLUME ASSORTMENT TABLE

(MINIMUM LENGTH 3m)

VOLUMES TO SPECIFIED TOP DIAMETERS O.B. AS A PERCENTAGE OF OVERBARK VOLUME

mean dbh cm	Top Diameter in centimetres																			mean dbh cm
	to tip	7*	8	10	12	14	16	18	20	22	24	26	28	30	32	34	36	38	40	
10	128	100	68	35	7	1														10
11	120	100	78	49	14	3														11
12	116	100	85	61	24	8	2													12
13	112	100	89	71	36	15	4	1												13
14	110	100	92	78	48	23	9	2												14
15	108	100	94	83	59	34	16	6	1											15
16	107	100	95	87	69	45	24	10	2											16
17	106	100	96	89	76	55	33	16	4	1										17
18	105	100	97	91	81	63	43	24	8	3										18
19	104	100	97	93	84	70	52	33	13	5	2									19
20	104	100	98	94	87	76	60	41	19	9	3	1								20
21	103	100	98	95	89	80	66	49	26	13	6	2								21
22	103	100	99	96	91	83	72	56	34	19	10	4	1							22
23	102	100	99	96	92	86	76	62	41	25	14	7	3							23
24	102	100	99	97	93	88	80	68	49	32	19	10	5	1						24
25	102	100	99	97	94	90	83	72	55	39	25	14	7	2	1					25
26	102	100	99	98	95	91	85	76	61	45	30	19	10	4	2					26
27	102	100	99	98	96	92	87	79	66	51	37	24	15	7	3	1				27
28	102	100	100	98	96	93	88	82	70	56	42	29	19	9	5	2	1			28
29	101	100	100	98	96	94	90	84	74	61	48	35	23	13	8	4	2	1		29
30	101	100	100	98	97	94	91	86	77	65	52	40	28	17	10	6	3	1		30
31	101	100	100	99	97	95	92	87	79	69	57	45	33	21	14	8	5	2	1	31
32	101	100	100	99	97	95	93	88	81	72	61	49	37	25	17	11	7	4	2	32
33	101	100	100	99	98	96	93	89	83	75	64	53	41	29	20	14	9	5	3	33
34	101	100	100	99	98	96	94	90	85	77	67	57	45	33	24	17	12	7	4	34
35	101	100	100	99	98	96	94	91	86	79	70	60	49	37	28	20	14	9	6	35
36	101	100	100	99	98	97	95	92	88	81	73	63	53	41	32	24	17	12	8	36
37	101	100	100	99	98	97	95	93	89	83	75	66	56	45	36	27	20	15	10	37
38	101	100	100	99	98	97	96	93	90	84	77	68	59	48	39	31	23	17	12	38
39	101	100	100	99	98	97	96	94	91	86	79	71	62	52	43	34	27	20	15	39
40	101	100	100	99	98	97	96	94	91	87	80	73	64	54	46	37	30	23	17	40
41	100	100	100	99	99	98	96	95	92	88	82	75	67	57	49	41	33	26	20	41
42	100	100	100	99	99	98	97	95	92	89	84	77	69	60	52	43	36	29	23	42
43	100	100	100	99	99	98	97	95	93	89	85	78	71	62	54	46	39	32	26	43
44	100	100	100	99	99	98	97	96	93	90	86	80	73	65	57	49	41	34	28	44
45	100	100	100	99	99	98	97	96	94	91	87	81	75	67	59	51	44	37	31	45
46	100	100	100	99	99	98	97	96	94	91	88	82	76	68	61	54	46	40	33	46
47	100	100	100	99	99	98	97	96	95	92	88	84	78	70	63	56	49	42	36	47
48	100	100	100	99	99	98	98	97	95	92	89	85	79	72	65	58	51	45	38	48
49	100	100	100	99	99	98	98	97	95	93	90	86	80	74	67	60	53	47	40	49
50	100	100	100	99	99	99	98	97	96	93	90	87	82	76	69	62	56	49	43	50

* The volume to 7cm top diameter assumes the conventional minimum length of 1.3m.

No minimum length has been assumed in calculating the 'to tip' percent -ages.

This table can be used for all conifers, but for broadleaved species its use should be restricted to stands with a mean dbh of 30cm or less.

STAND OVERBARK VOLUME ASSORTMENT TABLE

(MINIMUM LENGTH 4m)

VOLUMES TO SPECIFIED TOP DIAMETERS O.B. AS A PERCENTAGE OF OVERBARK VOLUME

mean dbh cm	Top Diameter in centimetres																			mean dbh cm
	to tip	7*	8	10	12	14	16	18	20	22	24	26	28	30	32	34	36	38	40	
10	128	100	43	16	4															10
11	120	100	58	27	8	1														11
12	116	100	72	41	17	5	1													12
13	112	100	82	54	27	10	2													13
14	110	100	88	66	39	17	6	1												14
15	108	100	92	76	51	27	11	3												15
16	107	100	94	83	62	37	18	7	1											16
17	106	100	96	87	71	48	27	12	3											17
18	105	100	97	90	78	58	37	19	5	1										18
19	104	100	97	92	83	67	46	27	10	3	1									19
20	104	100	98	94	86	73	55	36	15	6	2									20
21	103	100	98	95	89	78	63	44	21	10	4	1								21
22	103	100	99	96	91	82	69	52	29	16	7	3								22
23	102	100	99	96	92	85	74	59	37	22	11	5	1							23
24	102	100	99	97	93	87	79	66	44	28	16	8	3	1						24
25	102	100	99	97	94	89	82	70	51	35	21	12	5	2						25
26	102	100	99	98	95	91	84	74	57	41	27	16	7	3	1					26
27	102	100	99	98	96	92	86	78	63	48	33	21	10	5	2					27
28	102	100	100	98	96	93	88	81	68	54	39	27	14	8	4	1				28
29	101	100	100	98	96	94	90	83	72	59	45	32	19	11	6	2	1			29
30	101	100	100	98	97	94	91	85	75	63	50	37	23	15	9	4	2			30
31	101	100	100	99	97	95	92	87	78	67	55	42	28	19	12	6	3	1		31
32	101	100	100	99	97	95	93	88	80	71	59	47	33	23	15	8	5	2	1	32
33	101	100	100	99	98	96	93	89	82	74	63	51	37	27	19	11	7	3	2	33
34	101	100	100	99	98	96	94	90	84	76	66	55	42	31	23	14	9	5	3	34
35	101	100	100	99	98	96	94	91	86	78	69	59	46	35	26	17	12	7	4	35
36	101	100	100	99	98	97	95	92	87	80	72	62	50	39	30	21	15	10	6	36
37	101	100	100	99	98	97	95	93	88	82	74	65	53	43	34	24	17	12	8	37
38	101	100	100	99	98	97	96	93	89	84	76	67	56	47	37	27	20	15	10	38
39	101	100	100	99	98	97	96	94	90	85	78	70	60	50	41	31	24	18	13	39
40	101	100	100	99	98	97	96	94	91	86	80	72	62	53	44	34	27	20	15	40
41	100	100	100	99	99	98	96	95	92	88	82	74	65	56	47	38	30	23	18	41
42	100	100	100	99	99	98	97	95	92	89	83	76	67	59	50	41	33	26	20	42
43	100	100	100	99	99	98	97	95	93	89	84	77	69	61	53	44	36	29	23	43
44	100	100	100	99	99	98	97	96	93	90	86	79	71	64	56	46	39	32	26	44
45	100	100	100	99	99	98	97	96	94	91	87	81	73	66	58	49	42	35	28	45
46	100	100	100	99	99	98	97	96	94	91	88	82	75	68	60	52	44	37	31	46
47	100	100	100	99	99	98	97	96	95	92	88	84	77	70	62	54	47	40	33	47
48	100	100	100	99	99	98	98	97	95	92	89	85	78	72	64	56	49	43	36	48
49	100	100	100	99	99	98	98	97	95	93	90	86	79	73	66	58	51	45	38	49
50	100	100	100	99	99	99	98	97	96	93	90	87	81	75	68	60	54	47	41	50

* The volume to 7cm top diameter assumes the conventional minimum length of 1.3m.

No minimum length has been assumed in calculating the 'to tip' percent -ages.

This table can be used for all conifers,but for broadleaved species its use should be restricted to stands with a mean dbh of 30cm or less.

STAND UNDERBARK VOLUME ASSORTMENT TABLE FOR PINES, LARCHES AND DOUGLAS FIR

(MINIMUM LENGTH 3m)

UNDERBARK VOLUMES TO SPECIFIED TOP DIAMETERS U.B. AS A PERCENT OF VOLUME O.B.★

mean dbh cm	Top Diameters underbark in centimetres																		mean dbh cm
	7	8	10	12	14	16	18	20	22	24	26	28	30	32	34	36	38	40	
10	52	47	19	2															10
11	64	59	30	6	1														11
12	73	68	42	13	3														12
13	78	74	53	21	7	2													13
14	81	78	61	31	13	4	1												14
15	83	80	67	41	20	8	2												15
16	83	81	72	50	28	13	5	1											16
17	84	82	74	57	37	20	8	2											17
18	84	82	76	63	45	27	13	4	1										18
19	84	82	78	67	52	35	19	7	2	1									19
20	84	83	79	71	58	42	26	11	4	1									20
21	84	83	80	73	62	48	32	16	7	3									21
22	84	83	80	75	66	53	39	21	11	5	1								22
23	84	83	81	76	69	58	44	27	15	8	3	1							23
24	84	83	81	77	71	62	49	33	20	11	4	2							24
25	84	84	82	78	73	65	54	38	25	15	7	3	1						25
26	84	84	82	79	75	67	57	43	30	19	10	5	2						26
27	85	84	82	80	76	69	61	48	35	24	13	7	3	1					27
28	85	84	83	80	77	71	63	52	40	28	17	10	4	2	1				28
29	85	84	83	81	78	73	66	55	44	33	21	13	7	3	1				29
30	85	84	83	81	78	74	68	58	48	37	25	16	9	5	3	1			30
31	85	84	83	82	79	75	69	61	51	41	29	20	12	7	4	1			31
32	85	84	83	82	80	76	71	63	54	44	32	24	15	9	6	2	1		32
33	85	84	83	82	80	77	72	65	57	47	36	27	18	12	7	4	2	1	33
34	85	84	84	82	81	78	73	67	59	50	39	31	21	15	10	5	3	1	34
35	85	84	84	83	81	78	74	68	61	53	43	34	24	17	12	7	4	2	35
36	85	84	84	83	81	79	75	70	63	55	46	37	27	20	14	9	6	3	36
37	85	84	84	83	82	79	76	71	65	57	48	40	30	23	17	11	7	4	37
38	85	84	84	83	82	80	77	72	66	59	51	43	33	26	19	13	9	6	38
39	85	84	84	83	82	80	77	73	68	61	53	45	36	29	22	15	11	7	39
40	85	84	84	83	82	81	78	74	69	63	55	47	39	31	24	18	13	9	40
41	85	84	84	84	83	81	78	75	70	64	57	50	41	34	27	20	15	11	41
42	85	84	84	84	83	81	79	76	72	66	59	52	43	36	29	22	17	12	42
43	85	84	84	84	83	82	80	76	73	67	61	54	46	39	32	25	19	14	43
44	85	85	84	84	83	82	80	77	74	69	62	56	48	41	34	27	21	16	44
45	85	85	84	84	83	82	80	78	74	70	64	57	50	43	36	29	23	18	45
46	85	85	84	84	83	82	81	78	75	71	65	59	52	45	38	31	25	20	46
47	85	85	84	84	83	82	81	79	76	72	66	60	53	47	40	33	27	22	47
48	85	85	84	84	84	83	81	79	76	73	67	62	55	49	42	35	29	24	48
49	85	85	84	84	84	83	82	80	77	73	68	63	57	50	44	37	31	26	49
50	85	85	84	84	84	83	82	80	77	74	70	64	58	52	46	39	33	27	50

★ Stand volume overbark is measured to the normal conventions of 7 cm top diameter o.b. and 1.3m minimum length.

STAND UNDERBARK VOLUME ASSORTMENT TABLE FOR SPRUCES AND OTHER CONIFERS

(MINIMUM LENGTH 3m)

UNDERBARK VOLUMES TO SPECIFIED TOP DIAMETERS U.B. AS A PERCENT OF VOLUME O.B.★

mean dbh cm	Top Diameters underbark in centimetres																		mean dbh cm
	7	8	10	12	14	16	18	20	22	24	26	28	30	32	34	36	38	40	
10	72	67	32	6															10
11	81	77	45	12	3														11
12	86	82	57	21	6														12
13	88	85	67	32	12	2													13
14	89	86	73	43	20	5	1												14
15	89	87	77	53	29	9	3												15
16	89	88	81	61	38	15	6	1											16
17	90	88	82	68	47	22	10	3	1										17
18	90	89	84	73	55	31	16	6	2										18
19	90	89	85	76	61	39	22	10	4	1									19
20	90	89	86	79	66	47	30	16	7	2									20
21	90	89	87	81	71	54	37	22	11	4	1								21
22	90	90	87	82	74	60	44	28	16	6	2	1							22
23	90	90	88	83	77	65	50	35	21	9	4	2							23
24	90	90	88	85	79	69	56	41	27	14	7	3	1						24
25	90	90	89	85	80	72	61	47	33	18	10	5	2	1					25
26	90	90	89	86	82	74	65	52	38	23	14	8	4	2					26
27	90	90	89	87	83	77	68	56	43	28	18	11	6	3	1				27
28	90	90	89	87	84	79	71	60	48	34	23	14	8	4	2				28
29	90	90	90	88	85	80	73	64	53	39	27	18	11	7	3	1			29
30	90	90	90	88	86	82	75	67	56	43	32	22	15	9	4	2	1		30
31	91	90	90	89	86	83	77	69	60	48	37	27	18	12	6	3	1		31
32	91	91	90	89	87	84	79	72	63	51	41	31	22	15	8	5	2	1	32
33	91	91	90	89	87	84	80	73	66	55	45	35	26	18	11	7	4	1	33
34	91	91	90	89	88	85	81	75	68	58	48	39	30	22	14	9	5	2	34
35	91	91	90	90	88	86	82	77	70	61	52	42	33	25	17	11	7	4	35
36	91	91	90	90	88	86	83	78	72	63	55	46	37	28	20	14	9	5	36
37	91	91	91	90	89	87	84	79	73	66	57	49	40	32	23	16	11	7	37
38	91	91	91	90	89	87	84	80	75	68	60	51	43	35	26	19	14	9	38
39	91	91	91	90	89	87	85	81	76	69	62	54	46	38	29	22	16	11	39
40	91	91	91	90	89	88	85	82	77	71	64	56	48	40	32	25	19	13	40
41	91	91	91	90	89	88	86	83	78	72	66	58	51	43	34	27	21	15	41
42	91	91	91	90	90	88	86	83	79	74	67	60	53	46	37	30	24	17	42
43	91	91	91	91	90	89	87	84	81	75	70	63	56	48	40	33	26	20	43
44	91	91	91	91	90	89	87	85	81	77	71	65	58	51	42	35	29	22	44
45	91	91	91	91	90	89	87	85	82	78	72	66	60	53	45	38	31	24	45
46	91	91	91	91	90	89	88	86	83	79	74	68	61	55	47	40	33	27	46
47	91	91	91	91	90	90	88	86	83	80	75	69	63	57	49	42	36	29	47
48	91	91	91	91	90	90	88	86	84	81	76	71	65	58	51	44	38	31	48
49	91	91	91	91	91	90	89	87	84	81	77	72	66	60	53	46	40	33	49
50	92	92	91	91	91	90	89	87	85	82	78	73	68	62	55	48	42	35	50

★ Stand volume overbark is measured to the normal conventions of 7 cm top diameter o.b. and 1.3m minimum length.

SINGLE TREE LENGTH ASSORTMENT TABLE TO OVERBARK TOP DIAMETERS

(MINIMUM LENGTH 1·3m)

dbh Class cm	LENGTHS TO SPECIFIED TOP DIAMETERS — Top Diameter overbark in centimetres																		dbh Class cm
	7	8	10	12	14	16	18	20	22	24	26	28	30	32	34	36	38	40	
	Total Height 9 m																		
10	5.0	3.9	1.3																10
15	5.8	5.6	4.9	3.9	2.4														15
20	6.4	6.2	5.7	5.1	4.3	3.4	2.4	1.3											20
25	6.8	6.7	6.3	5.9	5.5	4.9	4.3	3.5	2.8	1.8									25
	Total Height 12 m																		
10	6.4	5.4	1.3																10
15	8.3	7.6	6.0	4.4	2.5														15
20	9.1	8.7	7.9	7.0	5.6	4.3	2.7	1.3											20
25	9.3	9.2	8.6	8.0	7.3	6.4	5.3	4.0	2.8	1.9									25
30	9.7	9.5	9.1	8.8	8.4	7.8	7.1	6.0	5.0	3.9	3.0	2.1	1.3						30
	Total Height 15 m																		
10	8.0	6.6	1.3																10
15	10.7	9.9	8.2	6.0	3.1														15
20	11.6	11.1	10.0	8.8	7.2	5.4	3.5	1.3											20
25	12.0	11.8	11.1	10.3	9.2	8.0	6.7	5.3	3.8	2.1									25
30	12.3	12.1	11.6	11.0	10.3	9.5	8.5	7.3	6.0	4.8	3.7	2.5	1.3						30
35	12.5	12.4	12.1	11.6	11.1	10.4	9.7	8.8	7.8	6.8	5.8	4.8	3.8	2.8	1.8				35
40	12.6	12.5	12.3	11.9	11.6	11.1	10.5	9.8	9.0	8.2	7.3	6.4	5.5	4.6	3.8	2.9	2.1	1.3	40
	Total Height 18 m																		
15	13.0	12.4	10.3	7.5	3.7														15
20	14.1	13.7	12.4	10.8	8.8	6.6	4.1	1.3											20
25	14.7	14.4	13.6	12.6	11.3	9.9	8.2	6.3	4.3	2.3									25
30	14.9	14.7	14.2	13.5	12.6	11.6	10.3	8.8	7.3	5.8	4.3	2.8	1.3						30
35	15.2	15.0	14.5	14.0	13.3	12.6	11.6	10.5	9.3	8.2	7.0	5.8	4.6	3.3	2.0				35
40	15.3	15.3	14.8	14.3	13.8	13.2	12.4	11.6	10.8	9.9	8.9	7.9	6.9	5.8	4.6	3.5	2.4	1.3	40
	Total Height 21 m																		
15	16.3	15.8	11.9	7.9	3.3														15
20	17.2	16.9	14.8	12.5	10.5	8.0	4.5	1.3											20
25	17.8	17.4	16.2	15.0	13.6	11.9	9.8	7.5	5.2	2.5									25
30	17.9	17.7	16.9	16.0	15.0	13.6	12.1	10.3	8.6	6.7	4.9	3.1	1.3						30
35	18.1	17.9	17.4	16.6	16.0	15.1	14.0	12.5	11.0	9.3	7.8	6.3	4.9	3.4	2.0				35
40	18.4	18.1	17.5	16.9	16.3	15.4	14.6	13.5	12.5	11.2	9.7	8.2	7.2	5.9	4.7	3.6	2.4	1.3	40
45	18.4	18.2	17.7	17.2	16.5	15.8	15.1	14.2	13.4	12.3	11.3	10.0	8.8	7.5	6.4	5.3	4.3	3.4	45
50	18.6	18.3	17.8	17.3	16.7	16.0	15.3	14.6	13.8	12.9	11.9	10.8	9.8	8.8	7.9	7.1	6.2	5.4	50

SINGLE TREE LENGTH ASSORTMENT TABLE TO OVERBARK TOP DIAMETERS

(MINIMUM LENGTH 1·3m)

L E N G T H S   T O   S P E C I F I E D   T O P   D I A M E T E R S

dbh Class cm	Top Diameter overbark in centimetres 7	8	10	12	14	16	18	20	22	24	26	28	30	32	34	36	38	40	dbh Class cm
Total Height 24 m																			
20	19.9	19.7	18.0	16.0	13.3	9.7	5.8	1.3											20
25	20.4	20.3	19.1	17.9	16.1	14.2	11.5	8.7	5.7	3.0									25
30	20.6	20.5	19.6	18.7	17.7	16.2	14.8	12.7	10.3	7.9	5.5	3.4	1.3						30
35	20.8	20.7	20.1	19.4	18.5	17.4	16.1	14.5	12.8	11.0	8.8	6.8	5.1	3.5	2.0				35
40	21.0	20.8	20.3	19.6	18.9	18.0	17.0	15.8	14.4	13.0	11.5	9.9	8.1	6.1	4.8	3.7	2.5	1.3	40
45	21.1	21.0	20.5	20.0	19.3	18.4	17.5	16.5	15.4	14.3	13.1	11.8	10.3	8.8	7.3	5.9	4.6	3.5	45
50	21.2	21.1	20.6	20.1	19.4	18.6	17.9	17.0	16.1	15.1	14.1	13.0	11.8	10.6	9.3	8.2	7.1	6.1	50
55	21.3	21.2	20.7	20.1	19.5	18.8	18.2	17.5	16.8	16.0	15.1	14.1	13.2	12.2	11.2	10.2	9.3	8.3	55
Total Height 27 m																			
20	22.7	22.3	20.3	17.8	15.0	10.7	5.6	1.3											20
25	23.2	22.9	21.7	20.4	18.4	16.5	13.6	10.1	6.3	2.9									25
30	23.5	23.2	22.3	21.3	20.0	18.4	16.4	14.1	11.6	8.8	5.9	3.4	1.3						30
35	23.5	23.5	22.7	21.9	20.8	19.6	18.2	16.5	14.5	12.3	9.9	7.5	5.5	3.7	2.0				35
40	23.9	23.7	23.0	22.3	21.3	20.3	19.2	17.9	16.4	14.8	13.0	11.1	9.2	7.3	5.5	3.9	2.5	1.3	40
45	24.0	23.7	23.2	22.5	21.8	20.9	19.9	18.8	17.6	16.3	15.1	13.5	11.9	10.2	8.4	6.7	5.2	3.9	45
50	24.1	23.9	23.3	22.7	22.0	21.2	20.4	19.5	18.6	17.5	16.5	15.3	14.0	12.6	11.1	9.6	8.2	6.8	50
55	24.2	24.0	23.5	22.9	22.2	21.5	20.8	20.0	19.2	18.3	17.4	16.3	15.2	14.2	13.0	11.7	10.5	9.2	55
60	24.3	24.1	23.5	23.0	22.4	21.8	21.2	20.5	19.8	18.9	18.1	17.2	16.2	15.2	14.1	13.0	11.9	10.8	60
Total Height 30 m																			
30	26.5	26.1	25.2	24.0	22.6	20.9	18.9	16.4	13.4	10.6	7.7	4.4	1.3						30
35	26.8	26.4	25.6	24.7	23.6	22.2	20.7	18.8	16.5	14.1	11.6	8.8	6.5	4.3	2.2				35
40	26.9	26.6	26.0	25.1	24.1	23.0	21.8	20.3	18.6	16.8	15.0	12.9	10.8	8.5	6.1	4.0	2.5	1.3	40
45	27.0	26.7	26.2	25.4	24.6	23.6	22.9	21.5	20.1	18.7	17.3	15.6	14.0	12.1	9.8	7.6	5.8	4.1	45
50	27.1	26.8	26.3	25.6	24.8	24.1	23.2	22.2	21.1	19.9	18.7	17.3	15.9	14.3	12.4	10.5	8.8	7.2	50
55	27.2	26.9	26.4	25.9	25.2	24.4	23.6	22.8	21.8	20.8	19.8	18.6	17.4	16.0	14.5	13.0	11.5	10.1	55
60	27.3	27.0	26.5	26.0	25.4	24.7	24.0	23.2	22.4	21.4	20.5	19.4	18.4	17.4	16.2	15.0	13.8	12.5	60
Total Height 33 m																			
40	29.8	29.3	28.7	27.8	26.7	25.5	24.2	22.6	20.7	19.0	17.2	15.0	12.4	9.3	6.3	4.0	2.5	1.3	40
45	29.8	29.5	28.9	28.2	27.3	26.3	25.2	23.9	22.4	21.0	19.5	17.7	15.7	13.5	10.9	8.4	6.3	4.6	45
50	29.9	29.5	29.1	28.5	27.7	26.9	26.0	24.9	23.7	22.5	21.2	19.8	18.2	16.3	14.3	12.2	10.0	7.9	50
55	30.0	29.6	29.2	28.7	27.9	27.2	26.4	25.5	24.5	23.4	22.4	21.0	19.7	18.1	16.4	14.6	12.9	11.2	55
60	30.1	29.7	29.3	28.8	28.2	27.5	26.9	26.1	25.2	24.3	23.3	22.1	20.9	19.6	18.3	16.8	15.3	13.8	60
Total Height 36 m																			
40	32.8	32.3	31.8	31.0	30.0	28.9	27.5	25.7	23.7	21.4	19.3	16.9	14.3	11.4	8.5	5.6	3.3	1.3	40
45	32.9	32.4	31.9	31.2	30.3	29.3	28.2	26.7	25.1	23.4	21.9	20.0	18.1	16.0	12.8	9.7	7.1	5.0	45
50	32.9	32.5	32.0	31.4	30.7	29.9	28.9	27.7	26.4	25.0	23.7	22.2	20.6	18.7	16.3	13.6	11.0	8.5	50
55	33.0	32.6	32.3	31.6	31.0	30.2	29.4	28.5	27.4	26.3	25.2	23.8	22.4	20.8	18.9	17.0	14.3	12.1	55
60	33.1	32.7	32.3	31.8	31.2	30.5	29.8	29.0	28.2	27.2	26.2	25.0	23.7	22.2	20.5	18.6	16.8	15.0	60

SINGLE TREE LENGTH ASSORTMENT TABLE TO UNDERBARK TOP DIAMETERS FOR PINES, LARCHES AND DOUGLAS FIR

(MINIMUM LENGTH 1·3m)

dbh Class cm	LENGTHS TO SPECIFIED TOP DIAMETERS																		dbh Class cm
	Top Diameter underbark in centimetres																		
	7	8	10	12	14	16	18	20	22	24	26	28	30	32	34	36	38	40	
	Total Height 9 m																		
10	4.5	2.6																	10
15	5.7	5.2	4.4	3.0															15
20	6.3	6.0	5.4	4.6	3.7	2.7	1.6												20
25	6.8	6.5	6.1	5.6	5.1	4.5	3.7	2.9	1.9										25
	Total Height 12 m																		
10	5.9	3.4																	10
15	8.0	6.8	5.1	3.2															15
20	8.9	8.3	7.4	6.2	4.8	3.1	1.6												20
25	9.3	8.9	8.3	7.6	6.7	5.6	4.3	3.0	1.9										25
30	9.6	9.3	8.9	8.6	8.0	7.3	6.3	5.1	4.0	3.0	2.0								30
	Total Height 15 m																		
10	7.3	4.0																	10
15	10.3	9.0	7.0	4.3															15
20	11.4	10.6	9.3	7.8	6.0	4.1	1.8												20
25	11.9	11.4	10.6	9.6	8.4	7.0	5.6	4.0	2.3										25
30	12.2	11.9	11.3	10.6	9.8	8.7	7.6	6.2	4.9	3.7	2.4								30
35	12.4	12.2	11.8	11.3	10.6	9.9	9.0	7.9	6.9	5.8	4.7	3.6	2.5						35
40	12.6	12.4	12.1	11.7	11.2	10.7	9.9	9.1	8.3	7.3	6.3	5.3	4.3	3.4	2.5	1.6			40
	Total Height 18 m																		
15	12.7	11.3	8.8	5.3															15
20	13.9	13.0	11.5	9.6	7.4	4.8	1.9												20
25	14.6	14.0	13.0	11.9	10.4	8.7	6.7	4.6	2.4										25
30	14.8	14.4	13.8	13.0	11.9	10.6	9.1	7.5	5.9	4.3	2.7								30
35	15.1	14.7	14.2	13.6	12.8	11.9	10.7	9.5	8.3	7.0	5.7	4.3	2.9						35
40	15.3	15.0	14.6	14.0	13.4	12.6	11.8	10.9	10.0	8.9	7.8	6.6	5.4	4.2	2.9	1.7			40
	Total Height 21 m																		
15	16.0	13.9	9.8	5.2															15
20	17.0	15.9	13.6	11.3	8.9	5.5	2.0												20
25	17.6	16.8	15.6	14.2	12.5	10.4	8.1	5.5	2.7										25
30	17.8	17.3	16.4	15.4	14.1	12.5	10.7	8.9	6.8	4.9	2.9								30
35	18.0	17.6	16.9	16.2	15.4	14.3	12.8	11.2	9.5	7.8	6.2	4.6	3.0						35
40	18.2	17.8	17.2	16.5	15.7	14.8	13.7	12.6	11.3	9.6	8.0	6.9	5.5	4.2	3.0	1.7			40
45	18.3	18.0	17.4	16.8	16.0	15.3	14.4	13.5	12.4	11.2	9.8	8.5	7.2	6.0	4.8	3.8	2.8	1.8	45
50	18.5	18.1	17.5	17.0	16.3	15.5	14.7	13.9	13.0	11.9	10.7	9.6	8.6	7.6	6.6	5.7	4.8	3.8	50

SINGLE TREE LENGTH ASSORTMENT TABLE TO UNDERBARK TOP DIAMETERS FOR PINES, LARCHES AND DOUGLAS FIR

(MINIMUM LENGTH 1·3m)

dbh Class cm	LENGTHS TO SPECIFIED TOP DIAMETERS — Top Diameter underbark in centimetres																	dbh Class cm
	7	8	10	12	14	16	18	20	22	24	26	28	30	32	34	36	38	40	
	Total Height 24 m																		
20	19.8	18.9	16.9	14.4	11.0	6.9	2.3												20
25	20.4	19.7	18.5	16.8	14.9	12.3	9.3	6.1	3.2										25
30	20.6	20.1	19.1	18.1	16.7	15.2	13.2	10.7	8.1	5.5	3.1								30
35	20.8	20.4	19.7	18.9	17.8	16.4	14.8	13.1	11.1	8.8	6.6	4.7	3.0						35
40	20.9	20.6	19.9	19.2	18.3	17.2	16.0	14.6	13.1	11.5	9.7	7.7	5.7	4.3	3.0	1.7			40
45	21.1	20.8	20.2	19.6	18.7	17.8	16.7	15.6	14.4	13.1	11.6	10.0	8.3	6.7	5.2	3.9	2.8	1.8	45
50	21.2	20.9	20.3	19.7	18.9	18.1	17.2	16.3	15.2	14.1	12.9	11.6	10.2	8.9	7.7	6.5	5.3	4.2	50
55	21.2	20.9	20.4	19.7	19.0	18.4	17.7	16.9	16.0	15.0	14.0	13.0	11.9	10.8	9.7	8.6	7.5	6.4	55
	Total Height 27 m																		
20	22.5	21.3	19.0	16.2	12.2	7.1	2.3												20
25	23.1	22.3	21.0	19.2	17.2	14.4	10.9	6.9	3.2										25
30	23.4	22.8	21.8	20.5	18.9	17.0	14.6	12.0	9.0	5.9	3.1								30
35	23.5	23.1	22.3	21.3	20.0	18.6	16.9	14.8	12.5	9.9	7.3	5.1	3.2						35
40	23.8	23.3	22.6	21.7	20.7	19.5	18.2	16.6	14.9	13.0	10.9	8.8	6.8	4.9	3.2	1.7			40
45	23.9	23.4	22.8	22.1	21.2	20.2	19.1	17.8	16.4	15.0	13.3	11.6	9.7	7.7	5.9	4.4	3.1	1.9	45
50	24.0	23.6	23.0	22.3	21.5	20.7	19.7	18.7	17.6	16.4	15.1	13.7	12.2	10.5	8.9	7.3	5.8	4.4	50
55	24.1	23.7	23.2	22.5	21.7	21.0	20.2	19.3	18.4	17.4	16.2	15.0	13.8	12.5	11.1	9.7	8.2	6.7	55
60	24.2	23.8	23.3	22.7	22.0	21.4	20.7	19.9	19.0	18.1	17.1	16.0	14.9	13.7	12.5	11.2	9.9	8.7	60
	Total Height 30 m																		
30	26.3	25.7	24.6	23.2	21.5	19.5	17.0	13.8	10.7	7.7	4.1								30
35	26.6	26.0	25.1	24.0	22.7	21.1	19.2	16.9	14.3	11.6	8.6	6.0	3.7						35
40	26.7	26.3	25.5	24.5	23.4	22.1	20.6	18.8	17.0	15.0	12.7	10.3	7.8	5.3	3.2	1.7			40
45	26.8	26.4	25.8	24.9	24.0	23.1	21.8	20.3	18.8	17.3	15.5	13.6	11.4	9.0	6.7	4.7	3.1	1.8	45
50	27.0	26.6	25.9	25.1	24.3	23.4	22.4	21.3	20.0	18.7	17.2	15.6	13.7	11.6	9.6	7.8	6.1	4.7	50
55	27.1	26.7	26.1	25.4	24.7	23.9	23.0	21.9	20.9	19.8	18.5	17.1	15.6	13.9	12.2	10.6	9.0	7.6	55
60	27.1	26.7	26.2	25.6	24.9	24.2	23.4	22.5	21.5	20.5	19.3	18.2	17.0	15.7	14.4	13.0	11.5	10.1	60
	Total Height 33 m																		
40	29.6	29.0	28.2	27.2	25.9	24.6	23.0	21.0	19.1	17.2	14.7	11.8	8.4	5.4	3.2	1.7			40
45	29.6	29.2	28.5	27.7	26.7	25.5	24.2	22.6	21.1	19.5	17.5	15.3	12.7	9.9	7.3	5.3	3.6	2.1	45
50	29.7	29.3	28.8	28.0	27.2	26.3	25.1	23.9	22.5	21.2	19.6	17.8	15.7	13.5	11.1	8.7	6.5	4.6	50
55	29.8	29.4	28.9	28.2	27.5	26.6	25.7	24.6	23.5	22.4	20.9	19.4	17.6	15.7	13.7	11.8	9.9	8.1	55
60	29.9	29.5	29.0	28.4	27.7	27.1	26.3	25.3	24.3	23.3	22.0	20.6	19.2	17.7	16.0	14.4	12.8	11.2	60
	Total Height 36 m																		
40	32.6	32.1	31.3	30.4	29.2	27.9	26.1	24.0	21.6	19.3	16.6	13.8	10.5	7.3	4.4	2.0			40
45	32.6	32.2	31.5	30.7	29.7	28.5	27.0	25.3	23.5	21.8	19.8	17.7	15.0	11.5	8.4	5.8	3.7	2.1	45
50	32.7	32.3	31.7	31.0	30.2	29.2	27.9	26.6	25.1	23.7	22.0	20.2	18.0	15.2	12.2	9.4	7.0	5.0	50
55	32.8	32.5	31.9	31.2	30.5	29.6	28.7	27.6	26.4	25.2	23.7	22.1	20.2	18.1	15.6	12.9	10.6	8.5	55
60	32.9	32.5	32.0	31.4	30.8	30.0	29.2	28.3	27.2	26.2	24.8	23.4	21.7	19.7	17.7	15.6	13.7	11.8	60

SINGLE TREE LENGTH ASSORTMENT TABLE TO UNDERBARK TOP DIAMETERS FOR SPRUCES AND OTHER CONIFERS

(MINIMUM LENGTH 1·3m)

dbh Class cm	LENGTHS TO SPECIFIED TOP DIAMETERS — Top Diameter underbark in centimetres																		dbh Class cm
	7	8	10	12	14	16	18	20	22	24	26	28	30	32	34	36	38	40	
Total Height 9 m																			
10	4.8	3.5																	10
15	5.8	5.5	4.7	3.5															15
20	6.4	6.1	5.6	4.9	4.0	3.1	2.0												20
25	6.8	6.6	6.3	5.8	5.3	4.7	4.0	3.2	2.3										25
Total Height 12 m																			
10	6.2	4.7																	10
15	8.2	7.3	5.7	3.9															15
20	9.0	8.6	7.7	6.6	5.2	3.7	2.1												20
25	9.3	9.1	8.5	7.8	7.0	6.0	4.8	3.5	2.3										25
30	9.6	9.4	9.1	8.7	8.2	7.6	6.7	5.6	4.5	3.4	2.5	1.6							30
Total Height 15 m																			
10	7.8	5.8																	10
15	10.6	9.6	7.7	5.2															15
20	11.5	10.9	9.8	8.4	6.7	4.7	2.6												20
25	12.0	11.6	10.9	10.0	8.8	7.5	6.1	4.6	3.0										25
30	12.3	12.0	11.5	10.8	10.0	9.1	8.0	6.8	5.5	4.3	3.0	1.8							30
35	12.5	12.3	12.0	11.5	10.9	10.1	9.3	8.3	7.3	6.3	5.2	4.2	3.1	2.1					35
40	12.6	12.5	12.2	11.8	11.4	10.9	10.2	9.4	8.6	7.7	6.8	5.9	4.9	4.0	3.2	2.3	1.5		40
Total Height 18 m																			
15	12.9	12.0	9.7	6.5															15
20	14.1	13.5	12.1	10.2	8.1	5.7	3.0												20
25	14.7	14.3	13.4	12.3	10.9	9.3	7.4	5.4	3.3										25
30	14.9	14.6	14.0	13.3	12.3	11.1	9.7	8.1	6.6	5.0	3.5	1.9							30
35	15.1	14.9	14.4	13.8	13.1	12.2	11.2	10.0	8.8	7.6	6.3	5.1	3.8	2.4					35
40	15.3	15.2	14.7	14.2	13.6	12.9	12.1	11.2	10.3	9.4	8.4	7.3	6.2	5.0	3.8	2.7	1.6		40
Total Height 21 m																			
15	16.2	15.2	11.1	6.7															15
20	17.2	16.5	14.4	12.0	9.7	6.8	3.2												20
25	17.7	17.2	15.9	14.6	13.1	11.2	8.9	6.5	3.9										25
30	17.9	17.6	16.7	15.7	14.6	13.1	11.4	9.6	7.7	5.8	3.9	2.0							30
35	18.1	17.8	17.2	16.4	15.7	14.7	13.4	11.8	10.2	8.5	7.0	5.5	4.0	2.5					35
40	18.3	18.0	17.4	16.7	16.0	15.1	14.1	13.1	11.9	10.4	8.8	7.6	6.3	5.1	3.9	2.7	1.6		40
45	18.4	18.1	17.6	17.0	16.3	15.5	14.7	13.8	12.9	11.8	10.5	9.2	8.0	6.8	5.7	4.6	3.6	2.7	45
50	18.6	18.2	17.7	17.2	16.5	15.8	15.0	14.2	13.4	12.4	11.3	10.2	9.2	8.2	7.3	6.4	5.6	4.7	50

SINGLE TREE LENGTH ASSORTMENT TABLE TO UNDERBARK TOP DIAMETERS FOR SPRUCES AND OTHER CONIFERS

(MINIMUM LENGTH 1·3m)

LENGTHS TO SPECIFIED TOP DIAMETERS

dbh Class cm	Top Diameter underbark in centimetres																		dbh Class cm
	7	8	10	12	14	16	18	20	22	24	26	28	30	32	34	36	38	40	
Total Height 24 m																			
20	19.9	19.4	17.6	15.3	12.2	8.3	4.0												20
25	20.4	20.1	18.9	17.4	15.5	13.3	10.4	7.4	4.4										25
30	20.6	20.4	19.4	18.4	17.2	15.7	14.0	11.6	9.1	6.7	4.3	2.1							30
35	20.8	20.6	20.0	19.2	18.1	16.9	15.4	13.8	11.9	9.9	7.7	5.7	4.0	2.5					35
40	21.0	20.7	20.2	19.4	18.6	17.6	16.5	15.2	13.7	12.2	10.6	8.8	6.9	5.2	4.0	2.8	1.6		40
45	21.1	20.9	20.4	19.8	19.0	18.1	17.1	16.0	14.9	13.7	12.3	10.9	9.3	7.8	6.3	4.9	3.8	2.7	45
50	21.2	21.0	20.5	19.9	19.2	18.4	17.6	16.6	15.6	14.6	13.5	12.3	11.0	9.8	8.5	7.4	6.3	5.3	50
55	21.2	21.1	20.6	19.9	19.3	18.6	17.9	17.2	16.4	15.5	14.5	13.6	12.6	11.5	10.5	9.5	8.5	7.5	55
Total Height 27 m																			
20	22.6	22.0	19.8	17.1	13.7	8.9	3.9												20
25	23.2	22.7	21.4	19.9	17.8	15.5	12.2	8.5	4.7										25
30	23.5	23.1	22.1	21.0	19.5	17.7	15.5	13.0	10.3	7.3	4.5	2.1							30
35	23.5	23.3	22.5	21.6	20.4	19.1	17.5	15.6	13.5	11.1	8.6	6.3	4.3	2.6					35
40	23.9	23.5	22.8	22.0	21.0	19.9	18.7	17.3	15.6	13.9	11.9	10.0	8.0	6.1	4.4	2.9	1.6		40
45	24.0	23.6	23.0	22.3	21.5	20.5	19.5	18.3	17.0	15.6	14.2	12.5	10.8	9.0	7.2	5.6	4.2	3.0	45
50	24.1	23.8	23.2	22.5	21.7	20.9	20.1	19.1	18.0	17.0	15.8	14.5	13.1	11.6	10.0	8.6	7.1	5.8	50
55	24.2	23.9	23.3	22.7	22.0	21.3	20.5	19.7	18.8	17.8	16.8	15.7	14.5	13.3	12.1	10.8	9.5	8.1	55
60	24.3	24.0	23.4	22.9	22.2	21.6	20.9	20.2	19.3	18.5	17.6	16.6	15.6	14.5	13.4	12.2	11.0	9.9	60
Total Height 30 m																			
30	26.4	26.0	25.0	23.6	22.1	20.2	17.9	15.1	12.0	9.1	5.9	2.5							30
35	26.7	26.3	25.4	24.4	23.1	21.7	19.9	17.8	15.4	12.8	10.0	7.4	5.1	2.9					35
40	26.9	26.5	25.8	24.8	23.8	22.6	21.2	19.5	17.8	15.9	13.8	11.6	9.3	6.9	4.6	2.9	1.6		40
45	27.0	26.6	26.0	25.2	24.3	23.4	22.3	20.9	19.4	18.0	16.4	14.7	12.8	10.6	8.3	6.3	4.5	3.0	45
50	27.1	26.7	26.2	25.4	24.6	23.8	22.8	21.7	20.5	19.3	17.9	16.5	14.9	13.0	11.1	9.2	7.6	6.1	50
55	27.2	26.8	26.3	25.7	24.9	24.1	23.3	22.4	21.3	20.3	19.1	17.9	16.5	15.0	13.5	11.9	10.4	9.0	55
60	27.3	26.9	26.4	25.8	25.2	24.4	23.7	22.8	21.9	21.0	19.9	18.8	17.7	16.6	15.3	14.1	12.8	11.5	60
Total Height 33 m																			
40	29.7	29.2	28.5	27.5	26.3	25.0	23.6	21.8	19.9	18.1	15.9	13.4	10.4	7.3	4.7	2.9	1.6		40
45	29.8	29.4	28.8	28.0	27.0	25.9	24.7	23.2	21.7	20.2	18.5	16.5	14.3	11.8	9.1	6.9	5.0	3.5	45
50	29.8	29.5	29.0	28.3	27.5	26.6	25.6	24.4	23.1	21.8	20.4	18.8	17.0	15.0	12.8	10.6	8.4	6.4	50
55	30.0	29.6	29.1	28.5	27.7	26.9	26.0	25.1	24.0	22.9	21.6	20.2	18.7	16.9	15.1	13.3	11.6	9.8	55
60	30.1	29.6	29.2	28.6	28.0	27.3	26.6	25.7	24.7	23.8	22.6	21.4	20.1	18.7	17.2	15.7	14.2	12.7	60
Total Height 36 m																			
40	32.7	32.2	31.6	30.7	29.6	28.4	26.8	24.8	22.6	20.3	17.9	15.4	12.5	9.4	6.4	3.9	1.8		40
45	32.8	32.3	31.7	30.9	30.0	28.9	27.6	26.0	24.3	22.6	20.8	18.9	16.7	13.8	10.6	7.8	5.5	3.7	45
50	32.9	32.4	31.9	31.2	30.4	29.5	28.4	27.1	25.7	24.3	22.8	21.2	19.4	17.1	14.4	11.6	9.1	6.9	50
55	32.9	32.6	32.2	31.4	30.7	29.9	29.0	28.0	26.9	25.7	24.4	23.0	21.4	19.5	17.5	15.0	12.6	10.5	55
60	33.0	32.6	32.2	31.6	31.0	30.3	29.5	28.6	27.7	26.7	25.5	24.2	22.7	21.1	19.2	17.3	15.4	13.6	60

STAND TABLE FOR CONIFERS

PERCENTAGE DISTRIBUTION OF NUMBERS OF TREES

mean dbh cm	Breast Height Diameter Class in centimetres														mean dbh cm
	5	10	15	20	25	30	35	40	45	50	55	60	65	70	
10	19	71	10												10
11	8	73	19												11
12	3	66	29	2											12
13	1	53	42	4											13
14		39	53	8											14
15		26	60	14											15
16		16	61	21	2										16
17		9	57	30	4										17
18		5	50	38	7										18
19		2	41	45	11	1									19
20		1	31	50	16	2									20
21			23	51	22	4									21
22			16	48	29	7									22
23			11	43	34	10	2								23
24			7	38	38	14	3								24
25			5	32	40	18	5								25
26			3	27	40	22	7	1							26
27			2	22	39	26	9	2							27
28			2	17	37	29	12	3							28
29			1	14	34	31	15	5							29
30				11	31	32	18	7	1						30
31				9	27	32	21	9	2						31
32				7	24	31	23	11	4						32
33				6	21	30	24	13	5	1					33
34				4	18	29	25	15	7	2					34
35				4	15	27	26	17	8	3					35
36				3	13	25	26	18	10	5					36
37				1	12	23	25	20	12	6	1				37
38					11	21	25	20	13	7	3				38
39					9	19	25	21	14	8	4				39
40					8	18	23	21	15	9	5	1			40
41					6	16	22	22	16	10	6	2			41
42					5	15	21	21	17	11	7	3			42
43					4	13	20	21	17	12	8	5			43
44					3	12	19	20	18	13	9	5	1		44
45					2	11	17	20	18	14	9	6	3		45
46						11	17	19	18	14	10	7	4		46
47						10	15	18	18	15	11	7	5	1	47
48						8	15	18	18	15	11	8	5	2	48
49						7	14	17	17	15	12	9	6	3	49
50						6	13	16	17	15	12	9	7	5	50
	5	10	15	20	25	30	35	40	45	50	55	60	65	70	

NOTE The diameters given for the breast height diameter classes are the central values for each class. Thus the 10 cm diameter class includes dbh 8-12 cm inclusive, 15 cm-13-17 cm, 20 cm-18-22 cm, etc. The lowest class of 5 cm, includes all trees with dbh of 7 cm and less.

STOCK TABLE FOR CONIFERS

PERCENTAGE DISTRIBUTION OF VOLUME

mean dbh cm	Breast Height Diameter Class in centimetres													mean dbh cm
	10	15	20	25	30	35	40	45	50	55	60	65	70	
10	81	19												10
11	67	33												11
12	51	46	3											12
13	35	57	8											13
14	22	63	15											14
15	12	62	26											15
16	6	56	35	3										16
17	3	46	43	8										17
18	1	35	50	14										18
19		26	52	20	2									19
20		17	52	27	4									20
21		11	47	34	8									21
22		7	41	39	13									22
23		4	34	43	17	2								23
24		3	27	43	22	5								24
25		2	21	41	27	9								25
26		1	16	39	31	12	1							26
27			12	35	34	16	3							27
28			9	31	35	19	6							28
29			7	26	35	22	10							29
30			5	22	34	25	12	2						30
31			4	19	31	27	14	5						31
32			3	15	30	28	17	7						32
33			2	13	27	29	19	9	1					33
34			2	11	24	28	21	11	3					34
35			1	9	22	27	22	13	6					35
36			1	7	19	26	23	15	9					36
37				7	17	25	24	16	9	2				37
38				6	15	23	23	18	11	4				38
39				5	13	22	23	18	12	7				39
40				4	12	20	23	19	13	8	1			40
41				4	11	18	22	19	14	9	3			41
42				3	9	17	21	20	15	10	5			42
43				2	9	16	19	19	16	11	8			43
44				1	8	15	19	19	16	12	8	2		44
45				1	7	13	18	19	16	13	9	4		45
46					7	12	17	18	17	13	10	6		46
47					6	12	16	18	16	14	10	7	1	47
48					5	11	15	17	16	14	11	8	3	48
49					4	10	15	17	16	14	11	8	5	49
50					4	9	14	16	16	14	11	9	7	50
	10	15	20	25	30	35	40	45	50	55	60	65	70	

NOTE The diameters given for breast height diameter classes are the central values for each class. Thus the 15cm diameter class includes dbh 13-17cm inclusive, 20cm-18-22cm, etc. The lowest class of 10cm, includes all trees with dbh of 12cm to 7cm inclusive.

7. SAWN SOFTWOOD SIZES

The following tables have been extracted from *British Standard 4471 (1969)*.

Table 59

1. Basic Lengths of Sawn Softwood (in Metres)

1·80	2·10	3·00	4·20	5·10	6·00
	2·40	3·30	4·50	5·40	6·30
	2·70	3·60	4·80	5·70	
		3·90			

Table 60

2. Basic Cross-Dimensional Sizes of Sawn Softwood (in Millimetres)

	75	100	125	150	175	200	225	250	300
16	x	x	x	x					
19	x	x	x	x					
22	x	x	x	x					
25	x	x	x	x	x	x	x	x	x
32	x	x	x	x	x	x	x	x	x
36	x	x	x	x					
38	x	x	x	x	x	x	x		
40	x	x	x	x	x	x	x		
44	x	x	x	x	x	x	x	x	x
50	x	x	x	x	x	x	x	x	x
63		x	x	x	x	x	x		
75		x	x	x	x	x	x	x	x
100		x		x		x		x	x
150				x		x			x
200						x			
250								x	
300									x

Note: The above extracts are reproduced by permission of the British Standards Institution, 2 Park Street, London W1A 2BS.

Plane Figures

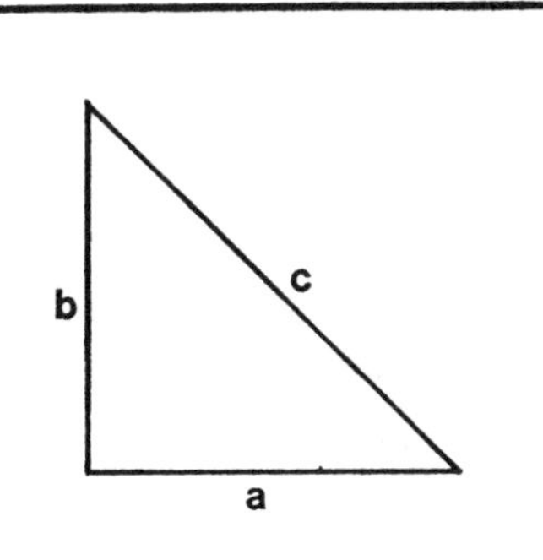

Right Angled Triangle

$$c = \sqrt{a^2 + b^2}$$
$$a = \sqrt{c^2 - b^2}$$
$$b = \sqrt{c^2 - a^2}$$
$$\text{area} = \tfrac{1}{2}ab$$

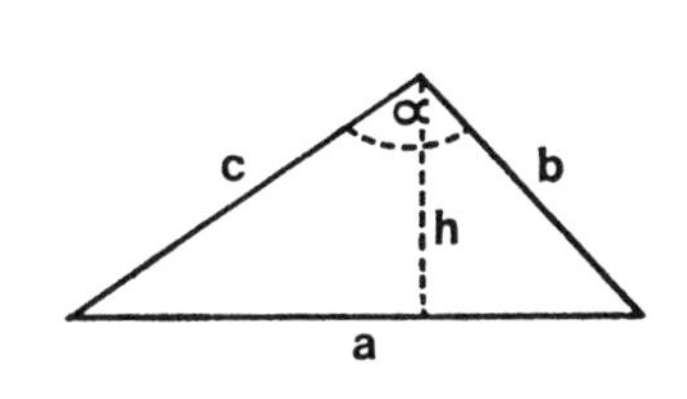

Oblique Triangle

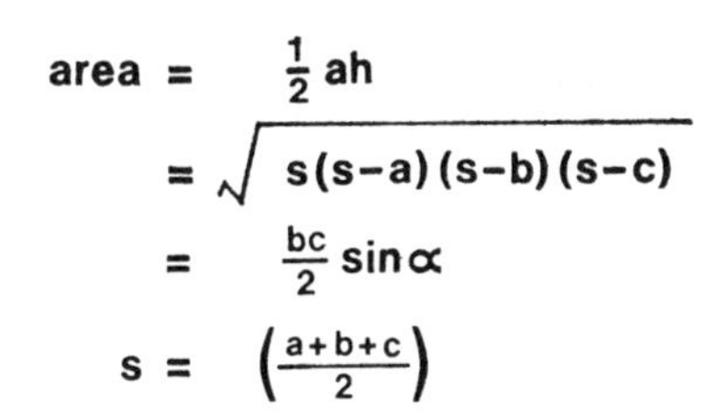

$$\text{area} = \tfrac{1}{2}ah$$
$$= \sqrt{s(s-a)(s-b)(s-c)}$$
$$= \frac{bc}{2}\sin\alpha$$
$$s = \left(\frac{a+b+c}{2}\right)$$

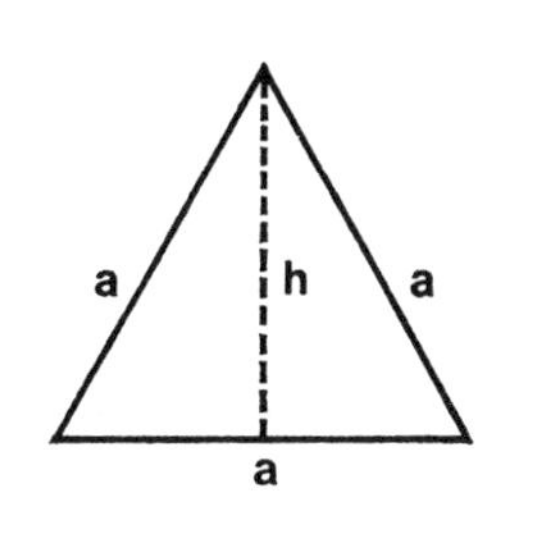

Equilateral Triangle

$$\text{area} = \tfrac{1}{2}ah = 0.433a^2$$
$$= 0.577h^2$$
$$h = 0.866a$$
$$a = 1.155h$$
$$a = 1.520\sqrt{\text{area}}$$

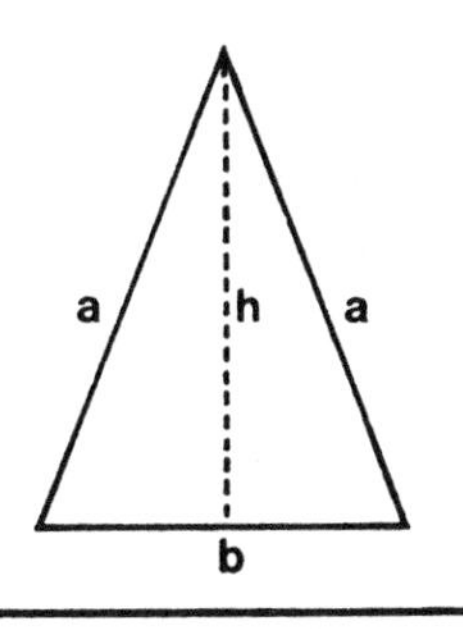

Isosceles Triangle

$$\text{area} = \tfrac{1}{2}bh$$
$$h = \sqrt{\left(a+\frac{b}{2}\right)\left(a-\frac{b}{2}\right)}$$

Plane Figures (*contd*)

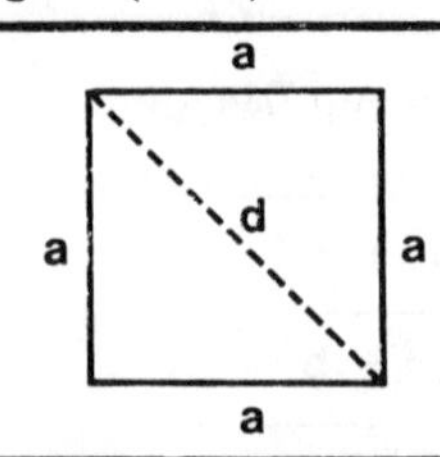

Square

$$\text{area} = a^2 = \frac{d^2}{2}$$

$$d = 1.414a = 1.414\sqrt{\text{area}}$$

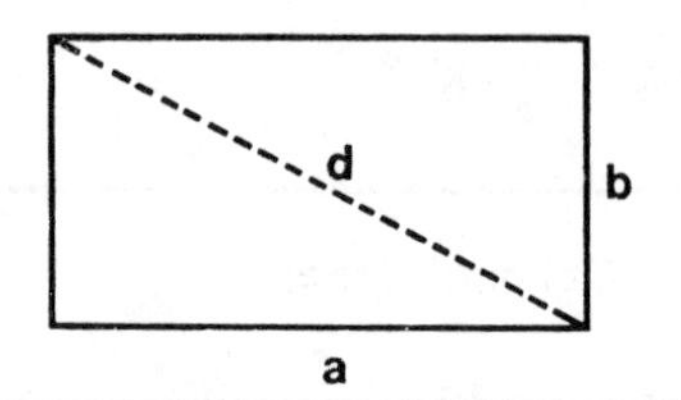

Rectangle

$$\text{area} = ab$$

$$d = \sqrt{a^2 + b^2}$$

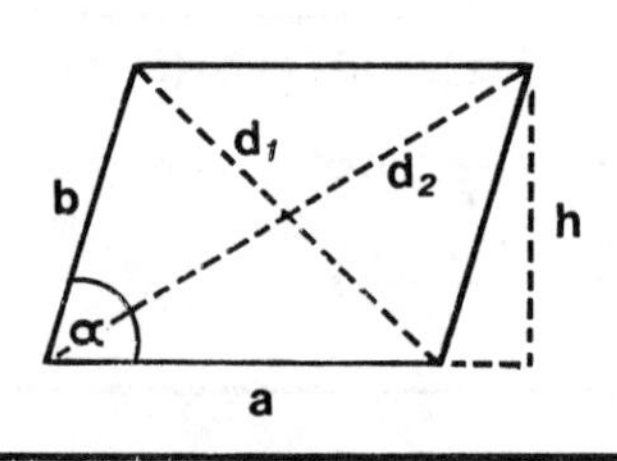

Parallelogram

$$\text{area} = ah = ab \sin \alpha$$

$$d_1 = \sqrt{a^2 + b^2 - 2ab \cos \alpha}$$

$$d_2 = \sqrt{a^2 + b^2 + 2ab \cos \alpha}$$

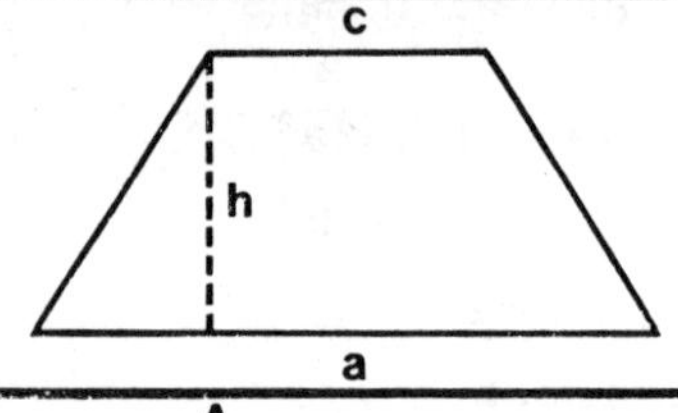

Trapezium

$$\text{area} = \frac{a+c}{2} h$$

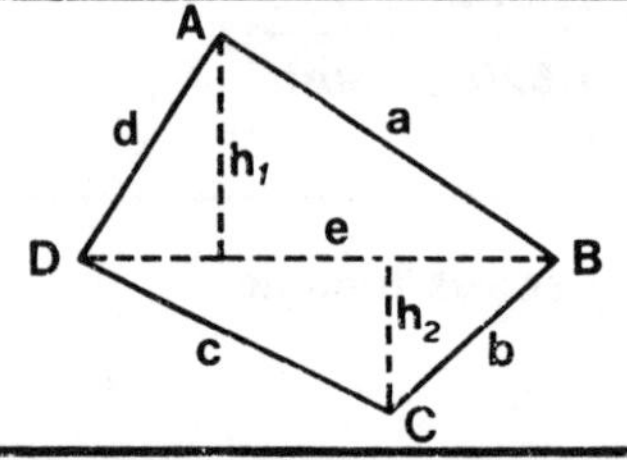

Trapezoid

$$\text{area} = \frac{e}{2}(h_1 + h_2)$$

$$= \frac{1}{2}(ad \sin A) + \frac{1}{2}(bc \sin C)$$

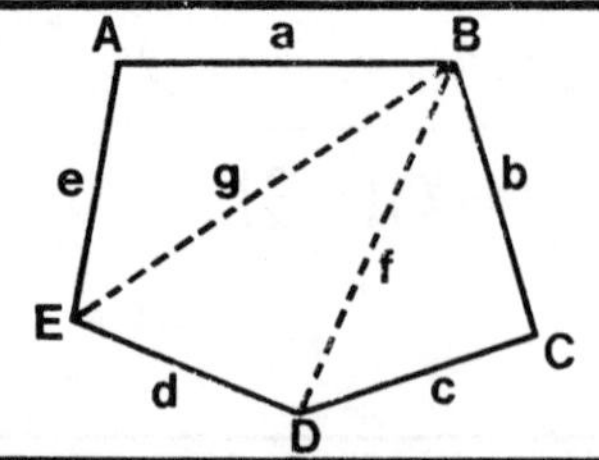

Pentagon

$$f^2 = c^2 + b^2 - 2cb \cos C$$

$$g^2 = e^2 + a^2 - 2ea \cos A$$

$$\text{area} = \triangle AEB + \triangle BED + \triangle BCD$$

(see oblique triangle area above)

Plane Figures (*contd*)

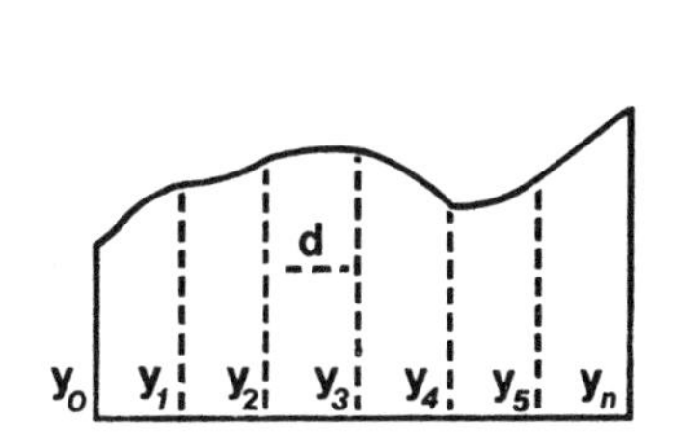	**Irregular Figure** Simpson's Rule (where n is even):- $\text{area} = \frac{d}{3}\left((y_0 + y_n) + 4(y_1 + y_3 + \ldots. y_{n-1}) + 2(y_2 + y_4 + \ldots. y_{n-2})\right)$ **Trapezoidal Rule** (where n is an odd number):- $\text{area} = d\left(\frac{1}{2}(y_0 + y_n) + y_1 + y_2 + \ldots. y_{n-1}\right)$
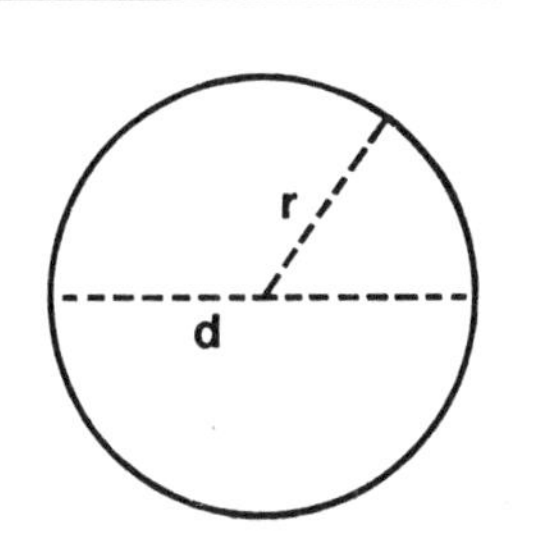	**Circle** $\pi = 3.141\ 592\ 653\ 90$ $\text{area} = \frac{\pi d^2}{4} = \pi r^2$ $\text{Circumference} = \pi d = 2\pi r$
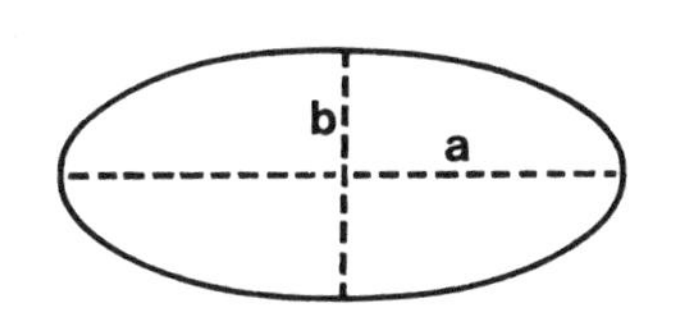	**Ellipse** $\text{area} = \pi ab$
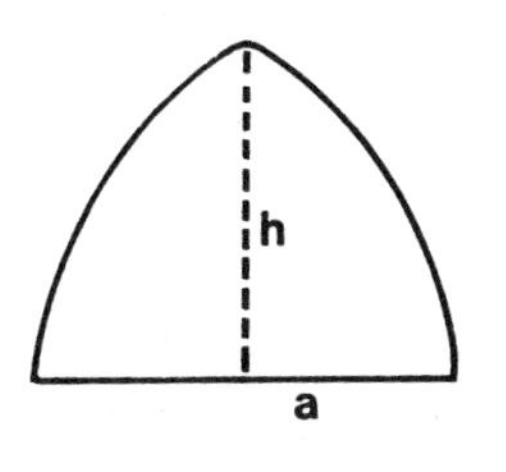	**Parabola** $\text{area} = \frac{2}{3}ah$

Solids

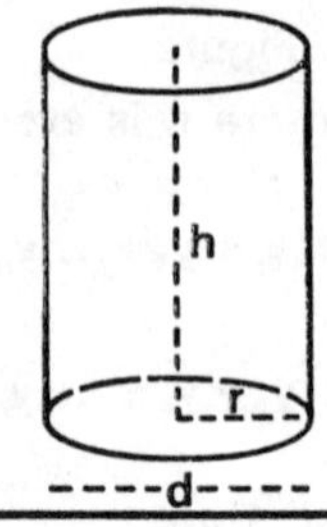

Cylinder

Volume $= \pi r^2 h = \frac{\pi d^2 h}{4}$

Surface area $= 2(\pi r h + \pi r^2)$

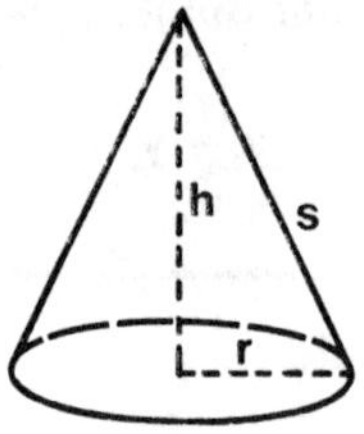

Cone

Volume $= \frac{\pi r^2 h}{3} = \frac{\pi d^2 h}{12}$

Surface area $= \pi r s + \pi r^2$

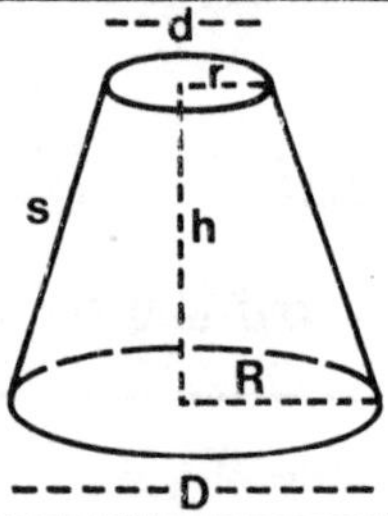

Frustrum of Cone

Volume $= \frac{\pi}{3}(R^2 + Rr + r^2)h$

$= \frac{\pi}{12}(D^2 + Dd + d^2)h$

Surface area $= \pi s(R + r) + \pi r^2 + \pi R^2$

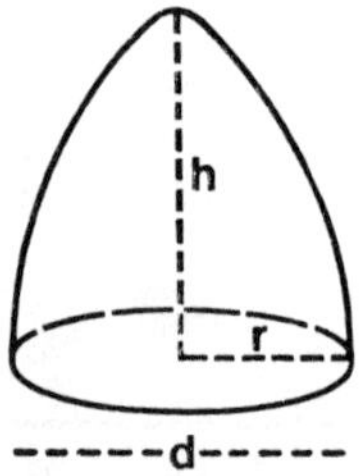

Paraboloid

Volume $= \pi r^2 \frac{h}{2} = \frac{\pi d^2 h}{8}$

Surface area $= \frac{2\pi r}{12h^2}\left((r^2 + 4h^2)^{3/2} - r^3\right) + \pi r^2$

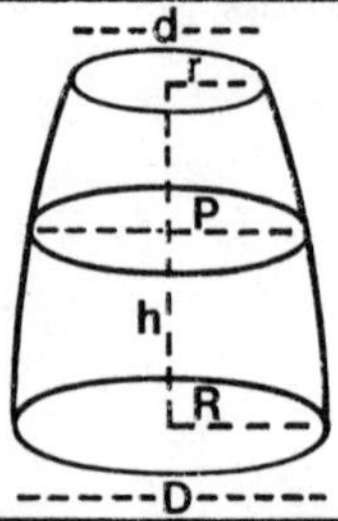

Frustrum of Paraboloid

Volume $= \frac{\pi h}{2}(R^2 + r^2)$

$= \frac{\pi h}{8}(D^2 + d^2)$ or $\frac{\pi h P^2}{4}$

Surface area $=$ (area of paraboloid (base R) less area of paraboloid (base r)) $+ \pi R^2 + \pi r^2$

Solids (*contd*)

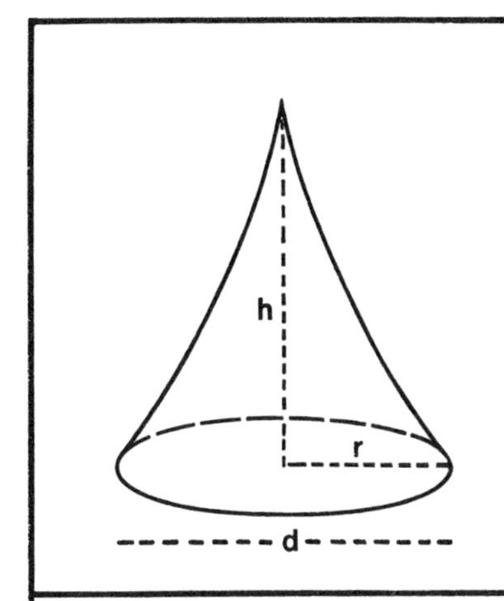

Neiloid

Volume $= \frac{\pi}{4} r^2 h = \frac{\pi}{16} d^2 h$

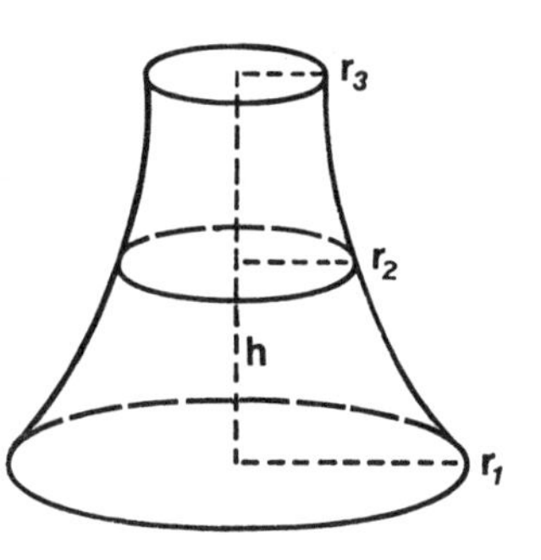

Frustrum of Neiloid

Volume $= \frac{\pi h}{6} (r_1^2 + 4r_2^2 + r_3^2)$

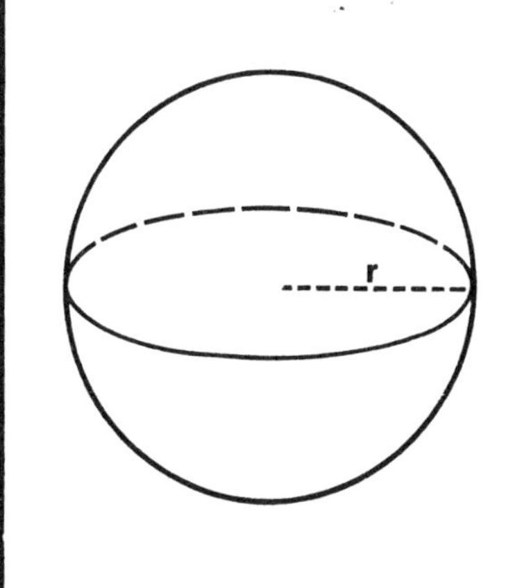

Sphere

Volume $= \frac{4 \pi r^3}{3}$

Surface area $= 4 \pi r^2$

9. PRECISE CONVERSION FACTORS

1. Length

Unit		Millimetre mm	Centimetre cm	Metre m	Kilometre km
1 Millimetre	=	**1**	0·1	0·001	
1 Centimetre	=	10	**1**	0·01	
1 Metre	=	1 000	100	**1**	0·001
1 Kilometre	=	1 000 000	100 000	1 000	**1**
1 Inch	=	25·4	2·54	0·025 4	
1 Foot	=	304·8	30·48	0·304 8	
1 Yard	=	914·4	91·44	0·914 4	0·000 914
1 Chain (100 links)	=	20 116·8	2 011·68	20·116 8	0·020 117
1 Mile	=	1 609 344	160 934·4	1 609·344	1·609 344

Note: The conversion factors that have been underlined are SI units and are

Inch in	Foot ft	Yard yd	Chain (100 links)	Mile
0·039 370	0·003 281			
0·393 701	0·032 808	0·010 936		
39·370 079	3·280 840	1·093 613	0·049 710	0·000 621
	3 280·840	1 093·613	49·709 695	0·621 371
1	0·083 333	0·027 778		
12	**1**	0·333 333	0·015 152	0·000 189
36	3	**1**	0·045 455	0·000 568
792	66	22	**1**	0·012 5
	5 280	1 760	80	**1**

exact conversion factors.

2. Area

Unit	Square Millimetre mm^2	Square Centimetre cm^2	Square Metre m^2	are	hectare ha	Square Kilometre km^2
1 Square Millimetre =	1	0·01				
1 Square Centimetre =	10^{2}	1	0·0001			
1 Square Metre =	10^{6}	10^{4}	1	0·01	0·000 1	0·000 001
1 are =	10^{8}	10^{6}	10^{2}	1	0·01	0·000 1
1 hectare =	10^{10}	10^{8}	10^{4}	10^{2}	1	0·01
1 Square Kilometre =	10^{12}	10^{10}	10^{6}	10^{4}	10^{2}	1
1 Square Inch =	645·16	6·451 6				
1 Square Foot =		929·030 4	0·092 903 04			
1 Square Foot Quarter Girth =			0·118 288			
1 Square Yard =			0·836 127	0·008 361	0·000 084	
1 Square Chain =			404·685 64	4·046 856	0·040 469	
1 Acre =			4 046·856	40·468 564	0·404 686	0·004 047
1 Square Mile =					258·998 811	2·589 988

Note: The conversion factors that have that been underlined are SI units

Square Inch in²	Square Foot ft²	Square Foot quarter girth ft² q.g.	Square Yard yd²	Square Chain	Acre	Square Mile
0·001 550						
0·155 000	0·001 076					
	10·763 9	8·453 955 547	1·195 99	0·002 471		
			119·599	0·247 105	0·024 711	
			11 959·9	24·710 54	2·471 054	0·003 861
			1195 990·0	2 471·05	247·105 4	0·386 102
1	0·006 944		0·000 772			
144	1		0·111 111	0·000 230		
	1·273 239 5	1				
1 296	9		1	0·002 066	0·000 207	
	4 356		484	1	0·1	0·000 156
	43 560		4 840	10	1	0·001 563
			3 097 600	6 400	640	1

and are exact conversion factors.

3. Volume

Unit	Cubic Millimetre mm^3	Cubic Centimetre cm^3	Cubic Metre m^3	Cubic Inch in^3	Cubic Foot ft^3
1 Cubic Millimetre =	**1**	0·001		0·000 061	
1 Cubic Centimetre =	10^3	**1**	0·000 001	0·061 024	0·000 035
1 Cubic Metre =	10^9	10^6	**1**	61 023·744	35·314 67
1 Cubic Inch =	16 387·064	16·387 064	0·000 016	**1**	0·000 578 7
1 Cubic Foot =		28 316·847	0·028 316 846 592	1 728	**1**
1 Hoppus Foot =			0·036 054		1·273 239 5
1 Cubic Yard =			0·764 554 857 984	46 656	27
1 Cord =			3·624 556		128
1 Petrograd Standard =			4·672 280		165
1 Gothenburg Standard =			5·097 032		180
1 Cubic Fathom =			6·116 439		216

Note: The conversion factors that have been underlined are SI units and are

Hoppus Foot H. ft.	Cubic Yard yd³	Cord	Petrograd Standard	Gothenburg Standard	Cubic Fathom
27·736 074	1·307 951	0·275 896	0·214 028	0·196 193	0·163 494
0·785 398	0·037 037	0·007 813	0·006 061	0·005 556	0·004 630
1		0·009 947	0·007 717	0·007 074	0·005 895
	1				
100·531		1	0·775 758	0·711 111	0·592 593
129·591		1·289 063	1	0·916 667	0·763 889
141·372		1·406 250	1·090 909	1	0·833 333
169·646		1·687 500	1·309 091	1·2	1

exact conversion factors.

4. Miscellaneous (diameter/girth: quantities per unit area)

1 centimetre diameter	=	0·309 212 inches *quarter girth*
1 centimetre diameter	=	1·236 85 inches *true* girth
1 inch *quarter* girth	=	3·234 03 centimetres diameter
1 inch *true* girth	=	0·808 507 centimetres diameter
1 square metre per hectare	=	3·421 194 square feet (*quarter-girth*) per acre
1 square metre per hectare	=	4·356 square feet (*true*) per acre
1 square foot (*quarter-girth*) per acre	=	0·292 296 square metres per hectare
1 square foot (*true*) per acre	=	0·229 568 4 square metres per hectare
1 cubic metre per hectare	=	11·224 4 hoppus feet per acre
1 cubic metre per hectare	=	14·291 34 cubic feet per acre
1 hoppus foot per acre	=	0·089 091 6 cubic metres per hectare
1 cubic foot per acre	=	0·069 972 45 cubic metres per hectare

10. ABBREVIATIONS

1. Species Abbreviations

SP	Scots pine	*Pinus sylvestris*
CP	Corsican pine	*Pinus nigra* var. *maritima*
LP	Lodgepole pine	*Pinus contorta*
SS	Sitka spruce	*Picea sitchensis*
NS	Norway spruce	*Picea abies*
OMS	Serbian/Omorika spruce	*Picea omorika*
EL	European larch	*Larix decidua*
JL	Japanese larch	*Larix kaempferi*
HL	Hybrid larch	*Larix x eurolepis*
DF	Douglas fir	*Pseudotsuga menziesii*
WH	Western hemlock	*Tsuga heterophylla*
RC	Red cedar	*Thuja plicata*
LC	Lawson cypress	*Chamaecyparis lawsoniana*
GF	Grand fir	*Abies grandis*
NF	Noble fir	*Abies procera*
Oak	Pedunculate/Sessile oak	*Quercus robur/petraea*
Be	Beech	*Fagus sylvatica*
SAB	Sycamore/Ash/Birch	*Acer pseudoplatanus/Fraxinus excelsior/ Betula pubescens/pendula*
Po	Hybrid poplars	*Populus* x *euramericana*

2. Other Abbreviations

cc	—	cubic centimetre
cm	—	centimetre
dbh	—	diameter at breast height
gm	—	gram
ha	—	hectare
ht	—	height
m	—	metre
mm	—	millimetre
m^2	—	square metre
m^3	—	cubic metre
ob	—	over bark
td	—	top diameter
ub	—	under bark

PART VI TABLES

VOLUME IN CUBIC METRES

Length in Metres	Mid-diameter in centimetres								Length in Metres
	7	8	9	10	11	12	13	14	
1.0	0.004	0.005	0.006	0.008	0.010	0.011	0.013	0.015	1.0
1.1	0.004	0.006	0.007	0.009	0.010	0.012	0.015	0.017	1.1
1.2	0.005	0.006	0.008	0.009	0.011	0.014	0.016	0.018	1.2
1.3	0.005	0.007	0.008	0.010	0.012	0.015	0.017	0.020	1.3
1.4	0.005	0.007	0.009	0.011	0.013	0.016	0.019	0.022	1.4
1.5	0.006	0.008	0.010	0.012	0.014	0.017	0.020	0.023	1.5
1.6	0.006	0.008	0.010	0.013	0.015	0.018	0.021	0.025	1.6
1.7	0.007	0.009	0.011	0.013	0.016	0.019	0.023	0.026	1.7
1.8	0.007	0.009	0.011	0.014	0.017	0.020	0.024	0.028	1.8
1.9	0.007	0.010	0.012	0.015	0.018	0.021	0.025	0.029	1.9
2.0	0.008	0.010	0.013	0.016	0.019	0.023	0.027	0.031	2.0
2.1	0.008	0.011	0.013	0.016	0.020	0.024	0.028	0.032	2.1
2.2	0.008	0.011	0.014	0.017	0.021	0.025	0.029	0.034	2.2
2.3	0.009	0.012	0.015	0.018	0.022	0.026	0.031	0.035	2.3
2.4	0.009	0.012	0.015	0.019	0.023	0.027	0.032	0.037	2.4
2.5	0.010	0.013	0.016	0.020	0.024	0.028	0.033	0.038	2.5
2.6	0.010	0.013	0.017	0.020	0.025	0.029	0.035	0.040	2.6
2.7	0.010	0.014	0.017	0.021	0.026	0.031	0.036	0.042	2.7
2.8	0.011	0.014	0.018	0.022	0.027	0.032	0.037	0.043	2.8
2.9	0.011	0.015	0.018	0.023	0.028	0.033	0.038	0.045	2.9
3.0	0.012	0.015	0.019	0.024	0.029	0.034	0.040	0.046	3.0
3.1	0.012	0.016	0.020	0.024	0.029	0.035	0.041	0.048	3.1
3.2	0.012	0.016	0.020	0.025	0.030	0.036	0.042	0.049	3.2
3.3	0.013	0.017	0.021	0.026	0.031	0.037	0.044	0.051	3.3
3.4	0.013	0.017	0.022	0.027	0.032	0.038	0.045	0.052	3.4
3.5	0.013	0.018	0.022	0.027	0.033	0.040	0.046	0.054	3.5
3.6	0.014	0.018	0.023	0.028	0.034	0.041	0.048	0.055	3.6
3.7	0.014	0.019	0.024	0.029	0.035	0.042	0.049	0.057	3.7
3.8	0.015	0.019	0.024	0.030	0.036	0.043	0.050	0.058	3.8
3.9	0.015	0.020	0.025	0.031	0.037	0.044	0.052	0.060	3.9
4.0	0.015	0.020	0.025	0.031	0.038	0.045	0.053	0.062	4.0
4.1	0.016	0.021	0.026	0.032	0.039	0.046	0.054	0.063	4.1
4.2	0.016	0.021	0.027	0.033	0.040	0.048	0.056	0.065	4.2
4.3	0.017	0.022	0.027	0.034	0.041	0.049	0.057	0.066	4.3
4.4	0.017	0.022	0.028	0.035	0.042	0.050	0.058	0.068	4.4
4.5	0.017	0.023	0.029	0.035	0.043	0.051	0.060	0.069	4.5
4.6	0.018	0.023	0.029	0.036	0.044	0.052	0.061	0.071	4.6
4.7	0.018	0.024	0.030	0.037	0.045	0.053	0.062	0.072	4.7
4.8	0.018	0.024	0.031	0.038	0.046	0.054	0.064	0.074	4.8
4.9	0.019	0.025	0.031	0.038	0.047	0.055	0.065	0.075	4.9
5.0	0.019	0.025	0.032	0.039	0.048	0.057	0.066	0.077	5.0
5.1	0.020	0.026	0.032	0.040	0.048	0.058	0.068	0.079	5.1
5.2	0.020	0.026	0.033	0.041	0.049	0.059	0.069	0.080	5.2
5.3	0.020	0.027	0.034	0.042	0.050	0.060	0.070	0.082	5.3
5.4	0.021	0.027	0.034	0.042	0.051	0.061	0.072	0.083	5.4

Length in Metres	VOLUME IN CUBIC METRES								Length in Metres
	Mid-diameter in centimetres								
	7	8	9	10	11	12	13	14	
5.5	0.021	0.028	0.035	0.043	0.052	0.062	0.073	0.085	5.5
5.6	0.022	0.028	0.036	0.044	0.053	0.063	0.074	0.086	5.6
5.7	0.022	0.029	0.036	0.045	0.054	0.064	0.076	0.088	5.7
5.8	0.022	0.029	0.037	0.046	0.055	0.066	0.077	0.089	5.8
5.9	0.023	0.030	0.038	0.046	0.056	0.067	0.078	0.091	5.9
6.0	0.023	0.030	0.038	0.047	0.057	0.068	0.080	0.092	6.0
6.1	0.023	0.031	0.039	0.048	0.058	0.069	0.081	0.094	6.1
6.2	0.024	0.031	0.039	0.049	0.059	0.070	0.082	0.095	6.2
6.3	0.024	0.032	0.040	0.049	0.060	0.071	0.084	0.097	6.3
6.4	0.025	0.032	0.041	0.050	0.061	0.072	0.085	0.099	6.4
6.5	0.025	0.033	0.041	0.051	0.062	0.074	0.086	0.100	6.5
6.6	0.025	0.033	0.042	0.052	0.063	0.075	0.088	0.102	6.6
6.7	0.026	0.034	0.043	0.053	0.064	0.076	0.089	0.103	6.7
6.8	0.026	0.034	0.043	0.053	0.065	0.077	0.090	0.105	6.8
6.9	0.027	0.035	0.044	0.054	0.066	0.078	0.092	0.106	6.9
7.0	0.027	0.035	0.045	0.055	0.067	0.079	0.093	0.108	7.0
7.1	0.027	0.036	0.045	0.056	0.067	0.080	0.094	0.109	7.1
7.2	0.028	0.036	0.046	0.057	0.068	0.081	0.096	0.111	7.2
7.3	0.028	0.037	0.046	0.057	0.069	0.083	0.097	0.112	7.3
7.4	0.028	0.037	0.047	0.058	0.070	0.084	0.098	0.114	7.4
7.5	0.029	0.038	0.048	0.059	0.071	0.085	0.100	0.115	7.5
7.6	0.029	0.038	0.048	0.060	0.072	0.086	0.101	0.117	7.6
7.7	0.030	0.039	0.049	0.060	0.073	0.087	0.102	0.119	7.7
7.8	0.030	0.039	0.050	0.061	0.074	0.088	0.104	0.120	7.8
7.9	0.030	0.040	0.050	0.062	0.075	0.089	0.105	0.122	7.9
8.0	0.031	0.040	0.051	0.063	0.076	0.090	0.106	0.123	8.0
8.1	0.031	0.041	0.052	0.064	0.077	0.092	0.108	0.125	8.1
8.2	0.032	0.041	0.052	0.064	0.078	0.093	0.109	0.126	8.2
8.3	0.032	0.042	0.053	0.065	0.079	0.094	0.110	0.128	8.3
8.4	0.032	0.042	0.053	0.066	0.080	0.095	0.111	0.129	8.4
8.5	0.033	0.043	0.054	0.067	0.081	0.096	0.113	0.131	8.5
8.6	0.033	0.043	0.055	0.068	0.082	0.097	0.114	0.132	8.6
8.7	0.033	0.044	0.055	0.068	0.083	0.098	0.115	0.134	8.7
8.8	0.034	0.044	0.056	0.069	0.084	0.100	0.117	0.135	8.8
8.9	0.034	0.045	0.057	0.070	0.085	0.101	0.118	0.137	8.9
9.0	0.035	0.045	0.057	0.071	0.086	0.102	0.119	0.139	9.0
9.1	0.035	0.046	0.058	0.071	0.086	0.103	0.121	0.140	9.1
9.2	0.035	0.046	0.059	0.072	0.087	0.104	0.122	0.142	9.2
9.3	0.036	0.047	0.059	0.073	0.088	0.105	0.123	0.143	9.3
9.4	0.036	0.047	0.060	0.074	0.089	0.106	0.125	0.145	9.4
9.5	0.037	0.048	0.060	0.075	0.090	0.107	0.126	0.146	9.5
9.6	0.037	0.048	0.061	0.075	0.091	0.109	0.127	0.148	9.6
9.7	0.037	0.049	0.062	0.076	0.092	0.110	0.129	0.149	9.7
9.8	0.038	0.049	0.062	0.077	0.093	0.111	0.130	0.151	9.8
9.9	0.038	0.050	0.063	0.078	0.094	0.112	0.131	0.152	9.9
10.0	0.038	0.050	0.064	0.079	0.095	0.113	0.133	0.154	10.0

VOLUME IN CUBIC METRES

Length in Metres	Mid-diameter in centimetres								Length in Metres
	15	16	17	18	19	20	21	22	
1.0	0.018	0.020	0.023	0.025	0.028	0.031	0.035	0.038	1.0
1.1	0.019	0.022	0.025	0.028	0.031	0.035	0.038	0.042	1.1
1.2	0.021	0.024	0.027	0.031	0.034	0.038	0.042	0.046	1.2
1.3	0.023	0.026	0.030	0.033	0.037	0.041	0.045	0.049	1.3
1.4	0.025	0.028	0.032	0.036	0.040	0.044	0.048	0.053	1.4
1.5	0.027	0.030	0.034	0.038	0.043	0.047	0.052	0.057	1.5
1.6	0.028	0.032	0.036	0.041	0.045	0.050	0.055	0.061	1.6
1.7	0.030	0.034	0.039	0.043	0.048	0.053	0.059	0.065	1.7
1.8	0.032	0.036	0.041	0.046	0.051	0.057	0.062	0.068	1.8
1.9	0.034	0.038	0.043	0.048	0.054	0.060	0.066	0.072	1.9
2.0	0.035	0.040	0.045	0.051	0.057	0.063	0.069	0.076	2.0
2.1	0.037	0.042	0.048	0.053	0.060	0.066	0.073	0.080	2.1
2.2	0.039	0.044	0.050	0.056	0.062	0.069	0.076	0.084	2.2
2.3	0.041	0.046	0.052	0.059	0.065	0.072	0.080	0.087	2.3
2.4	0.042	0.048	0.054	0.061	0.068	0.075	0.083	0.091	2.4
2.5	0.044	0.050	0.057	0.064	0.071	0.079	0.087	0.095	2.5
2.6	0.046	0.052	0.059	0.066	0.074	0.082	0.090	0.099	2.6
2.7	0.048	0.054	0.061	0.069	0.077	0.085	0.094	0.103	2.7
2.8	0.049	0.056	0.064	0.071	0.079	0.088	0.097	0.106	2.8
2.9	0.051	0.058	0.066	0.074	0.082	0.091	0.100	0.110	2.9
3.0	0.053	0.060	0.068	0.076	0.085	0.094	0.104	0.114	3.0
3.1	0.055	0.062	0.070	0.079	0.088	0.097	0.107	0.118	3.1
3.2	0.057	0.064	0.073	0.081	0.091	0.101	0.111	0.122	3.2
3.3	0.058	0.066	0.075	0.084	0.094	0.104	0.114	0.125	3.3
3.4	0.060	0.068	0.077	0.087	0.096	0.107	0.118	0.129	3.4
3.5	0.062	0.070	0.079	0.089	0.099	0.110	0.121	0.133	3.5
3.6	0.064	0.072	0.082	0.092	0.102	0.113	0.125	0.137	3.6
3.7	0.065	0.074	0.084	0.094	0.105	0.116	0.128	0.141	3.7
3.8	0.067	0.076	0.086	0.097	0.108	0.119	0.132	0.144	3.8
3.9	0.069	0.078	0.089	0.099	0.111	0.123	0.135	0.148	3.9
4.0	0.071	0.080	0.091	0.102	0.113	0.126	0.139	0.152	4.0
4.1	0.072	0.082	0.093	0.104	0.116	0.129	0.142	0.156	4.1
4.2	0.074	0.084	0.095	0.107	0.119	0.132	0.145	0.160	4.2
4.3	0.076	0.086	0.098	0.109	0.122	0.135	0.149	0.163	4.3
4.4	0.078	0.088	0.100	0.112	0.125	0.138	0.152	0.167	4.4
4.5	0.080	0.090	0.102	0.115	0.128	0.141	0.156	0.171	4.5
4.6	0.081	0.092	0.104	0.117	0.130	0.145	0.159	0.175	4.6
4.7	0.083	0.094	0.107	0.120	0.133	0.148	0.163	0.179	4.7
4.8	0.085	0.097	0.109	0.122	0.136	0.151	0.166	0.182	4.8
4.9	0.087	0.099	0.111	0.125	0.139	0.154	0.170	0.186	4.9
5.0	0.088	0.101	0.113	0.127	0.142	0.157	0.173	0.190	5.0
5.1	0.090	0.103	0.116	0.130	0.145	0.160	0.177	0.194	5.1
5.2	0.092	0.105	0.118	0.132	0.147	0.163	0.180	0.198	5.2
5.3	0.094	0.107	0.120	0.135	0.150	0.167	0.184	0.201	5.3
5.4	0.095	0.109	0.123	0.137	0.153	0.170	0.187	0.205	5.4

VOLUME IN CUBIC METRES

Length in Metres	Mid-diameter in centimetres								Length in Metres
	15	16	17	18	19	20	21	22	
5.5	0.097	0.111	0.125	0.140	0.156	0.173	0.190	0.209	5.5
5.6	0.099	0.113	0.127	0.143	0.159	0.176	0.194	0.213	5.6
5.7	0.101	0.115	0.129	0.145	0.162	0.179	0.197	0.217	5.7
5.8	0.102	0.117	0.132	0.148	0.164	0.182	0.201	0.220	5.8
5.9	0.104	0.119	0.134	0.150	0.167	0.185	0.204	0.224	5.9
6.0	0.106	0.121	0.136	0.153	0.170	0.188	0.208	0.228	6.0
6.1	0.108	0.123	0.138	0.155	0.173	0.192	0.211	0.232	6.1
6.2	0.110	0.125	0.141	0.158	0.176	0.195	0.215	0.236	6.2
6.3	0.111	0.127	0.143	0.160	0.179	0.198	0.218	0.239	6.3
6.4	0.113	0.129	0.145	0.163	0.181	0.201	0.222	0.243	6.4
6.5	0.115	0.131	0.148	0.165	0.184	0.204	0.225	0.247	6.5
6.6	0.117	0.133	0.150	0.168	0.187	0.207	0.229	0.251	6.6
6.7	0.118	0.135	0.152	0.170	0.190	0.210	0.232	0.255	6.7
6.8	0.120	0.137	0.154	0.173	0.193	0.214	0.236	0.258	6.8
6.9	0.122	0.139	0.157	0.176	0.196	0.217	0.239	0.262	6.9
7.0	0.124	0.141	0.159	0.178	0.198	0.220	0.242	0.266	7.0
7.1	0.125	0.143	0.161	0.181	0.201	0.223	0.246	0.270	7.1
7.2	0.127	0.145	0.163	0.183	0.204	0.226	0.249	0.274	7.2
7.3	0.129	0.147	0.166	0.186	0.207	0.229	0.253	0.277	7.3
7.4	0.131	0.149	0.168	0.188	0.210	0.232	0.256	0.281	7.4
7.5	0.133	0.151	0.170	0.191	0.213	0.236	0.260	0.285	7.5
7.6	0.134	0.153	0.173	0.193	0.215	0.239	0.263	0.289	7.6
7.7	0.136	0.155	0.175	0.196	0.218	0.242	0.267	0.293	7.7
7.8	0.138	0.157	0.177	0.198	0.221	0.245	0.270	0.297	7.8
7.9	0.140	0.159	0.179	0.201	0.224	0.248	0.274	0.300	7.9
8.0	0.141	0.161	0.182	0.204	0.227	0.251	0.277	0.304	8.0
8.1	0.143	0.163	0.184	0.206	0.230	0.254	0.281	0.308	8.1
8.2	0.145	0.165	0.186	0.209	0.232	0.258	0.284	0.312	8.2
8.3	0.147	0.167	0.188	0.211	0.235	0.261	0.287	0.316	8.3
8.4	0.148	0.169	0.191	0.214	0.238	0.264	0.291	0.319	8.4
8.5	0.150	0.171	0.193	0.216	0.241	0.267	0.294	0.323	8.5
8.6	0.152	0.173	0.195	0.219	0.244	0.270	0.298	0.327	8.6
8.7	0.154	0.175	0.197	0.221	0.247	0.273	0.301	0.331	8.7
8.8	0.156	0.177	0.200	0.224	0.250	0.276	0.305	0.335	8.8
8.9	0.157	0.179	0.202	0.226	0.252	0.280	0.308	0.338	8.9
9.0	0.159	0.181	0.204	0.229	0.255	0.283	0.312	0.342	9.0
9.1	0.161	0.183	0.207	0.232	0.258	0.286	0.315	0.346	9.1
9.2	0.163	0.185	0.209	0.234	0.261	0.289	0.319	0.350	9.2
9.3	0.164	0.187	0.211	0.237	0.264	0.292	0.322	0.354	9.3
9.4	0.166	0.189	0.213	0.239	0.267	0.295	0.326	0.357	9.4
9.5	0.168	0.191	0.216	0.242	0.269	0.298	0.329	0.361	9.5
9.6	0.170	0.193	0.218	0.244	0.272	0.302	0.333	0.365	9.6
9.7	0.171	0.195	0.220	0.247	0.275	0.305	0.336	0.369	9.7
9.8	0.173	0.197	0.222	0.249	0.278	0.308	0.339	0.373	9.8
9.9	0.175	0.199	0.225	0.252	0.281	0.311	0.343	0.376	9.9
10.0	0.177	0.201	0.227	0.254	0.284	0.314	0.346	0.380	10.0

Table 64 (contd)

VOLUME IN CUBIC METRES

Length in Metres	Mid-diameter in centimetres								Length in Metres
	23	24	25	26	27	28	29	30	
1.0	0.042	0.045	0.049	0.053	0.057	0.062	0.066	0.071	1.0
1.1	0.046	0.050	0.054	0.058	0.063	0.068	0.073	0.078	1.1
1.2	0.050	0.054	0.059	0.064	0.069	0.074	0.079	0.085	1.2
1.3	0.054	0.059	0.064	0.069	0.074	0.080	0.086	0.092	1.3
1.4	0.058	0.063	0.069	0.074	0.080	0.086	0.092	0.099	1.4
1.5	0.062	0.068	0.074	0.080	0.086	0.092	0.099	0.106	1.5
1.6	0.066	0.072	0.079	0.085	0.092	0.099	0.106	0.113	1.6
1.7	0.071	0.077	0.083	0.090	0.097	0.105	0.112	0.120	1.7
1.8	0.075	0.081	0.088	0.096	0.103	0.111	0.119	0.127	1.8
1.9	0.079	0.086	0.093	0.101	0.109	0.117	0.125	0.134	1.9
2.0	0.083	0.090	0.098	0.106	0.115	0.123	0.132	0.141	2.0
2.1	0.087	0.095	0.103	0.111	0.120	0.129	0.139	0.148	2.1
2.2	0.091	0.100	0.108	0.117	0.126	0.135	0.145	0.156	2.2
2.3	0.096	0.104	0.113	0.122	0.132	0.142	0.152	0.163	2.3
2.4	0.100	0.109	0.118	0.127	0.137	0.148	0.159	0.170	2.4
2.5	0.104	0.113	0.123	0.133	0.143	0.154	0.165	0.177	2.5
2.6	0.108	0.118	0.128	0.138	0.149	0.160	0.172	0.184	2.6
2.7	0.112	0.122	0.133	0.143	0.155	0.166	0.178	0.191	2.7
2.8	0.116	0.127	0.137	0.149	0.160	0.172	0.185	0.198	2.8
2.9	0.120	0.131	0.142	0.154	0.166	0.179	0.192	0.205	2.9
3.0	0.125	0.136	0.147	0.159	0.172	0.185	0.198	0.212	3.0
3.1	0.129	0.140	0.152	0.165	0.177	0.191	0.205	0.219	3.1
3.2	0.133	0.145	0.157	0.170	0.183	0.197	0.211	0.226	3.2
3.3	0.137	0.149	0.162	0.175	0.189	0.203	0.218	0.233	3.3
3.4	0.141	0.154	0.167	0.181	0.195	0.209	0.225	0.240	3.4
3.5	0.145	0.158	0.172	0.186	0.200	0.216	0.231	0.247	3.5
3.6	0.150	0.163	0.177	0.191	0.206	0.222	0.238	0.254	3.6
3.7	0.154	0.167	0.182	0.196	0.212	0.228	0.244	0.262	3.7
3.8	0.158	0.172	0.187	0.202	0.218	0.234	0.251	0.269	3.8
3.9	0.162	0.176	0.191	0.207	0.223	0.240	0.258	0.276	3.9
4.0	0.166	0.181	0.196	0.212	0.229	0.246	0.264	0.283	4.0
4.1	0.170	0.185	0.201	0.218	0.235	0.252	0.271	0.290	4.1
4.2	0.174	0.190	0.206	0.223	0.240	0.259	0.277	0.297	4.2
4.3	0.179	0.195	0.211	0.228	0.246	0.265	0.284	0.304	4.3
4.4	0.183	0.199	0.216	0.234	0.252	0.271	0.291	0.311	4.4
4.5	0.187	0.204	0.221	0.239	0.258	0.277	0.297	0.318	4.5
4.6	0.191	0.208	0.226	0.244	0.263	0.283	0.304	0.325	4.6
4.7	0.195	0.213	0.231	0.250	0.269	0.289	0.310	0.332	4.7
4.8	0.199	0.217	0.236	0.255	0.275	0.296	0.317	0.339	4.8
4.9	0.204	0.222	0.241	0.260	0.281	0.302	0.324	0.346	4.9
5.0	0.208	0.226	0.245	0.265	0.286	0.308	0.330	0.353	5.0
5.1	0.212	0.231	0.250	0.271	0.292	0.314	0.337	0.360	5.1
5.2	0.216	0.235	0.255	0.276	0.298	0.320	0.343	0.368	5.2
5.3	0.220	0.240	0.260	0.281	0.303	0.326	0.350	0.375	5.3
5.4	0.224	0.244	0.265	0.287	0.309	0.333	0.357	0.382	5.4

Length in Metres	VOLUME IN CUBIC METRES								Length in Metres
	Mid-diameter in centimetres								
	23	24	25	26	27	28	29	30	
5.5	0.229	0.249	0.270	0.292	0.315	0.339	0.363	0.389	5.5
5.6	0.233	0.253	0.275	0.297	0.321	0.345	0.370	0.396	5.6
5.7	0.237	0.258	0.280	0.303	0.326	0.351	0.376	0.403	5.7
5.8	0.241	0.262	0.285	0.308	0.332	0.357	0.383	0.410	5.8
5.9	0.245	0.267	0.290	0.313	0.338	0.363	0.390	0.417	5.9
6.0	0.249	0.271	0.295	0.319	0.344	0.369	0.396	0.424	6.0
6.1	0.253	0.276	0.299	0.324	0.349	0.376	0.403	0.431	6.1
6.2	0.258	0.280	0.304	0.329	0.355	0.382	0.410	0.438	6.2
6.3	0.262	0.285	0.309	0.334	0.361	0.388	0.416	0.445	6.3
6.4	0.266	0.290	0.314	0.340	0.366	0.394	0.423	0.452	6.4
6.5	0.270	0.294	0.319	0.345	0.372	0.400	0.429	0.459	6.5
6.6	0.274	0.299	0.324	0.350	0.378	0.406	0.436	0.467	6.6
6.7	0.278	0.303	0.329	0.356	0.384	0.413	0.443	0.474	6.7
6.8	0.283	0.308	0.334	0.361	0.389	0.419	0.449	0.481	6.8
6.9	0.287	0.312	0.339	0.366	0.395	0.425	0.456	0.488	6.9
7.0	0.291	0.317	0.344	0.372	0.401	0.431	0.462	0.495	7.0
7.1	0.295	0.321	0.349	0.377	0.407	0.437	0.469	0.502	7.1
7.2	0.299	0.326	0.353	0.382	0.412	0.443	0.476	0.509	7.2
7.3	0.303	0.330	0.358	0.388	0.418	0.449	0.482	0.516	7.3
7.4	0.307	0.335	0.363	0.393	0.424	0.456	0.489	0.523	7.4
7.5	0.312	0.339	0.368	0.398	0.429	0.462	0.495	0.530	7.5
7.6	0.316	0.344	0.373	0.404	0.435	0.468	0.502	0.537	7.6
7.7	0.320	0.348	0.378	0.409	0.441	0.474	0.509	0.544	7.7
7.8	0.324	0.353	0.383	0.414	0.447	0.480	0.515	0.551	7.8
7.9	0.328	0.357	0.388	0.419	0.452	0.486	0.522	0.558	7.9
8.0	0.332	0.362	0.393	0.425	0.458	0.493	0.528	0.565	8.0
8.1	0.337	0.366	0.398	0.430	0.464	0.499	0.535	0.573	8.1
8.2	0.341	0.371	0.403	0.435	0.469	0.505	0.542	0.580	8.2
8.3	0.345	0.375	0.407	0.441	0.475	0.511	0.548	0.587	8.3
8.4	0.349	0.380	0.412	0.446	0.481	0.517	0.555	0.594	8.4
8.5	0.353	0.385	0.417	0.451	0.487	0.523	0.561	0.601	8.5
8.6	0.357	0.389	0.422	0.457	0.492	0.530	0.568	0.608	8.6
8.7	0.361	0.394	0.427	0.462	0.498	0.536	0.575	0.615	8.7
8.8	0.366	0.398	0.432	0.467	0.504	0.542	0.581	0.622	8.8
8.9	0.370	0.403	0.437	0.473	0.510	0.548	0.588	0.629	8.9
9.0	0.374	0.407	0.442	0.478	0.515	0.554	0.594	0.636	9.0
9.1	0.378	0.412	0.447	0.483	0.521	0.560	0.601	0.643	9.1
9.2	0.382	0.416	0.452	0.488	0.527	0.566	0.608	0.650	9.2
9.3	0.386	0.421	0.457	0.494	0.532	0.573	0.614	0.657	9.3
9.4	0.391	0.425	0.461	0.499	0.538	0.579	0.621	0.664	9.4
9.5	0.395	0.430	0.466	0.504	0.544	0.585	0.627	0.672	9.5
9.6	0.399	0.434	0.471	0.510	0.550	0.591	0.634	0.679	9.6
9.7	0.403	0.439	0.476	0.515	0.555	0.597	0.641	0.686	9.7
9.8	0.407	0.443	0.481	0.520	0.561	0.603	0.647	0.693	9.8
9.9	0.411	0.448	0.486	0.526	0.567	0.610	0.654	0.700	9.9
10.0	0.415	0.452	0.491	0.531	0.573	0.616	0.661	0.707	10.0

VOLUME IN CUBIC METRES

Length in Metres	Mid-diameter in centimetres								Length in Metres
	31	32	33	34	35	36	37	38	
1.0	0.075	0.080	0.086	0.091	0.096	0.102	0.108	0.113	1.0
1.1	0.083	0.088	0.094	0.100	0.106	0.112	0.118	0.125	1.1
1.2	0.091	0.097	0.103	0.109	0.115	0.122	0.129	0.136	1.2
1.3	0.098	0.105	0.111	0.118	0.125	0.132	0.140	0.147	1.3
1.4	0.106	0.113	0.120	0.127	0.135	0.143	0.151	0.159	1.4
1.5	0.113	0.121	0.128	0.136	0.144	0.153	0.161	0.170	1.5
1.6	0.121	0.129	0.137	0.145	0.154	0.163	0.172	0.181	1.6
1.7	0.128	0.137	0.145	0.154	0.164	0.173	0.183	0.193	1.7
1.8	0.136	0.145	0.154	0.163	0.173	0.183	0.194	0.204	1.8
1.9	0.143	0.153	0.163	0.173	0.183	0.193	0.204	0.215	1.9
2.0	0.151	0.161	0.171	0.182	0.192	0.204	0.215	0.227	2.0
2.1	0.159	0.169	0.180	0.191	0.202	0.214	0.226	0.238	2.1
2.2	0.166	0.177	0.188	0.200	0.212	0.224	0.237	0.250	2.2
2.3	0.174	0.185	0.197	0.209	0.221	0.234	0.247	0.261	2.3
2.4	0.181	0.193	0.205	0.218	0.231	0.244	0.258	0.272	2.4
2.5	0.189	0.201	0.214	0.227	0.241	0.254	0.269	0.284	2.5
2.6	0.196	0.209	0.222	0.236	0.250	0.265	0.280	0.295	2.6
2.7	0.204	0.217	0.231	0.245	0.260	0.275	0.290	0.306	2.7
2.8	0.211	0.225	0.239	0.254	0.269	0.285	0.301	0.318	2.8
2.9	0.219	0.233	0.248	0.263	0.279	0.295	0.312	0.329	2.9
3.0	0.226	0.241	0.257	0.272	0.289	0.305	0.323	0.340	3.0
3.1	0.234	0.249	0.265	0.281	0.298	0.316	0.333	0.352	3.1
3.2	0.242	0.257	0.274	0.291	0.308	0.326	0.344	0.363	3.2
3.3	0.249	0.265	0.282	0.300	0.317	0.336	0.355	0.374	3.3
3.4	0.257	0.273	0.291	0.309	0.327	0.346	0.366	0.386	3.4
3.5	0.264	0.281	0.299	0.318	0.337	0.356	0.376	0.397	3.5
3.6	0.272	0.290	0.308	0.327	0.346	0.366	0.387	0.408	3.6
3.7	0.279	0.298	0.316	0.336	0.356	0.377	0.398	0.420	3.7
3.8	0.287	0.306	0.325	0.345	0.366	0.387	0.409	0.431	3.8
3.9	0.294	0.314	0.334	0.354	0.375	0.397	0.419	0.442	3.9
4.0	0.302	0.322	0.342	0.363	0.385	0.407	0.430	0.454	4.0
4.1	0.309	0.330	0.351	0.372	0.394	0.417	0.441	0.465	4.1
4.2	0.317	0.338	0.359	0.381	0.404	0.428	0.452	0.476	4.2
4.3	0.325	0.346	0.368	0.390	0.414	0.438	0.462	0.488	4.3
4.4	0.332	0.354	0.376	0.399	0.423	0.448	0.473	0.499	4.4
4.5	0.340	0.362	0.385	0.409	0.433	0.458	0.484	0.510	4.5
4.6	0.347	0.370	0.393	0.418	0.443	0.468	0.495	0.522	4.6
4.7	0.355	0.378	0.402	0.427	0.452	0.478	0.505	0.533	4.7
4.8	0.362	0.386	0.411	0.436	0.462	0.489	0.516	0.544	4.8
4.9	0.370	0.394	0.419	0.445	0.471	0.499	0.527	0.556	4.9
5.0	0.377	0.402	0.428	0.454	0.481	0.509	0.538	0.567	5.0
5.1	0.385	0.410	0.436	0.463	0.491	0.519	0.548	0.578	5.1
5.2	0.392	0.418	0.445	0.472	0.500	0.529	0.559	0.590	5.2
5.3	0.400	0.426	0.453	0.481	0.510	0.539	0.570	0.601	5.3
5.4	0.408	0.434	0.462	0.490	0.520	0.550	0.581	0.612	5.4

VOLUME IN CUBIC METRES

Length in Metres	Mid-diameter in centimetres								Length in Metres
	31	32	33	34	35	36	37	38	
5.5	0.415	0.442	0.470	0.499	0.529	0.560	0.591	0.624	5.5
5.6	0.423	0.450	0.479	0.508	0.539	0.570	0.602	0.635	5.6
5.7	0.430	0.458	0.488	0.518	0.548	0.580	0.613	0.646	5.7
5.8	0.438	0.466	0.496	0.527	0.558	0.590	0.624	0.658	5.8
5.9	0.445	0.475	0.505	0.536	0.568	0.601	0.634	0.669	5.9
6.0	0.453	0.483	0.513	0.545	0.577	0.611	0.645	0.680	6.0
6.1	0.460	0.491	0.522	0.554	0.587	0.621	0.656	0.692	6.1
6.2	0.468	0.499	0.530	0.563	0.597	0.631	0.667	0.703	6.2
6.3	0.476	0.507	0.539	0.572	0.606	0.641	0.677	0.714	6.3
6.4	0.483	0.515	0.547	0.581	0.616	0.651	0.688	0.726	6.4
6.5	0.491	0.523	0.556	0.590	0.625	0.662	0.699	0.737	6.5
6.6	0.498	0.531	0.564	0.599	0.635	0.672	0.710	0.749	6.6
6.7	0.506	0.539	0.573	0.608	0.645	0.682	0.720	0.760	6.7
6.8	0.513	0.547	0.582	0.617	0.654	0.692	0.731	0.771	6.8
6.9	0.521	0.555	0.590	0.626	0.664	0.702	0.742	0.783	6.9
7.0	0.528	0.563	0.599	0.636	0.673	0.713	0.753	0.794	7.0
7.1	0.536	0.571	0.607	0.645	0.683	0.723	0.763	0.805	7.1
7.2	0.543	0.579	0.616	0.654	0.693	0.733	0.774	0.817	7.2
7.3	0.551	0.587	0.624	0.663	0.702	0.743	0.785	0.828	7.3
7.4	0.559	0.595	0.633	0.672	0.712	0.753	0.796	0.839	7.4
7.5	0.566	0.603	0.641	0.681	0.722	0.763	0.806	0.851	7.5
7.6	0.574	0.611	0.650	0.690	0.731	0.774	0.817	0.862	7.6
7.7	0.581	0.619	0.659	0.699	0.741	0.784	0.828	0.873	7.7
7.8	0.589	0.627	0.667	0.708	0.750	0.794	0.839	0.885	7.8
7.9	0.596	0.635	0.676	0.717	0.760	0.804	0.849	0.896	7.9
8.0	0.604	0.643	0.684	0.726	0.770	0.814	0.860	0.907	8.0
8.1	0.611	0.651	0.693	0.735	0.779	0.824	0.871	0.919	8.1
8.2	0.619	0.659	0.701	0.744	0.789	0.835	0.882	0.930	8.2
8.3	0.626	0.668	0.710	0.754	0.799	0.845	0.892	0.941	8.3
8.4	0.634	0.676	0.718	0.763	0.808	0.855	0.903	0.953	8.4
8.5	0.642	0.684	0.727	0.772	0.818	0.865	0.914	0.964	8.5
8.6	0.649	0.692	0.736	0.781	0.827	0.875	0.925	0.975	8.6
8.7	0.657	0.700	0.744	0.790	0.837	0.886	0.935	0.987	8.7
8.8	0.664	0.708	0.753	0.799	0.847	0.896	0.946	0.998	8.8
8.9	0.672	0.716	0.761	0.808	0.856	0.906	0.957	1.009	8.9
9.0	0.679	0.724	0.770	0.817	0.866	0.916	0.968	1.021	9.0
9.1	0.687	0.732	0.778	0.826	0.876	0.926	0.978	1.032	9.1
9.2	0.694	0.740	0.787	0.835	0.885	0.936	0.989	1.043	9.2
9.3	0.702	0.748	0.795	0.844	0.895	0.947	1.000	1.055	9.3
9.4	0.709	0.756	0.804	0.853	0.904	0.957	1.011	1.066	9.4
9.5	0.717	0.764	0.813	0.863	0.914	0.967	1.021	1.077	9.5
9.6	0.725	0.772	0.821	0.872	0.924	0.977	1.032	1.089	9.6
9.7	0.732	0.780	0.830	0.881	0.933	0.987	1.043	1.100	9.7
9.8	0.740	0.788	0.838	0.890	0.943	0.998	1.054	1.111	9.8
9.9	0.747	0.796	0.847	0.899	0.952	1.008	1.064	1.123	9.9
10.0	0.755	0.804	0.855	0.908	0.962	1.018	1.075	1.134	10.0

Length in Metres	VOLUME IN CUBIC METRES								Length in Metres
	Mid-diameter in centimetres								
	39	40	41	42	43	44	45	46	
1.0	0.119	0.126	0.132	0.139	0.145	0.152	0.159	0.166	1.0
1.1	0.131	0.138	0.145	0.152	0.160	0.167	0.175	0.183	1.1
1.2	0.143	0.151	0.158	0.166	0.174	0.182	0.191	0.199	1.2
1.3	0.155	0.163	0.172	0.180	0.189	0.198	0.207	0.216	1.3
1.4	0.167	0.176	0.185	0.194	0.203	0.213	0.223	0.233	1.4
1.5	0.179	0.188	0.198	0.208	0.218	0.228	0.239	0.249	1.5
1.6	0.191	0.201	0.211	0.222	0.232	0.243	0.254	0.266	1.6
1.7	0.203	0.214	0.224	0.236	0.247	0.258	0.270	0.283	1.7
1.8	0.215	0.226	0.238	0.249	0.261	0.274	0.286	0.299	1.8
1.9	0.227	0.239	0.251	0.263	0.276	0.289	0.302	0.316	1.9
2.0	0.239	0.251	0.264	0.277	0.290	0.304	0.318	0.332	2.0
2.1	0.251	0.264	0.277	0.291	0.305	0.319	0.334	0.349	2.1
2.2	0.263	0.276	0.290	0.305	0.319	0.335	0.350	0.366	2.2
2.3	0.275	0.289	0.304	0.319	0.334	0.350	0.366	0.382	2.3
2.4	0.287	0.302	0.317	0.333	0.349	0.365	0.382	0.399	2.4
2.5	0.299	0.314	0.330	0.346	0.363	0.380	0.398	0.415	2.5
2.6	0.311	0.327	0.343	0.360	0.378	0.395	0.414	0.432	2.6
2.7	0.323	0.339	0.356	0.374	0.392	0.411	0.429	0.449	2.7
2.8	0.334	0.352	0.370	0.388	0.407	0.426	0.445	0.465	2.8
2.9	0.346	0.364	0.383	0.402	0.421	0.441	0.461	0.482	2.9
3.0	0.358	0.377	0.396	0.416	0.436	0.456	0.477	0.499	3.0
3.1	0.370	0.390	0.409	0.429	0.450	0.471	0.493	0.515	3.1
3.2	0.382	0.402	0.422	0.443	0.465	0.487	0.509	0.532	3.2
3.3	0.394	0.415	0.436	0.457	0.479	0.502	0.525	0.548	3.3
3.4	0.406	0.427	0.449	0.471	0.494	0.517	0.541	0.565	3.4
3.5	0.418	0.440	0.462	0.485	0.508	0.532	0.557	0.582	3.5
3.6	0.430	0.452	0.475	0.499	0.523	0.547	0.573	0.598	3.6
3.7	0.442	0.465	0.488	0.513	0.537	0.563	0.588	0.615	3.7
3.8	0.454	0.478	0.502	0.526	0.552	0.578	0.604	0.632	3.8
3.9	0.466	0.490	0.515	0.540	0.566	0.593	0.620	0.648	3.9
4.0	0.478	0.503	0.528	0.554	0.581	0.608	0.636	0.665	4.0
4.1	0.490	0.515	0.541	0.568	0.595	0.623	0.652	0.681	4.1
4.2	0.502	0.528	0.555	0.582	0.610	0.639	0.668	0.698	4.2
4.3	0.514	0.540	0.568	0.596	0.624	0.654	0.684	0.715	4.3
4.4	0.526	0.553	0.581	0.610	0.639	0.669	0.700	0.731	4.4
4.5	0.538	0.565	0.594	0.623	0.653	0.684	0.716	0.748	4.5
4.6	0.550	0.578	0.607	0.637	0.668	0.699	0.732	0.764	4.6
4.7	0.561	0.591	0.621	0.651	0.683	0.715	0.748	0.781	4.7
4.8	0.573	0.603	0.634	0.665	0.697	0.730	0.763	0.798	4.8
4.9	0.585	0.616	0.647	0.679	0.712	0.745	0.779	0.814	4.9
5.0	0.597	0.628	0.660	0.693	0.726	0.760	0.795	0.831	5.0
5.1	0.609	0.641	0.673	0.707	0.741	0.775	0.811	0.848	5.1
5.2	0.621	0.653	0.687	0.720	0.755	0.791	0.827	0.864	5.2
5.3	0.633	0.666	0.700	0.734	0.770	0.806	0.843	0.881	5.3
5.4	0.645	0.679	0.713	0.748	0.784	0.821	0.859	0.897	5.4

VOLUME IN CUBIC METRES

Length in Metres	Mid-diameter in centimetres								Length in Metres
	39	40	41	42	43	44	45	46	
5.5	0.657	0.691	0.726	0.762	0.799	0.836	0.875	0.914	5.5
5.6	0.669	0.704	0.739	0.776	0.813	0.851	0.891	0.931	5.6
5.7	0.681	0.716	0.753	0.790	0.828	0.867	0.907	0.947	5.7
5.8	0.693	0.729	0.766	0.804	0.842	0.882	0.922	0.964	5.8
5.9	0.705	0.741	0.779	0.817	0.857	0.897	0.938	0.981	5.9
6.0	0.717	0.754	0.792	0.831	0.871	0.912	0.954	0.997	6.0
6.1	0.729	0.767	0.805	0.845	0.886	0.928	0.970	1.014	6.1
6.2	0.741	0.779	0.819	0.859	0.900	0.943	0.986	1.030	6.2
6.3	0.753	0.792	0.832	0.873	0.915	0.958	1.002	1.047	6.3
6.4	0.765	0.804	0.845	0.887	0.929	0.973	1.018	1.064	6.4
6.5	0.776	0.817	0.858	0.901	0.944	0.988	1.034	1.080	6.5
6.6	0.788	0.829	0.871	0.914	0.958	1.004	1.050	1.097	6.6
6.7	0.800	0.842	0.885	0.928	0.973	1.019	1.066	1.113	6.7
6.8	0.812	0.855	0.898	0.942	0.987	1.034	1.081	1.130	6.8
6.9	0.824	0.867	0.911	0.956	1.002	1.049	1.097	1.147	6.9
7.0	0.836	0.880	0.924	0.970	1.017	1.064	1.113	1.163	7.0
7.1	0.848	0.892	0.937	0.984	1.031	1.080	1.129	1.180	7.1
7.2	0.860	0.905	0.951	0.998	1.046	1.095	1.145	1.197	7.2
7.3	0.872	0.917	0.964	1.011	1.060	1.110	1.161	1.213	7.3
7.4	0.884	0.930	0.977	1.025	1.075	1.125	1.177	1.230	7.4
7.5	0.896	0.942	0.990	1.039	1.089	1.140	1.193	1.246	7.5
7.6	0.908	0.955	1.003	1.053	1.104	1.156	1.209	1.263	7.6
7.7	0.920	0.968	1.017	1.067	1.118	1.171	1.225	1.280	7.7
7.8	0.932	0.980	1.030	1.081	1.133	1.186	1.241	1.296	7.8
7.9	0.944	0.993	1.043	1.094	1.147	1.201	1.256	1.313	7.9
8.0	0.956	1.005	1.056	1.108	1.162	1.216	1.272	1.330	8.0
8.1	0.968	1.018	1.069	1.122	1.176	1.232	1.288	1.346	8.1
8.2	0.980	1.030	1.083	1.136	1.191	1.247	1.304	1.363	8.2
8.3	0.992	1.043	1.096	1.150	1.205	1.262	1.320	1.379	8.3
8.4	1.003	1.056	1.109	1.164	1.220	1.277	1.336	1.396	8.4
8.5	1.015	1.068	1.122	1.178	1.234	1.292	1.352	1.413	8.5
8.6	1.027	1.081	1.135	1.191	1.249	1.308	1.368	1.429	8.6
8.7	1.039	1.093	1.149	1.205	1.263	1.323	1.384	1.446	8.7
8.8	1.051	1.106	1.162	1.219	1.278	1.338	1.400	1.462	8.8
8.9	1.063	1.118	1.175	1.233	1.292	1.353	1.415	1.479	8.9
9.0	1.075	1.131	1.188	1.247	1.307	1.368	1.431	1.496	9.0
9.1	1.087	1.144	1.201	1.261	1.322	1.384	1.447	1.512	9.1
9.2	1.099	1.156	1.215	1.275	1.336	1.399	1.463	1.529	9.2
9.3	1.111	1.169	1.228	1.288	1.351	1.414	1.479	1.546	9.3
9.4	1.123	1.181	1.241	1.302	1.365	1.429	1.495	1.562	9.4
9.5	1.135	1.194	1.254	1.316	1.380	1.445	1.511	1.579	9.5
9.6	1.147	1.206	1.267	1.330	1.394	1.460	1.527	1.595	9.6
9.7	1.159	1.219	1.281	1.344	1.409	1.475	1.543	1.612	9.7
9.8	1.171	1.232	1.294	1.358	1.423	1.490	1.559	1.629	9.8
9.9	1.183	1.244	1.307	1.372	1.438	1.505	1.575	1.645	9.9
10.0	1.195	1.257	1.320	1.385	1.452	1.521	1.590	1.662	10.0

VOLUME IN CUBIC METRES

Length in Metres	Mid-diameter in centimetres								Length in Metres
	47	48	49	50	51	52	53	54	
1.0	0.173	0.181	0.189	0.196	0.204	0.212	0.221	0.229	1.0
1.1	0.191	0.199	0.207	0.216	0.225	0.234	0.243	0.252	1.1
1.2	0.208	0.217	0.226	0.236	0.245	0.255	0.265	0.275	1.2
1.3	0.226	0.235	0.245	0.255	0.266	0.276	0.287	0.298	1.3
1.4	0.243	0.253	0.264	0.275	0.286	0.297	0.309	0.321	1.4
1.5	0.260	0.271	0.283	0.295	0.306	0.319	0.331	0.344	1.5
1.6	0.278	0.290	0.302	0.314	0.327	0.340	0.353	0.366	1.6
1.7	0.295	0.308	0.321	0.334	0.347	0.361	0.375	0.389	1.7
1.8	0.312	0.326	0.339	0.353	0.368	0.382	0.397	0.412	1.8
1.9	0.330	0.344	0.358	0.373	0.388	0.404	0.419	0.435	1.9
2.0	0.347	0.362	0.377	0.393	0.409	0.425	0.441	0.458	2.0
2.1	0.364	0.380	0.396	0.412	0.429	0.446	0.463	0.481	2.1
2.2	0.382	0.398	0.415	0.432	0.449	0.467	0.485	0.504	2.2
2.3	0.399	0.416	0.434	0.452	0.470	0.488	0.507	0.527	2.3
2.4	0.416	0.434	0.453	0.471	0.490	0.510	0.529	0.550	2.4
2.5	0.434	0.452	0.471	0.491	0.511	0.531	0.552	0.573	2.5
2.6	0.451	0.470	0.490	0.511	0.531	0.552	0.574	0.595	2.6
2.7	0.468	0.489	0.509	0.530	0.552	0.573	0.596	0.618	2.7
2.8	0.486	0.507	0.528	0.550	0.572	0.595	0.618	0.641	2.8
2.9	0.503	0.525	0.547	0.569	0.592	0.616	0.640	0.664	2.9
3.0	0.520	0.543	0.566	0.589	0.613	0.637	0.662	0.687	3.0
3.1	0.538	0.561	0.585	0.609	0.633	0.658	0.684	0.710	3.1
3.2	0.555	0.579	0.603	0.628	0.654	0.680	0.706	0.733	3.2
3.3	0.573	0.597	0.622	0.648	0.674	0.701	0.728	0.756	3.3
3.4	0.590	0.615	0.641	0.668	0.695	0.722	0.750	0.779	3.4
3.5	0.607	0.633	0.660	0.687	0.715	0.743	0.772	0.802	3.5
3.6	0.625	0.651	0.679	0.707	0.735	0.765	0.794	0.824	3.6
3.7	0.642	0.670	0.698	0.726	0.756	0.786	0.816	0.847	3.7
3.8	0.659	0.688	0.717	0.746	0.776	0.807	0.838	0.870	3.8
3.9	0.677	0.706	0.735	0.766	0.797	0.828	0.860	0.893	3.9
4.0	0.694	0.724	0.754	0.785	0.817	0.849	0.882	0.916	4.0
4.1	0.711	0.742	0.773	0.805	0.838	0.871	0.905	0.939	4.1
4.2	0.729	0.760	0.792	0.825	0.858	0.892	0.927	0.962	4.2
4.3	0.746	0.778	0.811	0.844	0.878	0.913	0.949	0.985	4.3
4.4	0.763	0.796	0.830	0.864	0.899	0.934	0.971	1.008	4.4
4.5	0.781	0.814	0.849	0.884	0.919	0.956	0.993	1.031	4.5
4.6	0.798	0.832	0.867	0.903	0.940	0.977	1.015	1.054	4.6
4.7	0.815	0.850	0.886	0.923	0.960	0.998	1.037	1.076	4.7
4.8	0.833	0.869	0.905	0.942	0.981	1.019	1.059	1.099	4.8
4.9	0.850	0.887	0.924	0.962	1.001	1.041	1.081	1.122	4.9
5.0	0.867	0.905	0.943	0.982	1.021	1.062	1.103	1.145	5.0
5.1	0.885	0.923	0.962	1.001	1.042	1.083	1.125	1.168	5.1
5.2	0.902	0.941	0.981	1.021	1.062	1.104	1.147	1.191	5.2
5.3	0.920	0.959	0.999	1.041	1.083	1.126	1.169	1.214	5.3
5.4	0.937	0.977	1.018	1.060	1.103	1.147	1.191	1.237	5.4

Length in Metres	VOLUME IN CUBIC METRES								Length in Metres
	Mid-diameter in centimetres								
	47	48	49	50	51	52	53	54	
5.5	0.954	0.995	1.037	1.080	1.124	1.168	1.213	1.260	5.5
5.6	0.972	1.013	1.056	1.100	1.144	1.189	1.235	1.283	5.6
5.7	0.989	1.031	1.075	1.119	1.164	1.211	1.258	1.305	5.7
5.8	1.006	1.050	1.094	1.139	1.185	1.232	1.280	1.328	5.8
5.9	1.024	1.068	1.113	1.158	1.205	1.253	1.302	1.351	5.9
6.0	1.041	1.086	1.131	1.178	1.226	1.274	1.324	1.374	6.0
6.1	1.058	1.104	1.150	1.198	1.246	1.295	1.346	1.397	6.1
6.2	1.076	1.122	1.169	1.217	1.267	1.317	1.368	1.420	6.2
6.3	1.093	1.140	1.188	1.237	1.287	1.338	1.390	1.443	6.3
6.4	1.110	1.158	1.207	1.257	1.307	1.359	1.412	1.466	6.4
6.5	1.128	1.176	1.226	1.276	1.328	1.380	1.434	1.489	6.5
6.6	1.145	1.194	1.245	1.296	1.348	1.402	1.456	1.512	6.6
6.7	1.162	1.212	1.263	1.316	1.369	1.423	1.478	1.534	6.7
6.8	1.180	1.230	1.282	1.335	1.389	1.444	1.500	1.557	6.8
6.9	1.197	1.249	1.301	1.355	1.410	1.465	1.522	1.580	6.9
7.0	1.214	1.267	1.320	1.374	1.430	1.487	1.544	1.603	7.0
7.1	1.232	1.285	1.339	1.394	1.450	1.508	1.566	1.626	7.1
7.2	1.249	1.303	1.358	1.414	1.471	1.529	1.588	1.649	7.2
7.3	1.267	1.321	1.377	1.433	1.491	1.550	1.611	1.672	7.3
7.4	1.284	1.339	1.395	1.453	1.512	1.572	1.633	1.695	7.4
7.5	1.301	1.357	1.414	1.473	1.532	1.593	1.655	1.718	7.5
7.6	1.319	1.375	1.433	1.492	1.553	1.614	1.677	1.741	7.6
7.7	1.336	1.393	1.452	1.512	1.573	1.635	1.699	1.763	7.7
7.8	1.353	1.411	1.471	1.532	1.593	1.656	1.721	1.786	7.8
7.9	1.371	1.430	1.490	1.551	1.614	1.678	1.743	1.809	7.9
8.0	1.388	1.448	1.509	1.571	1.634	1.699	1.765	1.832	8.0
8.1	1.405	1.466	1.527	1.590	1.655	1.720	1.787	1.855	8.1
8.2	1.423	1.484	1.546	1.610	1.675	1.741	1.809	1.878	8.2
8.3	1.440	1.502	1.565	1.630	1.696	1.763	1.831	1.901	8.3
8.4	1.457	1.520	1.584	1.649	1.716	1.784	1.853	1.924	8.4
8.5	1.475	1.538	1.603	1.669	1.736	1.805	1.875	1.947	8.5
8.6	1.492	1.556	1.622	1.689	1.757	1.826	1.897	1.970	8.6
8.7	1.509	1.574	1.641	1.708	1.777	1.848	1.919	1.992	8.7
8.8	1.527	1.592	1.659	1.728	1.798	1.869	1.941	2.015	8.8
8.9	1.544	1.611	1.678	1.748	1.818	1.890	1.964	2.038	8.9
9.0	1.561	1.629	1.697	1.767	1.839	1.911	1.986	2.061	9.0
9.1	1.579	1.647	1.716	1.787	1.859	1.933	2.008	2.084	9.1
9.2	1.596	1.665	1.735	1.806	1.879	1.954	2.030	2.107	9.2
9.3	1.613	1.683	1.754	1.826	1.900	1.975	2.052	2.130	9.3
9.4	1.631	1.701	1.773	1.846	1.920	1.996	2.074	2.153	9.4
9.5	1.648	1.719	1.791	1.865	1.941	2.018	2.096	2.176	9.5
9.6	1.666	1.737	1.810	1.885	1.961	2.039	2.118	2.199	9.6
9.7	1.683	1.755	1.829	1.905	1.982	2.060	2.140	2.222	9.7
9.8	1.700	1.773	1.848	1.924	2.002	2.081	2.162	2.244	9.8
9.9	1.718	1.791	1.867	1.944	2.022	2.102	2.184	2.267	9.9
10.0	1.735	1.810	1.886	1.963	2.043	2.124	2.206	2.290	10.0

VOLUME IN CUBIC METRES

Length in Metres	Mid-diameter in centimetres								Length in Metres
	55	56	57	58	59	60	61	62	
1.0	0.238	0.246	0.255	0.264	0.273	0.283	0.292	0.302	1.0
1.1	0.261	0.271	0.281	0.291	0.301	0.311	0.321	0.332	1.1
1.2	0.285	0.296	0.306	0.317	0.328	0.339	0.351	0.362	1.2
1.3	0.309	0.320	0.332	0.343	0.355	0.368	0.380	0.392	1.3
1.4	0.333	0.345	0.357	0.370	0.383	0.396	0.409	0.423	1.4
1.5	0.356	0.369	0.383	0.396	0.410	0.424	0.438	0.453	1.5
1.6	0.380	0.394	0.408	0.423	0.437	0.452	0.468	0.483	1.6
1.7	0.404	0.419	0.434	0.449	0.465	0.481	0.497	0.513	1.7
1.8	0.428	0.443	0.459	0.476	0.492	0.509	0.526	0.543	1.8
1.9	0.451	0.468	0.485	0.502	0.519	0.537	0.555	0.574	1.9
2.0	0.475	0.493	0.510	0.528	0.547	0.565	0.584	0.604	2.0
2.1	0.499	0.517	0.536	0.555	0.574	0.594	0.614	0.634	2.1
2.2	0.523	0.542	0.561	0.581	0.601	0.622	0.643	0.664	2.2
2.3	0.546	0.566	0.587	0.608	0.629	0.650	0.672	0.694	2.3
2.4	0.570	0.591	0.612	0.634	0.656	0.679	0.701	0.725	2.4
2.5	0.594	0.616	0.638	0.661	0.683	0.707	0.731	0.755	2.5
2.6	0.618	0.640	0.663	0.687	0.711	0.735	0.760	0.785	2.6
2.7	0.641	0.665	0.689	0.713	0.738	0.763	0.789	0.815	2.7
2.8	0.665	0.690	0.714	0.740	0.766	0.792	0.818	0.845	2.8
2.9	0.689	0.714	0.740	0.766	0.793	0.820	0.848	0.876	2.9
3.0	0.713	0.739	0.766	0.793	0.820	0.848	0.877	0.906	3.0
3.1	0.737	0.764	0.791	0.819	0.848	0.877	0.906	0.936	3.1
3.2	0.760	0.788	0.817	0.845	0.875	0.905	0.935	0.966	3.2
3.3	0.784	0.813	0.842	0.872	0.902	0.933	0.964	0.996	3.3
3.4	0.808	0.837	0.868	0.898	0.930	0.961	0.994	1.026	3.4
3.5	0.832	0.862	0.893	0.925	0.957	0.990	1.023	1.057	3.5
3.6	0.855	0.887	0.919	0.951	0.984	1.018	1.052	1.087	3.6
3.7	0.879	0.911	0.944	0.978	1.012	1.046	1.081	1.117	3.7
3.8	0.903	0.936	0.970	1.004	1.039	1.074	1.111	1.147	3.8
3.9	0.927	0.961	0.995	1.030	1.066	1.103	1.140	1.177	3.9
4.0	0.950	0.985	1.021	1.057	1.094	1.131	1.169	1.208	4.0
4.1	0.974	1.010	1.046	1.083	1.121	1.159	1.198	1.238	4.1
4.2	0.998	1.034	1.072	1.110	1.148	1.188	1.227	1.268	4.2
4.3	1.022	1.059	1.097	1.136	1.176	1.216	1.257	1.298	4.3
4.4	1.045	1.084	1.123	1.163	1.203	1.244	1.286	1.328	4.4
4.5	1.069	1.108	1.148	1.189	1.230	1.272	1.315	1.359	4.5
4.6	1.093	1.133	1.174	1.215	1.258	1.301	1.344	1.389	4.6
4.7	1.117	1.158	1.199	1.242	1.285	1.329	1.374	1.419	4.7
4.8	1.140	1.182	1.225	1.268	1.312	1.357	1.403	1.449	4.8
4.9	1.164	1.207	1.250	1.295	1.340	1.385	1.432	1.479	4.9
5.0	1.188	1.232	1.276	1.321	1.367	1.414	1.461	1.510	5.0
5.1	1.212	1.256	1.301	1.347	1.394	1.442	1.490	1.540	5.1
5.2	1.235	1.281	1.327	1.374	1.422	1.470	1.520	1.570	5.2
5.3	1.259	1.305	1.352	1.400	1.449	1.499	1.549	1.600	5.3
5.4	1.283	1.330	1.378	1.427	1.476	1.527	1.578	1.630	5.4

Length in Metres	VOLUME IN CUBIC METRES								Length in Metres
	Mid-diameter in centimetres								
	55	56	57	58	59	60	61	62	
5.5	1.307	1.355	1.403	1.453	1.504	1.555	1.607	1.660	5.5
5.6	1.330	1.379	1.429	1.480	1.531	1.583	1.637	1.691	5.6
5.7	1.354	1.404	1.455	1.506	1.558	1.612	1.666	1.721	5.7
5.8	1.378	1.429	1.480	1.532	1.586	1.640	1.695	1.751	5.8
5.9	1.402	1.453	1.506	1.559	1.613	1.668	1.724	1.781	5.9
6.0	1.425	1.478	1.531	1.585	1.640	1.696	1.753	1.811	6.0
6.1	1.449	1.502	1.557	1.612	1.668	1.725	1.783	1.842	6.1
6.2	1.473	1.527	1.582	1.638	1.695	1.753	1.812	1.872	6.2
6.3	1.497	1.552	1.608	1.665	1.722	1.781	1.841	1.902	6.3
6.4	1.521	1.576	1.633	1.691	1.750	1.810	1.870	1.932	6.4
6.5	1.544	1.601	1.659	1.717	1.777	1.838	1.900	1.962	6.5
6.6	1.568	1.626	1.684	1.744	1.804	1.866	1.929	1.993	6.6
6.7	1.592	1.650	1.710	1.770	1.832	1.894	1.958	2.023	6.7
6.8	1.616	1.675	1.735	1.797	1.859	1.923	1.987	2.053	6.8
6.9	1.639	1.699	1.761	1.823	1.886	1.951	2.016	2.083	6.9
7.0	1.663	1.724	1.786	1.849	1.914	1.979	2.046	2.113	7.0
7.1	1.687	1.749	1.812	1.876	1.941	2.007	2.075	2.144	7.1
7.2	1.711	1.773	1.837	1.902	1.968	2.036	2.104	2.174	7.2
7.3	1.734	1.798	1.863	1.929	1.996	2.064	2.133	2.204	7.3
7.4	1.758	1.823	1.888	1.955	2.023	2.092	2.163	2.234	7.4
7.5	1.782	1.847	1.914	1.982	2.050	2.121	2.192	2.264	7.5
7.6	1.806	1.872	1.939	2.008	2.078	2.149	2.221	2.294	7.6
7.7	1.829	1.897	1.965	2.034	2.105	2.177	2.250	2.325	7.7
7.8	1.853	1.921	1.990	2.061	2.132	2.205	2.280	2.355	7.8
7.9	1.877	1.946	2.016	2.087	2.160	2.234	2.309	2.385	7.9
8.0	1.901	1.970	2.041	2.114	2.187	2.262	2.338	2.415	8.0
8.1	1.924	1.995	2.067	2.140	2.215	2.290	2.367	2.445	8.1
8.2	1.948	2.020	2.092	2.167	2.242	2.318	2.396	2.476	8.2
8.3	1.972	2.044	2.118	2.193	2.269	2.347	2.426	2.506	8.3
8.4	1.996	2.069	2.143	2.219	2.297	2.375	2.455	2.536	8.4
8.5	2.019	2.094	2.169	2.246	2.324	2.403	2.484	2.566	8.5
8.6	2.043	2.118	2.195	2.272	2.351	2.432	2.513	2.596	8.6
8.7	2.067	2.143	2.220	2.299	2.379	2.460	2.543	2.627	8.7
8.8	2.091	2.167	2.246	2.325	2.406	2.488	2.572	2.657	8.8
8.9	2.114	2.192	2.271	2.351	2.433	2.516	2.601	2.687	8.9
9.0	2.138	2.217	2.297	2.378	2.461	2.545	2.630	2.717	9.0
9.1	2.162	2.241	2.322	2.404	2.488	2.573	2.659	2.747	9.1
9.2	2.186	2.266	2.348	2.431	2.515	2.601	2.689	2.778	9.2
9.3	2.210	2.291	2.373	2.457	2.543	2.630	2.718	2.808	9.3
9.4	2.233	2.315	2.399	2.484	2.570	2.658	2.747	2.838	9.4
9.5	2.257	2.340	2.424	2.510	2.597	2.686	2.776	2.868	9.5
9.6	2.281	2.364	2.450	2.536	2.625	2.714	2.806	2.898	9.6
9.7	2.305	2.389	2.475	2.563	2.652	2.743	2.835	2.928	9.7
9.8	2.328	2.414	2.501	2.589	2.679	2.771	2.864	2.959	9.8
9.9	2.352	2.438	2.526	2.616	2.707	2.799	2.893	2.989	9.9
10.0	2.376	2.463	2.552	2.642	2.734	2.827	2.922	3.019	10.0

VOLUME IN CUBIC METRES

Length in Metres	Mid-diameter in centimetres								Length in Metres
	63	64	65	66	67	68	69	70	
1.0	0.312	0.322	0.332	0.342	0.353	0.363	0.374	0.385	1.0
1.1	0.343	0.354	0.365	0.376	0.388	0.399	0.411	0.423	1.1
1.2	0.374	0.386	0.398	0.411	0.423	0.436	0.449	0.462	1.2
1.3	0.405	0.418	0.431	0.445	0.458	0.472	0.486	0.500	1.3
1.4	0.436	0.450	0.465	0.479	0.494	0.508	0.523	0.539	1.4
1.5	0.468	0.483	0.498	0.513	0.529	0.545	0.561	0.577	1.5
1.6	0.499	0.515	0.531	0.547	0.564	0.581	0.598	0.616	1.6
1.7	0.530	0.547	0.564	0.582	0.599	0.617	0.636	0.654	1.7
1.8	0.561	0.579	0.597	0.616	0.635	0.654	0.673	0.693	1.8
1.9	0.592	0.611	0.630	0.650	0.670	0.690	0.710	0.731	1.9
2.0	0.623	0.643	0.664	0.684	0.705	0.726	0.748	0.770	2.0
2.1	0.655	0.676	0.697	0.718	0.740	0.763	0.785	0.808	2.1
2.2	0.686	0.708	0.730	0.753	0.776	0.799	0.823	0.847	2.2
2.3	0.717	0.740	0.763	0.787	0.811	0.835	0.860	0.885	2.3
2.4	0.748	0.772	0.796	0.821	0.846	0.872	0.897	0.924	2.4
2.5	0.779	0.804	0.830	0.855	0.881	0.908	0.935	0.962	2.5
2.6	0.810	0.836	0.863	0.890	0.917	0.944	0.972	1.001	2.6
2.7	0.842	0.869	0.896	0.924	0.952	0.981	1.010	1.039	2.7
2.8	0.873	0.901	0.929	0.958	0.987	1.017	1.047	1.078	2.8
2.9	0.904	0.933	0.962	0.992	1.022	1.053	1.084	1.116	2.9
3.0	0.935	0.965	0.995	1.026	1.058	1.090	1.122	1.155	3.0
3.1	0.966	0.997	1.029	1.061	1.093	1.126	1.159	1.193	3.1
3.2	0.998	1.029	1.062	1.095	1.128	1.162	1.197	1.232	3.2
3.3	1.029	1.062	1.095	1.129	1.163	1.198	1.234	1.270	3.3
3.4	1.060	1.094	1.128	1.163	1.199	1.235	1.271	1.308	3.4
3.5	1.091	1.126	1.161	1.197	1.234	1.271	1.309	1.347	3.5
3.6	1.122	1.158	1.195	1.232	1.269	1.307	1.346	1.385	3.6
3.7	1.153	1.190	1.228	1.266	1.304	1.344	1.384	1.424	3.7
3.8	1.185	1.222	1.261	1.300	1.340	1.380	1.421	1.462	3.8
3.9	1.216	1.255	1.294	1.334	1.375	1.416	1.458	1.501	3.9
4.0	1.247	1.287	1.327	1.368	1.410	1.453	1.496	1.539	4.0
4.1	1.278	1.319	1.361	1.403	1.446	1.489	1.533	1.578	4.1
4.2	1.309	1.351	1.394	1.437	1.481	1.525	1.570	1.616	4.2
4.3	1.340	1.383	1.427	1.471	1.516	1.562	1.608	1.655	4.3
4.4	1.372	1.415	1.460	1.505	1.551	1.598	1.645	1.693	4.4
4.5	1.403	1.448	1.493	1.540	1.587	1.634	1.683	1.732	4.5
4.6	1.434	1.480	1.526	1.574	1.622	1.671	1.720	1.770	4.6
4.7	1.465	1.512	1.560	1.608	1.657	1.707	1.757	1.809	4.7
4.8	1.496	1.544	1.593	1.642	1.692	1.743	1.795	1.847	4.8
4.9	1.527	1.576	1.626	1.676	1.728	1.780	1.832	1.886	4.9
5.0	1.559	1.608	1.659	1.711	1.763	1.816	1.870	1.924	5.0
5.1	1.590	1.641	1.692	1.745	1.798	1.852	1.907	1.963	5.1
5.2	1.621	1.673	1.726	1.779	1.833	1.888	1.944	2.001	5.2
5.3	1.652	1.705	1.759	1.813	1.869	1.925	1.982	2.040	5.3
5.4	1.683	1.737	1.792	1.847	1.904	1.961	2.019	2.078	5.4

Length in Metres	VOLUME IN CUBIC METRES								Length in Metres
	Mid-diameter in centimetres								
	63	64	65	66	67	68	69	70	
5.5	1.714	1.769	1.825	1.882	1.939	1.997	2.057	2.117	5.5
5.6	1.746	1.802	1.858	1.916	1.974	2.034	2.094	2.155	5.6
5.7	1.777	1.834	1.891	1.950	2.010	2.070	2.131	2.194	5.7
5.8	1.808	1.866	1.925	1.984	2.045	2.106	2.169	2.232	5.8
5.9	1.839	1.898	1.958	2.019	2.080	2.143	2.206	2.271	5.9
6.0	1.870	1.930	1.991	2.053	2.115	2.179	2.244	2.309	6.0
6.1	1.902	1.962	2.024	2.087	2.151	2.215	2.281	2.348	6.1
6.2	1.933	1.995	2.057	2.121	2.186	2.252	2.318	2.386	6.2
6.3	1.964	2.027	2.091	2.155	2.221	2.288	2.356	2.425	6.3
6.4	1.995	2.059	2.124	2.190	2.256	2.324	2.393	2.463	6.4
6.5	2.026	2.091	2.157	2.224	2.292	2.361	2.431	2.501	6.5
6.6	2.057	2.123	2.190	2.258	2.327	2.397	2.468	2.540	6.6
6.7	2.089	2.155	2.223	2.292	2.362	2.433	2.505	2.578	6.7
6.8	2.120	2.188	2.256	2.326	2.397	2.470	2.543	2.617	6.8
6.9	2.151	2.220	2.290	2.361	2.433	2.506	2.580	2.655	6.9
7.0	2.182	2.252	2.323	2.395	2.468	2.542	2.617	2.694	7.0
7.1	2.213	2.284	2.356	2.429	2.503	2.578	2.655	2.732	7.1
7.2	2.244	2.316	2.389	2.463	2.538	2.615	2.692	2.771	7.2
7.3	2.276	2.348	2.422	2.497	2.574	2.651	2.730	2.809	7.3
7.4	2.307	2.381	2.456	2.532	2.609	2.687	2.767	2.848	7.4
7.5	2.338	2.413	2.489	2.566	2.644	2.724	2.804	2.886	7.5
7.6	2.369	2.445	2.522	2.600	2.679	2.760	2.842	2.925	7.6
7.7	2.400	2.477	2.555	2.634	2.715	2.796	2.879	2.963	7.7
7.8	2.431	2.509	2.588	2.669	2.750	2.833	2.917	3.002	7.8
7.9	2.463	2.541	2.621	2.703	2.785	2.869	2.954	3.040	7.9
8.0	2.494	2.574	2.655	2.737	2.821	2.905	2.991	3.079	8.0
8.1	2.525	2.606	2.688	2.771	2.856	2.942	3.029	3.117	8.1
8.2	2.556	2.638	2.721	2.805	2.891	2.978	3.066	3.156	8.2
8.3	2.587	2.670	2.754	2.840	2.926	3.014	3.104	3.194	8.3
8.4	2.618	2.702	2.787	2.874	2.962	3.051	3.141	3.233	8.4
8.5	2.650	2.734	2.821	2.908	2.997	3.087	3.178	3.271	8.5
8.6	2.681	2.767	2.854	2.942	3.032	3.123	3.216	3.310	8.6
8.7	2.712	2.799	2.887	2.976	3.067	3.160	3.253	3.348	8.7
8.8	2.743	2.831	2.920	3.011	3.103	3.196	3.291	3.387	8.8
8.9	2.774	2.863	2.953	3.045	3.138	3.232	3.328	3.425	8.9
9.0	2.806	2.895	2.986	3.079	3.173	3.269	3.365	3.464	9.0
9.1	2.837	2.927	3.020	3.113	3.208	3.305	3.403	3.502	9.1
9.2	2.868	2.960	3.053	3.147	3.244	3.341	3.440	3.541	9.2
9.3	2.899	2.992	3.086	3.182	3.279	3.377	3.478	3.579	9.3
9.4	2.930	3.024	3.119	3.216	3.314	3.414	3.515	3.618	9.4
9.5	2.961	3.056	3.152	3.250	3.349	3.450	3.552	3.656	9.5
9.6	2.993	3.088	3.186	3.284	3.385	3.486	3.590	3.695	9.6
9.7	3.024	3.120	3.219	3.319	3.420	3.523	3.627	3.733	9.7
9.8	3.055	3.153	3.252	3.353	3.455	3.559	3.664	3.771	9.8
9.9	3.086	3.185	3.285	3.387	3.490	3.595	3.702	3.810	9.9
10.0	3.117	3.217	3.318	3.421	3.526	3.632	3.739	3.848	10.0

VOLUME IN CUBIC METRES

Length in Metres	Mid-diameter in centimetres								Length in Metres
	71	72	73	74	75	76	77	78	
1.0	0.396	0.407	0.419	0.430	0.442	0.454	0.466	0.478	1.0
1.1	0.436	0.448	0.460	0.473	0.486	0.499	0.512	0.526	1.1
1.2	0.475	0.489	0.502	0.516	0.530	0.544	0.559	0.573	1.2
1.3	0.515	0.529	0.544	0.559	0.574	0.590	0.605	0.621	1.3
1.4	0.554	0.570	0.586	0.602	0.619	0.635	0.652	0.669	1.4
1.5	0.594	0.611	0.628	0.645	0.663	0.680	0.698	0.717	1.5
1.6	0.633	0.651	0.670	0.688	0.707	0.726	0.745	0.765	1.6
1.7	0.673	0.692	0.712	0.731	0.751	0.771	0.792	0.812	1.7
1.8	0.713	0.733	0.753	0.774	0.795	0.817	0.838	0.860	1.8
1.9	0.752	0.774	0.795	0.817	0.839	0.862	0.885	0.908	1.9
2.0	0.792	0.814	0.837	0.860	0.884	0.907	0.931	0.956	2.0
2.1	0.831	0.855	0.879	0.903	0.928	0.953	0.978	1.003	2.1
2.2	0.871	0.896	0.921	0.946	0.972	0.998	1.024	1.051	2.2
2.3	0.911	0.936	0.963	0.989	1.016	1.043	1.071	1.099	2.3
2.4	0.950	0.977	1.004	1.032	1.060	1.089	1.118	1.147	2.4
2.5	0.990	1.018	1.046	1.075	1.104	1.134	1.164	1.195	2.5
2.6	1.029	1.059	1.088	1.118	1.149	1.179	1.211	1.242	2.6
2.7	1.069	1.099	1.130	1.161	1.193	1.225	1.257	1.290	2.7
2.8	1.109	1.140	1.172	1.204	1.237	1.270	1.304	1.338	2.8
2.9	1.148	1.181	1.214	1.247	1.281	1.316	1.350	1.386	2.9
3.0	1.188	1.221	1.256	1.290	1.325	1.361	1.397	1.434	3.0
3.1	1.227	1.262	1.297	1.333	1.370	1.406	1.444	1.481	3.1
3.2	1.267	1.303	1.339	1.376	1.414	1.452	1.490	1.529	3.2
3.3	1.307	1.344	1.381	1.419	1.458	1.497	1.537	1.577	3.3
3.4	1.346	1.384	1.423	1.462	1.502	1.542	1.583	1.625	3.4
3.5	1.386	1.425	1.465	1.505	1.546	1.588	1.630	1.672	3.5
3.6	1.425	1.466	1.507	1.548	1.590	1.633	1.676	1.720	3.6
3.7	1.465	1.506	1.549	1.591	1.635	1.678	1.723	1.768	3.7
3.8	1.504	1.547	1.590	1.634	1.679	1.724	1.770	1.816	3.8
3.9	1.544	1.588	1.632	1.677	1.723	1.769	1.816	1.864	3.9
4.0	1.584	1.629	1.674	1.720	1.767	1.815	1.863	1.911	4.0
4.1	1.623	1.669	1.716	1.763	1.811	1.860	1.909	1.959	4.1
4.2	1.663	1.710	1.758	1.806	1.856	1.905	1.956	2.007	4.2
4.3	1.702	1.751	1.800	1.849	1.900	1.951	2.002	2.055	4.3
4.4	1.742	1.791	1.842	1.892	1.944	1.996	2.049	2.102	4.4
4.5	1.782	1.832	1.883	1.935	1.988	2.041	2.095	2.150	4.5
4.6	1.821	1.873	1.925	1.978	2.032	2.087	2.142	2.198	4.6
4.7	1.861	1.914	1.967	2.021	2.076	2.132	2.189	2.246	4.7
4.8	1.900	1.954	2.009	2.064	2.121	2.177	2.235	2.294	4.8
4.9	1.940	1.995	2.051	2.107	2.165	2.223	2.282	2.341	4.9
5.0	1.980	2.036	2.093	2.150	2.209	2.268	2.328	2.389	5.0
5.1	2.019	2.076	2.135	2.193	2.253	2.314	2.375	2.437	5.1
5.2	2.059	2.117	2.176	2.236	2.297	2.359	2.421	2.485	5.2
5.3	2.098	2.158	2.218	2.279	2.341	2.404	2.468	2.533	5.3
5.4	2.138	2.199	2.260	2.322	2.386	2.450	2.515	2.580	5.4

VOLUME IN CUBIC METRES

Length in Metres	Mid-diameter in centimetres								Length in Metres
	71	72	73	74	75	76	77	78	
5.5	2.178	2.239	2.302	2.365	2.430	2.495	2.561	2.628	5.5
5.6	2.217	2.280	2.344	2.408	2.474	2.540	2.608	2.676	5.6
5.7	2.257	2.321	2.386	2.451	2.518	2.586	2.654	2.724	5.7
5.8	2.296	2.361	2.428	2.494	2.562	2.631	2.701	2.771	5.8
5.9	2.336	2.402	2.469	2.537	2.607	2.677	2.747	2.819	5.9
6.0	2.376	2.443	2.511	2.581	2.651	2.722	2.794	2.867	6.0
6.1	2.415	2.484	2.553	2.624	2.695	2.767	2.841	2.915	6.1
6.2	2.455	2.524	2.595	2.667	2.739	2.813	2.887	2.963	6.2
6.3	2.494	2.565	2.637	2.710	2.783	2.858	2.934	3.010	6.3
6.4	2.534	2.606	2.679	2.753	2.827	2.903	2.980	3.058	6.4
6.5	2.573	2.646	2.720	2.796	2.872	2.949	3.027	3.106	6.5
6.6	2.613	2.687	2.762	2.839	2.916	2.994	3.073	3.154	6.6
6.7	2.653	2.728	2.804	2.882	2.960	3.039	3.120	3.201	6.7
6.8	2.692	2.769	2.846	2.925	3.004	3.085	3.167	3.249	6.8
6.9	2.732	2.809	2.888	2.968	3.048	3.130	3.213	3.297	6.9
7.0	2.771	2.850	2.930	3.011	3.093	3.176	3.260	3.345	7.0
7.1	2.811	2.891	2.972	3.054	3.137	3.221	3.306	3.393	7.1
7.2	2.851	2.931	3.013	3.097	3.181	3.266	3.353	3.440	7.2
7.3	2.890	2.972	3.055	3.140	3.225	3.312	3.399	3.488	7.3
7.4	2.930	3.013	3.097	3.183	3.269	3.357	3.446	3.536	7.4
7.5	2.969	3.054	3.139	3.226	3.313	3.402	3.492	3.584	7.5
7.6	3.009	3.094	3.181	3.269	3.358	3.448	3.539	3.632	7.6
7.7	3.049	3.135	3.223	3.312	3.402	3.493	3.586	3.679	7.7
7.8	3.088	3.176	3.265	3.355	3.446	3.538	3.632	3.727	7.8
7.9	3.128	3.216	3.306	3.398	3.490	3.584	3.679	3.775	7.9
8.0	3.167	3.257	3.348	3.441	3.534	3.629	3.725	3.823	8.0
8.1	3.207	3.298	3.390	3.484	3.578	3.675	3.772	3.870	8.1
8.2	3.247	3.339	3.432	3.527	3.623	3.720	3.818	3.918	8.2
8.3	3.286	3.379	3.474	3.570	3.667	3.765	3.865	3.966	8.3
8.4	3.326	3.420	3.516	3.613	3.711	3.811	3.912	4.014	8.4
8.5	3.365	3.461	3.558	3.656	3.755	3.856	3.958	4.062	8.5
8.6	3.405	3.501	3.599	3.699	3.799	3.901	4.005	4.109	8.6
8.7	3.444	3.542	3.641	3.742	3.844	3.947	4.051	4.157	8.7
8.8	3.484	3.583	3.683	3.785	3.888	3.992	4.098	4.205	8.8
8.9	3.524	3.624	3.725	3.828	3.932	4.037	4.144	4.253	8.9
9.0	3.563	3.664	3.767	3.871	3.976	4.083	4.191	4.301	9.0
9.1	3.603	3.705	3.809	3.914	4.020	4.128	4.238	4.348	9.1
9.2	3.642	3.746	3.851	3.957	4.064	4.174	4.284	4.396	9.2
9.3	3.682	3.786	3.892	4.000	4.109	4.219	4.331	4.444	9.3
9.4	3.722	3.827	3.934	4.043	4.153	4.264	4.377	4.492	9.4
9.5	3.761	3.868	3.976	4.086	4.197	4.310	4.424	4.539	9.5
9.6	3.801	3.909	4.018	4.129	4.241	4.355	4.470	4.587	9.6
9.7	3.840	3.949	4.060	4.172	4.285	4.400	4.517	4.635	9.7
9.8	3.880	3.990	4.102	4.215	4.330	4.446	4.563	4.683	9.8
9.9	3.920	4.031	4.144	4.258	4.374	4.491	4.610	4.731	9.9
10.0	3.959	4.071	4.185	4.301	4.418	4.536	4.657	4.778	10.0

Length in Metres	VOLUME IN CUBIC METRES								Length in Metres
	Mid-diameter in centimetres								
	79	80	81	82	83	84	85	86	
1.0	0.490	0.503	0.515	0.528	0.541	0.554	0.567	0.581	1.0
1.1	0.539	0.553	0.567	0.581	0.595	0.610	0.624	0.639	1.1
1.2	0.588	0.603	0.618	0.634	0.649	0.665	0.681	0.697	1.2
1.3	0.637	0.653	0.670	0.687	0.703	0.720	0.738	0.755	1.3
1.4	0.686	0.704	0.721	0.739	0.757	0.776	0.794	0.813	1.4
1.5	0.735	0.754	0.773	0.792	0.812	0.831	0.851	0.871	1.5
1.6	0.784	0.804	0.824	0.845	0.866	0.887	0.908	0.929	1.6
1.7	0.833	0.855	0.876	0.898	0.920	0.942	0.965	0.987	1.7
1.8	0.882	0.905	0.928	0.951	0.974	0.998	1.021	1.046	1.8
1.9	0.931	0.955	0.979	1.003	1.028	1.053	1.078	1.104	1.9
2.0	0.980	1.005	1.031	1.056	1.082	1.108	1.135	1.162	2.0
2.1	1.029	1.056	1.082	1.109	1.136	1.164	1.192	1.220	2.1
2.2	1.078	1.106	1.134	1.162	1.190	1.219	1.248	1.278	2.2
2.3	1.127	1.156	1.185	1.215	1.244	1.275	1.305	1.336	2.3
2.4	1.176	1.206	1.237	1.267	1.299	1.330	1.362	1.394	2.4
2.5	1.225	1.257	1.288	1.320	1.353	1.385	1.419	1.452	2.5
2.6	1.274	1.307	1.340	1.373	1.407	1.441	1.475	1.510	2.6
2.7	1.323	1.357	1.391	1.426	1.461	1.496	1.532	1.568	2.7
2.8	1.372	1.407	1.443	1.479	1.515	1.552	1.589	1.626	2.8
2.9	1.421	1.458	1.494	1.531	1.569	1.607	1.646	1.685	2.9
3.0	1.470	1.508	1.546	1.584	1.623	1.663	1.702	1.743	3.0
3.1	1.520	1.558	1.597	1.637	1.677	1.718	1.759	1.801	3.1
3.2	1.569	1.608	1.649	1.690	1.731	1.773	1.816	1.859	3.2
3.3	1.618	1.659	1.700	1.743	1.785	1.829	1.873	1.917	3.3
3.4	1.667	1.709	1.752	1.796	1.840	1.884	1.929	1.975	3.4
3.5	1.716	1.759	1.804	1.848	1.894	1.940	1.986	2.033	3.5
3.6	1.765	1.810	1.855	1.901	1.948	1.995	2.043	2.091	3.6
3.7	1.814	1.860	1.907	1.954	2.002	2.050	2.100	2.149	3.7
3.8	1.863	1.910	1.958	2.007	2.056	2.106	2.156	2.207	3.8
3.9	1.912	1.960	2.010	2.060	2.110	2.161	2.213	2.265	3.9
4.0	1.961	2.011	2.061	2.112	2.164	2.217	2.270	2.324	4.0
4.1	2.010	2.061	2.113	2.165	2.218	2.272	2.327	2.382	4.1
4.2	2.059	2.111	2.164	2.218	2.272	2.328	2.383	2.440	4.2
4.3	2.108	2.161	2.216	2.271	2.327	2.383	2.440	2.498	4.3
4.4	2.157	2.212	2.267	2.324	2.381	2.438	2.497	2.556	4.4
4.5	2.206	2.262	2.319	2.376	2.435	2.494	2.554	2.614	4.5
4.6	2.255	2.312	2.370	2.429	2.489	2.549	2.610	2.672	4.6
4.7	2.304	2.362	2.422	2.482	2.543	2.605	2.667	2.730	4.7
4.8	2.353	2.413	2.473	2.535	2.597	2.660	2.724	2.788	4.8
4.9	2.402	2.463	2.525	2.588	2.651	2.715	2.781	2.846	4.9
5.0	2.451	2.513	2.576	2.641	2.705	2.771	2.837	2.904	5.0
5.1	2.500	2.564	2.628	2.693	2.759	2.826	2.894	2.962	5.1
5.2	2.549	2.614	2.680	2.746	2.814	2.882	2.951	3.021	5.2
5.3	2.598	2.664	2.731	2.799	2.868	2.937	3.007	3.079	5.3
5.4	2.647	2.714	2.783	2.852	2.922	2.993	3.064	3.137	5.4

VOLUME IN CUBIC METRES

Length in Metres	Mid-diameter in centimetres								Length in Metres
	79	80	81	82	83	84	85	86	
5.5	2.696	2.765	2.834	2.905	2.976	3.048	3.121	3.195	5.5
5.6	2.745	2.815	2.886	2.957	3.030	3.103	3.178	3.253	5.6
5.7	2.794	2.865	2.937	3.010	3.084	3.159	3.234	3.311	5.7
5.8	2.843	2.915	2.989	3.063	3.138	3.214	3.291	3.369	5.8
5.9	2.892	2.966	3.040	3.116	3.192	3.270	3.348	3.427	5.9
6.0	2.941	3.016	3.092	3.169	3.246	3.325	3.405	3.485	6.0
6.1	2.990	3.066	3.143	3.221	3.300	3.380	3.461	3.543	6.1
6.2	3.039	3.116	3.195	3.274	3.355	3.436	3.518	3.601	6.2
6.3	3.088	3.167	3.246	3.327	3.409	3.491	3.575	3.660	6.3
6.4	3.137	3.217	3.298	3.380	3.463	3.547	3.632	3.718	6.4
6.5	3.186	3.267	3.349	3.433	3.517	3.602	3.688	3.776	6.5
6.6	3.235	3.318	3.401	3.485	3.571	3.658	3.745	3.834	6.6
6.7	3.284	3.368	3.453	3.538	3.625	3.713	3.802	3.892	6.7
6.8	3.333	3.418	3.504	3.591	3.679	3.768	3.859	3.950	6.8
6.9	3.382	3.468	3.556	3.644	3.733	3.824	3.915	4.008	6.9
7.0	3.431	3.519	3.607	3.697	3.787	3.879	3.972	4.066	7.0
7.1	3.480	3.569	3.659	3.750	3.842	3.935	4.029	4.124	7.1
7.2	3.529	3.619	3.710	3.802	3.896	3.990	4.086	4.182	7.2
7.3	3.578	3.669	3.762	3.855	3.950	4.045	4.142	4.240	7.3
7.4	3.627	3.720	3.813	3.908	4.004	4.101	4.199	4.299	7.4
7.5	3.676	3.770	3.865	3.961	4.058	4.156	4.256	4.357	7.5
7.6	3.725	3.820	3.916	4.014	4.112	4.212	4.313	4.415	7.6
7.7	3.774	3.870	3.968	4.066	4.166	4.267	4.369	4.473	7.7
7.8	3.823	3.921	4.019	4.119	4.220	4.323	4.426	4.531	7.8
7.9	3.872	3.971	4.071	4.172	4.274	4.378	4.483	4.589	7.9
8.0	3.921	4.021	4.122	4.225	4.328	4.433	4.540	4.647	8.0
8.1	3.970	4.071	4.174	4.278	4.383	4.489	4.596	4.705	8.1
8.2	4.019	4.122	4.225	4.330	4.437	4.544	4.653	4.763	8.2
8.3	4.068	4.172	4.277	4.383	4.491	4.600	4.710	4.821	8.3
8.4	4.117	4.222	4.329	4.436	4.545	4.655	4.767	4.879	8.4
8.5	4.166	4.273	4.380	4.489	4.599	4.710	4.823	4.937	8.5
8.6	4.215	4.323	4.432	4.542	4.653	4.766	4.880	4.996	8.6
8.7	4.264	4.373	4.483	4.594	4.707	4.821	4.937	5.054	8.7
8.8	4.313	4.423	4.535	4.647	4.761	4.877	4.994	5.112	8.8
8.9	4.362	4.474	4.586	4.700	4.815	4.932	5.050	5.170	8.9
9.0	4.411	4.524	4.638	4.753	4.870	4.988	5.107	5.228	9.0
9.1	4.461	4.574	4.689	4.806	4.924	5.043	5.164	5.286	9.1
9.2	4.510	4.624	4.741	4.859	4.978	5.098	5.221	5.344	9.2
9.3	4.559	4.675	4.792	4.911	5.032	5.154	5.277	5.402	9.3
9.4	4.608	4.725	4.844	4.964	5.086	5.209	5.334	5.460	9.4
9.5	4.657	4.775	4.895	5.017	5.140	5.265	5.391	5.518	9.5
9.6	4.706	4.825	4.947	5.070	5.194	5.320	5.448	5.576	9.6
9.7	4.755	4.876	4.998	5.123	5.248	5.376	5.504	5.635	9.7
9.8	4.804	4.926	5.050	5.175	5.302	5.431	5.561	5.693	9.8
9.9	4.853	4.976	5.101	5.228	5.356	5.486	5.618	5.751	9.9
10.0	4.902	5.027	5.153	5.281	5.411	5.542	5.674	5.809	10.0

VOLUME IN CUBIC METRES

Length in Metres	Mid-diameter in centimetres								Length in Metres
	87	88	89	90	91	92	93	94	
1.0	0.594	0.608	0.622	0.636	0.650	0.665	0.679	0.694	1.0
1.1	0.654	0.669	0.684	0.700	0.715	0.731	0.747	0.763	1.1
1.2	0.713	0.730	0.747	0.763	0.780	0.798	0.815	0.833	1.2
1.3	0.773	0.791	0.809	0.827	0.846	0.864	0.883	0.902	1.3
1.4	0.832	0.851	0.871	0.891	0.911	0.931	0.951	0.972	1.4
1.5	0.892	0.912	0.933	0.954	0.976	0.997	1.019	1.041	1.5
1.6	0.951	0.973	0.995	1.018	1.041	1.064	1.087	1.110	1.6
1.7	1.011	1.034	1.058	1.081	1.106	1.130	1.155	1.180	1.7
1.8	1.070	1.095	1.120	1.145	1.171	1.197	1.223	1.249	1.8
1.9	1.129	1.156	1.182	1.209	1.236	1.263	1.291	1.319	1.9
2.0	1.189	1.216	1.244	1.272	1.301	1.330	1.359	1.388	2.0
2.1	1.248	1.277	1.306	1.336	1.366	1.396	1.427	1.457	2.1
2.2	1.308	1.338	1.369	1.400	1.431	1.462	1.494	1.527	2.2
2.3	1.367	1.399	1.431	1.463	1.496	1.529	1.562	1.596	2.3
2.4	1.427	1.460	1.493	1.527	1.561	1.595	1.630	1.666	2.4
2.5	1.486	1.521	1.555	1.590	1.626	1.662	1.698	1.735	2.5
2.6	1.546	1.581	1.617	1.654	1.691	1.728	1.766	1.804	2.6
2.7	1.605	1.642	1.680	1.718	1.756	1.795	1.834	1.874	2.7
2.8	1.665	1.703	1.742	1.781	1.821	1.861	1.902	1.943	2.8
2.9	1.724	1.764	1.804	1.845	1.886	1.928	1.970	2.013	2.9
3.0	1.783	1.825	1.866	1.909	1.951	1.994	2.038	2.082	3.0
3.1	1.843	1.885	1.929	1.972	2.016	2.061	2.106	2.151	3.1
3.2	1.902	1.946	1.991	2.036	2.081	2.127	2.174	2.221	3.2
3.3	1.962	2.007	2.053	2.099	2.146	2.194	2.242	2.290	3.3
3.4	2.021	2.068	2.115	2.163	2.211	2.260	2.310	2.360	3.4
3.5	2.081	2.129	2.177	2.227	2.276	2.327	2.378	2.429	3.5
3.6	2.140	2.190	2.240	2.290	2.341	2.393	2.445	2.498	3.6
3.7	2.200	2.250	2.302	2.354	2.406	2.460	2.513	2.568	3.7
3.8	2.259	2.311	2.364	2.417	2.471	2.526	2.581	2.637	3.8
3.9	2.318	2.372	2.426	2.481	2.537	2.593	2.649	2.707	3.9
4.0	2.378	2.433	2.488	2.545	2.602	2.659	2.717	2.776	4.0
4.1	2.437	2.494	2.551	2.608	2.667	2.726	2.785	2.845	4.1
4.2	2.497	2.554	2.613	2.672	2.732	2.792	2.853	2.915	4.2
4.3	2.556	2.615	2.675	2.736	2.797	2.858	2.921	2.984	4.3
4.4	2.616	2.676	2.737	2.799	2.862	2.925	2.989	3.053	4.4
4.5	2.675	2.737	2.800	2.863	2.927	2.991	3.057	3.123	4.5
4.6	2.735	2.798	2.862	2.926	2.992	3.058	3.125	3.192	4.6
4.7	2.794	2.859	2.924	2.990	3.057	3.124	3.193	3.262	4.7
4.8	2.853	2.919	2.986	3.054	3.122	3.191	3.261	3.331	4.8
4.9	2.913	2.980	3.048	3.117	3.187	3.257	3.329	3.400	4.9
5.0	2.972	3.041	3.111	3.181	3.252	3.324	3.396	3.470	5.0
5.1	3.032	3.102	3.173	3.244	3.317	3.390	3.464	3.539	5.1
5.2	3.091	3.163	3.235	3.308	3.382	3.457	3.532	3.609	5.2
5.3	3.151	3.224	3.297	3.372	3.447	3.523	3.600	3.678	5.3
5.4	3.210	3.284	3.359	3.435	3.512	3.590	3.668	3.747	5.4

VOLUME IN CUBIC METRES

Length in Metres	Mid-diameter in centimetres								Length in Metres
	87	88	89	90	91	92	93	94	
5.5	3.270	3.345	3.422	3.499	3.577	3.656	3.736	3.817	5.5
5.6	3.329	3.406	3.484	3.563	3.642	3.723	3.804	3.886	5.6
5.7	3.388	3.467	3.546	3.626	3.707	3.789	3.872	3.956	5.7
5.8	3.448	3.528	3.608	3.690	3.772	3.856	3.940	4.025	5.8
5.9	3.507	3.588	3.670	3.753	3.837	3.922	4.008	4.094	5.9
6.0	3.567	3.649	3.733	3.817	3.902	3.989	4.076	4.164	6.0
6.1	3.626	3.710	3.795	3.881	3.967	4.055	4.144	4.233	6.1
6.2	3.686	3.771	3.857	3.944	4.032	4.122	4.212	4.303	6.2
6.3	3.745	3.832	3.919	4.008	4.097	4.188	4.280	4.372	6.3
6.4	3.805	3.893	3.982	4.071	4.162	4.254	4.347	4.441	6.4
6.5	3.864	3.953	4.044	4.135	4.228	4.321	4.415	4.511	6.5
6.6	3.923	4.014	4.106	4.199	4.293	4.387	4.483	4.580	6.6
6.7	3.983	4.075	4.168	4.262	4.358	4.454	4.551	4.650	6.7
6.8	4.042	4.136	4.230	4.326	4.423	4.520	4.619	4.719	6.8
6.9	4.102	4.197	4.293	4.390	4.488	4.587	4.687	4.788	6.9
7.0	4.161	4.257	4.355	4.453	4.553	4.653	4.755	4.858	7.0
7.1	4.221	4.318	4.417	4.517	4.618	4.720	4.823	4.927	7.1
7.2	4.280	4.379	4.479	4.580	4.683	4.786	4.891	4.997	7.2
7.3	4.340	4.440	4.541	4.644	4.748	4.853	4.959	5.066	7.3
7.4	4.399	4.501	4.604	4.708	4.813	4.919	5.027	5.135	7.4
7.5	4.459	4.562	4.666	4.771	4.878	4.986	5.095	5.205	7.5
7.6	4.518	4.622	4.728	4.835	4.943	5.052	5.163	5.274	7.6
7.7	4.577	4.683	4.790	4.899	5.008	5.119	5.231	5.344	7.7
7.8	4.637	4.744	4.852	4.962	5.073	5.185	5.298	5.413	7.8
7.9	4.696	4.805	4.915	5.026	5.138	5.252	5.366	5.482	7.9
8.0	4.756	4.866	4.977	5.089	5.203	5.318	5.434	5.552	8.0
8.1	4.815	4.927	5.039	5.153	5.268	5.385	5.502	5.621	8.1
8.2	4.875	4.987	5.101	5.217	5.333	5.451	5.570	5.691	8.2
8.3	4.934	5.048	5.164	5.280	5.398	5.518	5.638	5.760	8.3
8.4	4.994	5.109	5.226	5.344	5.463	5.584	5.706	5.829	8.4
8.5	5.053	5.170	5.288	5.407	5.528	5.650	5.774	5.899	8.5
8.6	5.112	5.231	5.350	5.471	5.593	5.717	5.842	5.968	8.6
8.7	5.172	5.291	5.412	5.535	5.658	5.783	5.910	6.038	8.7
8.8	5.231	5.352	5.475	5.598	5.723	5.850	5.978	6.107	8.8
8.9	5.291	5.413	5.537	5.662	5.788	5.916	6.046	6.176	8.9
9.0	5.350	5.474	5.599	5.726	5.853	5.983	6.114	6.246	9.0
9.1	5.410	5.535	5.661	5.789	5.919	6.049	6.182	6.315	9.1
9.2	5.469	5.596	5.723	5.853	5.984	6.116	6.249	6.385	9.2
9.3	5.529	5.656	5.786	5.916	6.049	6.182	6.317	6.454	9.3
9.4	5.588	5.717	5.848	5.980	6.114	6.249	6.385	6.523	9.4
9.5	5.647	5.778	5.910	6.044	6.179	6.315	6.453	6.593	9.5
9.6	5.707	5.839	5.972	6.107	6.244	6.382	6.521	6.662	9.6
9.7	5.766	5.900	6.034	6.171	6.309	6.448	6.589	6.732	9.7
9.8	5.826	5.960	6.097	6.234	6.374	6.515	6.657	6.801	9.8
9.9	5.885	6.021	6.159	6.298	6.439	6.581	6.725	6.870	9.9
10.0	5.945	6.082	6.221	6.362	6.504	6.648	6.793	6.940	10.0

VOLUME IN CUBIC METRES

Length in Metres	Mid-diameter in centimetres								Length in Metres
	95	96	97	98	99	100	101	102	
1.0	0.709	0.724	0.739	0.754	0.770	0.785	0.801	0.817	1.0
1.1	0.780	0.796	0.813	0.830	0.847	0.864	0.881	0.899	1.1
1.2	0.851	0.869	0.887	0.905	0.924	0.942	0.961	0.981	1.2
1.3	0.921	0.941	0.961	0.981	1.001	1.021	1.042	1.062	1.3
1.4	0.992	1.013	1.035	1.056	1.078	1.100	1.122	1.144	1.4
1.5	1.063	1.086	1.108	1.131	1.155	1.178	1.202	1.226	1.5
1.6	1.134	1.158	1.182	1.207	1.232	1.257	1.282	1.307	1.6
1.7	1.205	1.230	1.256	1.282	1.309	1.335	1.362	1.389	1.7
1.8	1.276	1.303	1.330	1.358	1.386	1.414	1.442	1.471	1.8
1.9	1.347	1.375	1.404	1.433	1.463	1.492	1.522	1.553	1.9
2.0	1.418	1.448	1.478	1.509	1.540	1.571	1.602	1.634	2.0
2.1	1.489	1.520	1.552	1.584	1.617	1.649	1.682	1.716	2.1
2.2	1.559	1.592	1.626	1.659	1.693	1.728	1.763	1.798	2.2
2.3	1.630	1.665	1.700	1.735	1.770	1.806	1.843	1.879	2.3
2.4	1.701	1.737	1.774	1.810	1.847	1.885	1.923	1.961	2.4
2.5	1.772	1.810	1.847	1.886	1.924	1.963	2.003	2.043	2.5
2.6	1.843	1.882	1.921	1.961	2.001	2.042	2.083	2.125	2.6
2.7	1.914	1.954	1.995	2.037	2.078	2.121	2.163	2.206	2.7
2.8	1.985	2.027	2.069	2.112	2.155	2.199	2.243	2.288	2.8
2.9	2.056	2.099	2.143	2.187	2.232	2.278	2.323	2.370	2.9
3.0	2.126	2.171	2.217	2.263	2.309	2.356	2.404	2.451	3.0
3.1	2.197	2.244	2.291	2.338	2.386	2.435	2.484	2.533	3.1
3.2	2.268	2.316	2.365	2.414	2.463	2.513	2.564	2.615	3.2
3.3	2.339	2.389	2.439	2.489	2.540	2.592	2.644	2.697	3.3
3.4	2.410	2.461	2.513	2.565	2.617	2.670	2.724	2.778	3.4
3.5	2.481	2.533	2.586	2.640	2.694	2.749	2.804	2.860	3.5
3.6	2.552	2.606	2.660	2.715	2.771	2.827	2.884	2.942	3.6
3.7	2.623	2.678	2.734	2.791	2.848	2.906	2.964	3.023	3.7
3.8	2.694	2.751	2.808	2.866	2.925	2.985	3.044	3.105	3.8
3.9	2.764	2.823	2.882	2.942	3.002	3.063	3.125	3.187	3.9
4.0	2.835	2.895	2.956	3.017	3.079	3.142	3.205	3.269	4.0
4.1	2.906	2.968	3.030	3.093	3.156	3.220	3.285	3.350	4.1
4.2	2.977	3.040	3.104	3.168	3.233	3.299	3.365	3.432	4.2
4.3	3.048	3.112	3.178	3.243	3.310	3.377	3.445	3.514	4.3
4.4	3.119	3.185	3.252	3.319	3.387	3.456	3.525	3.595	4.4
4.5	3.190	3.257	3.325	3.394	3.464	3.534	3.605	3.677	4.5
4.6	3.261	3.330	3.399	3.470	3.541	3.613	3.685	3.759	4.6
4.7	3.331	3.402	3.473	3.545	3.618	3.691	3.766	3.840	4.7
4.8	3.402	3.474	3.547	3.621	3.695	3.770	3.846	3.922	4.8
4.9	3.473	3.547	3.621	3.696	3.772	3.848	3.926	4.004	4.9
5.0	3.544	3.619	3.695	3.771	3.849	3.927	4.006	4.086	5.0
5.1	3.615	3.691	3.769	3.847	3.926	4.006	4.086	4.167	5.1
5.2	3.686	3.764	3.843	3.922	4.003	4.084	4.166	4.249	5.2
5.3	3.757	3.836	3.917	3.998	4.080	4.163	4.246	4.331	5.3
5.4	3.828	3.909	3.990	4.073	4.157	4.241	4.326	4.412	5.4

VOLUME IN CUBIC METRES

Length in Metres	Mid-diameter in centimetres								Length in Metres
	95	96	97	98	99	100	101	102	
5.5	3.899	3.981	4.064	4.149	4.234	4.320	4.407	4.494	5.5
5.6	3.969	4.053	4.138	4.224	4.311	4.398	4.487	4.576	5.6
5.7	4.040	4.126	4.212	4.299	4.388	4.477	4.567	4.658	5.7
5.8	4.111	4.198	4.286	4.375	4.465	4.555	4.647	4.739	5.8
5.9	4.182	4.271	4.360	4.450	4.542	4.634	4.727	4.821	5.9
6.0	4.253	4.343	4.434	4.526	4.619	4.712	4.807	4.903	6.0
6.1	4.324	4.415	4.508	4.601	4.696	4.791	4.887	4.984	6.1
6.2	4.395	4.488	4.582	4.677	4.773	4.869	4.967	5.066	6.2
6.3	4.466	4.560	4.656	4.752	4.850	4.948	5.047	5.148	6.3
6.4	4.536	4.632	4.729	4.827	4.927	5.027	5.128	5.230	6.4
6.5	4.607	4.705	4.803	4.903	5.003	5.105	5.208	5.311	6.5
6.6	4.678	4.777	4.877	4.978	5.080	5.184	5.288	5.393	6.6
6.7	4.749	4.850	4.951	5.054	5.157	5.262	5.368	5.475	6.7
6.8	4.820	4.922	5.025	5.129	5.234	5.341	5.448	5.556	6.8
6.9	4.891	4.994	5.099	5.205	5.311	5.419	5.528	5.638	6.9
7.0	4.962	5.067	5.173	5.280	5.388	5.498	5.608	5.720	7.0
7.1	5.033	5.139	5.247	5.355	5.465	5.576	5.688	5.802	7.1
7.2	5.104	5.212	5.321	5.431	5.542	5.655	5.769	5.883	7.2
7.3	5.174	5.284	5.395	5.506	5.619	5.733	5.849	5.965	7.3
7.4	5.245	5.356	5.468	5.582	5.696	5.812	5.929	6.047	7.4
7.5	5.316	5.429	5.542	5.657	5.773	5.890	6.009	6.128	7.5
7.6	5.387	5.501	5.616	5.733	5.850	5.969	6.089	6.210	7.6
7.7	5.458	5.573	5.690	5.808	5.927	6.048	6.169	6.292	7.7
7.8	5.529	5.646	5.764	5.884	6.004	6.126	6.249	6.374	7.8
7.9	5.600	5.718	5.838	5.959	6.081	6.205	6.329	6.455	7.9
8.0	5.671	5.791	5.912	6.034	6.158	6.283	6.409	6.537	8.0
8.1	5.741	5.863	5.986	6.110	6.235	6.362	6.490	6.619	8.1
8.2	5.812	5.935	6.060	6.185	6.312	6.440	6.570	6.700	8.2
8.3	5.883	6.008	6.134	6.261	6.389	6.519	6.650	6.782	8.3
8.4	5.954	6.080	6.207	6.336	6.466	6.597	6.730	6.864	8.4
8.5	6.025	6.152	6.281	6.412	6.543	6.676	6.810	6.946	8.5
8.6	6.096	6.225	6.355	6.487	6.620	6.754	6.890	7.027	8.6
8.7	6.167	6.297	6.429	6.562	6.697	6.833	6.970	7.109	8.7
8.8	6.238	6.370	6.503	6.638	6.774	6.911	7.050	7.191	8.8
8.9	6.309	6.442	6.577	6.713	6.851	6.990	7.131	7.272	8.9
9.0	6.379	6.514	6.651	6.789	6.928	7.069	7.211	7.354	9.0
9.1	6.450	6.587	6.725	6.864	7.005	7.147	7.291	7.436	9.1
9.2	6.521	6.659	6.799	6.940	7.082	7.226	7.371	7.518	9.2
9.3	6.592	6.732	6.873	7.015	7.159	7.304	7.451	7.599	9.3
9.4	6.663	6.804	6.946	7.090	7.236	7.383	7.531	7.681	9.4
9.5	6.734	6.876	7.020	7.166	7.313	7.461	7.611	7.763	9.5
9.6	6.805	6.949	7.094	7.241	7.390	7.540	7.691	7.844	9.6
9.7	6.876	7.021	7.168	7.317	7.467	7.618	7.771	7.926	9.7
9.8	6.946	7.093	7.242	7.392	7.544	7.697	7.852	8.008	9.8
9.9	7.017	7.166	7.316	7.468	7.621	7.775	7.932	8.090	9.9
10.0	7.088	7.238	7.390	7.543	7.698	7.854	8.012	8.171	10.0

VOLUME IN CUBIC METRES

Length in Metres	Mid-diameter in centimetres								Length in Metres
	103	104	105	106	107	108	109	110	
1.0	0.833	0.849	0.866	0.882	0.899	0.916	0.933	0.950	1.0
1.1	0.917	0.934	0.952	0.971	0.989	1.008	1.026	1.045	1.1
1.2	1.000	1.019	1.039	1.059	1.079	1.099	1.120	1.140	1.2
1.3	1.083	1.104	1.126	1.147	1.169	1.191	1.213	1.235	1.3
1.4	1.167	1.189	1.212	1.235	1.259	1.283	1.306	1.330	1.4
1.5	1.250	1.274	1.299	1.324	1.349	1.374	1.400	1.425	1.5
1.6	1.333	1.359	1.385	1.412	1.439	1.466	1.493	1.521	1.6
1.7	1.416	1.444	1.472	1.500	1.529	1.557	1.586	1.616	1.7
1.8	1.500	1.529	1.559	1.588	1.619	1.649	1.680	1.711	1.8
1.9	1.583	1.614	1.645	1.677	1.708	1.741	1.773	1.806	1.9
2.0	1.666	1.699	1.732	1.765	1.798	1.832	1.866	1.901	2.0
2.1	1.750	1.784	1.818	1.853	1.888	1.924	1.960	1.996	2.1
2.2	1.833	1.869	1.905	1.941	1.978	2.015	2.053	2.091	2.2
2.3	1.916	1.954	1.992	2.030	2.068	2.107	2.146	2.186	2.3
2.4	2.000	2.039	2.078	2.118	2.158	2.199	2.240	2.281	2.4
2.5	2.083	2.124	2.165	2.206	2.248	2.290	2.333	2.376	2.5
2.6	2.166	2.209	2.251	2.294	2.338	2.382	2.426	2.471	2.6
2.7	2.250	2.294	2.338	2.383	2.428	2.473	2.519	2.566	2.7
2.8	2.333	2.379	2.425	2.471	2.518	2.565	2.613	2.661	2.8
2.9	2.416	2.464	2.511	2.559	2.608	2.657	2.706	2.756	2.9
3.0	2.500	2.548	2.598	2.647	2.698	2.748	2.799	2.851	3.0
3.1	2.583	2.633	2.684	2.736	2.788	2.840	2.893	2.946	3.1
3.2	2.666	2.718	2.771	2.824	2.877	2.931	2.986	3.041	3.2
3.3	2.750	2.803	2.857	2.912	2.967	3.023	3.079	3.136	3.3
3.4	2.833	2.888	2.944	3.000	3.057	3.115	3.173	3.231	3.4
3.5	2.916	2.973	3.031	3.089	3.147	3.206	3.266	3.326	3.5
3.6	3.000	3.058	3.117	3.177	3.237	3.298	3.359	3.421	3.6
3.7	3.083	3.143	3.204	3.265	3.327	3.390	3.453	3.516	3.7
3.8	3.166	3.228	3.290	3.353	3.417	3.481	3.546	3.611	3.8
3.9	3.250	3.313	3.377	3.442	3.507	3.573	3.639	3.706	3.9
4.0	3.333	3.398	3.464	3.530	3.597	3.664	3.733	3.801	4.0
4.1	3.416	3.483	3.550	3.618	3.687	3.756	3.826	3.896	4.1
4.2	3.500	3.568	3.637	3.706	3.777	3.848	3.919	3.991	4.2
4.3	3.583	3.653	3.723	3.795	3.867	3.939	4.012	4.086	4.3
4.4	3.666	3.738	3.810	3.883	3.956	4.031	4.106	4.181	4.4
4.5	3.750	3.823	3.897	3.971	4.046	4.122	4.199	4.276	4.5
4.6	3.833	3.908	3.983	4.059	4.136	4.214	4.292	4.372	4.6
4.7	3.916	3.993	4.070	4.148	4.226	4.306	4.386	4.467	4.7
4.8	3.999	4.078	4.156	4.236	4.316	4.397	4.479	4.562	4.8
4.9	4.083	4.162	4.243	4.324	4.406	4.489	4.572	4.657	4.9
5.0	4.166	4.247	4.330	4.412	4.496	4.580	4.666	4.752	5.0
5.1	4.249	4.332	4.416	4.501	4.586	4.672	4.759	4.847	5.1
5.2	4.333	4.417	4.503	4.589	4.676	4.764	4.852	4.942	5.2
5.3	4.416	4.502	4.589	4.677	4.766	4.855	4.946	5.037	5.3
5.4	4.499	4.587	4.676	4.765	4.856	4.947	5.039	5.132	5.4

VOLUME IN CUBIC METRES

Length in Metres	Mid-diameter in centimetres								Length in Metres
	103	104	105	106	107	108	109	110	
5.5	4.583	4.672	4.762	4.854	4.946	5.038	5.132	5.227	5.5
5.6	4.666	4.757	4.849	4.942	5.036	5.130	5.226	5.322	5.6
5.7	4.749	4.842	4.936	5.030	5.125	5.222	5.319	5.417	5.7
5.8	4.833	4.927	5.022	5.118	5.215	5.313	5.412	5.512	5.8
5.9	4.916	5.012	5.109	5.207	5.305	5.405	5.505	5.607	5.9
6.0	4.999	5.097	5.195	5.295	5.395	5.497	5.599	5.702	6.0
6.1	5.083	5.182	5.282	5.383	5.485	5.588	5.692	5.797	6.1
6.2	5.166	5.267	5.369	5.471	5.575	5.680	5.785	5.892	6.2
6.3	5.249	5.352	5.455	5.560	5.665	5.771	5.879	5.987	6.3
6.4	5.333	5.437	5.542	5.648	5.755	5.863	5.972	6.082	6.4
6.5	5.416	5.522	5.628	5.736	5.845	5.955	6.065	6.177	6.5
6.6	5.499	5.607	5.715	5.824	5.935	6.046	6.159	6.272	6.6
6.7	5.583	5.692	5.802	5.913	6.025	6.138	6.252	6.367	6.7
6.8	5.666	5.777	5.888	6.001	6.115	6.229	6.345	6.462	6.8
6.9	5.749	5.861	5.975	6.089	6.204	6.321	6.439	6.557	6.9
7.0	5.833	5.946	6.061	6.177	6.294	6.413	6.532	6.652	7.0
7.1	5.916	6.031	6.148	6.266	6.384	6.504	6.625	6.747	7.1
7.2	5.999	6.116	6.234	6.354	6.474	6.596	6.719	6.842	7.2
7.3	6.083	6.201	6.321	6.442	6.564	6.687	6.812	6.937	7.3
7.4	6.166	6.286	6.408	6.530	6.654	6.779	6.905	7.032	7.4
7.5	6.249	6.371	6.494	6.619	6.744	6.871	6.998	7.127	7.5
7.6	6.333	6.456	6.581	6.707	6.834	6.962	7.092	7.223	7.6
7.7	6.416	6.541	6.667	6.795	6.924	7.054	7.185	7.318	7.7
7.8	6.499	6.626	6.754	6.883	7.014	7.145	7.278	7.413	7.8
7.9	6.583	6.711	6.841	6.972	7.104	7.237	7.372	7.508	7.9
8.0	6.666	6.796	6.927	7.060	7.194	7.329	7.465	7.603	8.0
8.1	6.749	6.881	7.014	7.148	7.284	7.420	7.558	7.698	8.1
8.2	6.832	6.966	7.100	7.236	7.373	7.512	7.652	7.793	8.2
8.3	6.916	7.051	7.187	7.325	7.463	7.604	7.745	7.888	8.3
8.4	6.999	7.136	7.274	7.413	7.553	7.695	7.838	7.983	8.4
8.5	7.082	7.221	7.360	7.501	7.643	7.787	7.932	8.078	8.5
8.6	7.166	7.306	7.447	7.589	7.733	7.878	8.025	8.173	8.6
8.7	7.249	7.391	7.533	7.678	7.823	7.970	8.118	8.268	8.7
8.8	7.332	7.475	7.620	7.766	7.913	8.062	8.212	8.363	8.8
8.9	7.416	7.560	7.707	7.854	8.003	8.153	8.305	8.458	8.9
9.0	7.499	7.645	7.793	7.942	8.093	8.245	8.398	8.553	9.0
9.1	7.582	7.730	7.880	8.030	8.183	8.336	8.491	8.648	9.1
9.2	7.666	7.815	7.966	8.119	8.273	8.428	8.585	8.743	9.2
9.3	7.749	7.900	8.053	8.207	8.363	8.520	8.678	8.838	9.3
9.4	7.832	7.985	8.139	8.295	8.452	8.611	8.771	8.933	9.4
9.5	7.916	8.070	8.226	8.383	8.542	8.703	8.865	9.028	9.5
9.6	7.999	8.155	8.313	8.472	8.632	8.794	8.958	9.123	9.6
9.7	8.082	8.240	8.399	8.560	8.722	8.886	9.051	9.218	9.7
9.8	8.166	8.325	8.486	8.648	8.812	8.978	9.145	9.313	9.8
9.9	8.249	8.410	8.572	8.736	8.902	9.069	9.238	9.408	9.9
10.0	8.332	8.495	8.659	8.825	8.992	9.161	9.331	9.503	10.0

Length in Metres	VOLUME IN CUBIC METRES								Length in Metres
	Mid-diameter in centimetres								
	111	112	113	114	115	116	117	118	
1.0	0.968	0.985	1.003	1.021	1.039	1.057	1.075	1.094	1.0
1.1	1.064	1.084	1.103	1.123	1.143	1.163	1.183	1.203	1.1
1.2	1.161	1.182	1.203	1.225	1.246	1.268	1.290	1.312	1.2
1.3	1.258	1.281	1.304	1.327	1.350	1.374	1.398	1.422	1.3
1.4	1.355	1.379	1.404	1.429	1.454	1.480	1.505	1.531	1.4
1.5	1.452	1.478	1.504	1.531	1.558	1.585	1.613	1.640	1.5
1.6	1.548	1.576	1.605	1.633	1.662	1.691	1.720	1.750	1.6
1.7	1.645	1.675	1.705	1.735	1.766	1.797	1.828	1.859	1.7
1.8	1.742	1.773	1.805	1.837	1.870	1.902	1.935	1.968	1.8
1.9	1.839	1.872	1.905	1.939	1.974	2.008	2.043	2.078	1.9
2.0	1.935	1.970	2.006	2.041	2.077	2.114	2.150	2.187	2.0
2.1	2.032	2.069	2.106	2.143	2.181	2.219	2.258	2.297	2.1
2.2	2.129	2.167	2.206	2.246	2.285	2.325	2.365	2.406	2.2
2.3	2.226	2.266	2.307	2.348	2.389	2.431	2.473	2.515	2.3
2.4	2.322	2.364	2.407	2.450	2.493	2.536	2.580	2.625	2.4
2.5	2.419	2.463	2.507	2.552	2.597	2.642	2.688	2.734	2.5
2.6	2.516	2.562	2.607	2.654	2.701	2.748	2.795	2.843	2.6
2.7	2.613	2.660	2.708	2.756	2.804	2.853	2.903	2.953	2.7
2.8	2.710	2.759	2.808	2.858	2.908	2.959	3.010	3.062	2.8
2.9	2.806	2.857	2.908	2.960	3.012	3.065	3.118	3.171	2.9
3.0	2.903	2.956	3.009	3.062	3.116	3.170	3.225	3.281	3.0
3.1	3.000	3.054	3.109	3.164	3.220	3.276	3.333	3.390	3.1
3.2	3.097	3.153	3.209	3.266	3.324	3.382	3.440	3.499	3.2
3.3	3.193	3.251	3.309	3.368	3.428	3.488	3.548	3.609	3.3
3.4	3.290	3.350	3.410	3.470	3.532	3.593	3.655	3.718	3.4
3.5	3.387	3.448	3.510	3.572	3.635	3.699	3.763	3.828	3.5
3.6	3.484	3.547	3.610	3.675	3.739	3.805	3.870	3.937	3.6
3.7	3.580	3.645	3.711	3.777	3.843	3.910	3.978	4.046	3.7
3.8	3.677	3.744	3.811	3.879	3.947	4.016	4.085	4.156	3.8
3.9	3.774	3.842	3.911	3.981	4.051	4.122	4.193	4.265	3.9
4.0	3.871	3.941	4.011	4.083	4.155	4.227	4.301	4.374	4.0
4.1	3.968	4.039	4.112	4.185	4.259	4.333	4.408	4.484	4.1
4.2	4.064	4.138	4.212	4.287	4.362	4.439	4.516	4.593	4.2
4.3	4.161	4.236	4.312	4.389	4.466	4.544	4.623	4.702	4.3
4.4	4.258	4.335	4.413	4.491	4.570	4.650	4.731	4.812	4.4
4.5	4.355	4.433	4.513	4.593	4.674	4.756	4.838	4.921	4.5
4.6	4.451	4.532	4.613	4.695	4.778	4.861	4.946	5.031	4.6
4.7	4.548	4.630	4.714	4.797	4.882	4.967	5.053	5.140	4.7
4.8	4.645	4.729	4.814	4.899	4.986	5.073	5.161	5.249	4.8
4.9	4.742	4.827	4.914	5.001	5.090	5.178	5.268	5.359	4.9
5.0	4.838	4.926	5.014	5.104	5.193	5.284	5.376	5.468	5.0
5.1	4.935	5.025	5.115	5.206	5.297	5.390	5.483	5.577	5.1
5.2	5.032	5.123	5.215	5.308	5.401	5.496	5.591	5.687	5.2
5.3	5.129	5.222	5.315	5.410	5.505	5.601	5.698	5.796	5.3
5.4	5.226	5.320	5.416	5.512	5.609	5.707	5.806	5.905	5.4

Length in Metres	VOLUME IN CUBIC METRES								Length in Metres
	Mid-diameter in centimetres								
	111	112	113	114	115	116	117	118	
5.5	5.322	5.419	5.516	5.614	5.713	5.813	5.913	6.015	5.5
5.6	5.419	5.517	5.616	5.716	5.817	5.918	6.021	6.124	5.6
5.7	5.516	5.616	5.716	5.818	5.921	6.024	6.128	6.233	5.7
5.8	5.613	5.714	5.817	5.920	6.024	6.130	6.236	6.343	5.8
5.9	5.709	5.813	5.917	6.022	6.128	6.235	6.343	6.452	5.9
6.0	5.806	5.911	6.017	6.124	6.232	6.341	6.451	6.562	6.0
6.1	5.903	6.010	6.118	6.226	6.336	6.447	6.558	6.671	6.1
6.2	6.000	6.108	6.218	6.328	6.440	6.552	6.666	6.780	6.2
6.3	6.096	6.207	6.318	6.430	6.544	6.658	6.773	6.890	6.3
6.4	6.193	6.305	6.418	6.532	6.648	6.764	6.881	6.999	6.4
6.5	6.290	6.404	6.519	6.635	6.751	6.869	6.988	7.108	6.5
6.6	6.387	6.502	6.619	6.737	6.855	6.975	7.096	7.218	6.6
6.7	6.484	6.601	6.719	6.839	6.959	7.081	7.203	7.327	6.7
6.8	6.580	6.699	6.820	6.941	7.063	7.186	7.311	7.436	6.8
6.9	6.677	6.798	6.920	7.043	7.167	7.292	7.418	7.546	6.9
7.0	6.774	6.896	7.020	7.145	7.271	7.398	7.526	7.655	7.0
7.1	6.871	6.995	7.120	7.247	7.375	7.503	7.633	7.764	7.1
7.2	6.967	7.093	7.221	7.349	7.479	7.609	7.741	7.874	7.2
7.3	7.064	7.192	7.321	7.451	7.582	7.715	7.848	7.983	7.3
7.4	7.161	7.290	7.421	7.553	7.686	7.821	7.956	8.093	7.4
7.5	7.258	7.389	7.522	7.655	7.790	7.926	8.063	8.202	7.5
7.6	7.354	7.488	7.622	7.757	7.894	8.032	8.171	8.311	7.6
7.7	7.451	7.586	7.722	7.859	7.998	8.138	8.279	8.421	7.7
7.8	7.548	7.685	7.822	7.961	8.102	8.243	8.386	8.530	7.8
7.9	7.645	7.783	7.923	8.064	8.206	8.349	8.494	8.639	7.9
8.0	7.742	7.882	8.023	8.166	8.310	8.455	8.601	8.749	8.0
8.1	7.838	7.980	8.123	8.268	8.413	8.560	8.709	8.858	8.1
8.2	7.935	8.079	8.224	8.370	8.517	8.666	8.816	8.967	8.2
8.3	8.032	8.177	8.324	8.472	8.621	8.772	8.924	9.077	8.3
8.4	8.129	8.276	8.424	8.574	8.725	8.877	9.031	9.186	8.4
8.5	8.225	8.374	8.524	8.676	8.829	8.983	9.139	9.295	8.5
8.6	8.322	8.473	8.625	8.778	8.933	9.089	9.246	9.405	8.6
8.7	8.419	8.571	8.725	8.880	9.037	9.194	9.354	9.514	8.7
8.8	8.516	8.670	8.825	8.982	9.140	9.300	9.461	9.624	8.8
8.9	8.612	8.768	8.926	9.084	9.244	9.406	9.569	9.733	8.9
9.0	8.709	8.867	9.026	9.186	9.348	9.511	9.676	9.842	9.0
9.1	8.806	8.965	9.126	9.288	9.452	9.617	9.784	9.952	9.1
9.2	8.903	9.064	9.226	9.390	9.556	9.723	9.891	10.06	9.2
9.3	8.999	9.162	9.327	9.493	9.660	9.829	9.999	10.17	9.3
9.4	9.096	9.261	9.427	9.595	9.764	9.934	10.11	10.28	9.4
9.5	9.193	9.359	9.527	9.697	9.868	10.04	10.21	10.39	9.5
9.6	9.290	9.458	9.628	9.799	9.971	10.15	10.32	10.50	9.6
9.7	9.387	9.556	9.728	9.901	10.08	10.25	10.43	10.61	9.7
9.8	9.483	9.655	9.828	10.00	10.18	10.36	10.54	10.72	9.8
9.9	9.580	9.754	9.928	10.10	10.28	10.46	10.64	10.83	9.9
10.0	9.677	9.852	10.03	10.21	10.39	10.57	10.75	10.94	10.0

VOLUME IN CUBIC METRES

Length in Metres	Mid-diameter in centimetres								Length in Metres
	119	120	121	122	123	124	125	126	
1.0	1.112	1.131	1.150	1.169	1.188	1.208	1.227	1.247	1.0
1.1	1.223	1.244	1.265	1.286	1.307	1.328	1.350	1.372	1.1
1.2	1.335	1.357	1.380	1.403	1.426	1.449	1.473	1.496	1.2
1.3	1.446	1.470	1.495	1.520	1.545	1.570	1.595	1.621	1.3
1.4	1.557	1.583	1.610	1.637	1.664	1.691	1.718	1.746	1.4
1.5	1.668	1.696	1.725	1.753	1.782	1.811	1.841	1.870	1.5
1.6	1.780	1.810	1.840	1.870	1.901	1.932	1.963	1.995	1.6
1.7	1.891	1.923	1.955	1.987	2.020	2.053	2.086	2.120	1.7
1.8	2.002	2.036	2.070	2.104	2.139	2.174	2.209	2.244	1.8
1.9	2.113	2.149	2.185	2.221	2.258	2.294	2.332	2.369	1.9
2.0	2.224	2.262	2.300	2.338	2.376	2.415	2.454	2.494	2.0
2.1	2.336	2.375	2.415	2.455	2.495	2.536	2.577	2.618	2.1
2.2	2.447	2.488	2.530	2.572	2.614	2.657	2.700	2.743	2.2
2.3	2.558	2.601	2.645	2.689	2.733	2.778	2.823	2.868	2.3
2.4	2.669	2.714	2.760	2.806	2.852	2.898	2.945	2.993	2.4
2.5	2.781	2.827	2.875	2.922	2.971	3.019	3.068	3.117	2.5
2.6	2.892	2.941	2.990	3.039	3.089	3.140	3.191	3.242	2.6
2.7	3.003	3.054	3.105	3.156	3.208	3.261	3.313	3.367	2.7
2.8	3.114	3.167	3.220	3.273	3.327	3.381	3.436	3.491	2.8
2.9	3.225	3.280	3.335	3.390	3.446	3.502	3.559	3.616	2.9
3.0	3.337	3.393	3.450	3.507	3.565	3.623	3.682	3.741	3.0
3.1	3.448	3.506	3.565	3.624	3.684	3.744	3.804	3.865	3.1
3.2	3.559	3.619	3.680	3.741	3.802	3.864	3.927	3.990	3.2
3.3	3.670	3.732	3.795	3.858	3.921	3.985	4.050	4.115	3.3
3.4	3.781	3.845	3.910	3.975	4.040	4.106	4.172	4.239	3.4
3.5	3.893	3.958	4.025	4.091	4.159	4.227	4.295	4.364	3.5
3.6	4.004	4.071	4.140	4.208	4.278	4.347	4.418	4.489	3.6
3.7	4.115	4.185	4.255	4.325	4.396	4.468	4.541	4.614	3.7
3.8	4.226	4.298	4.370	4.442	4.515	4.589	4.663	4.738	3.8
3.9	4.338	4.411	4.485	4.559	4.634	4.710	4.786	4.863	3.9
4.0	4.449	4.524	4.600	4.676	4.753	4.831	4.909	4.988	4.0
4.1	4.560	4.637	4.715	4.793	4.872	4.951	5.031	5.112	4.1
4.2	4.671	4.750	4.830	4.910	4.991	5.072	5.154	5.237	4.2
4.3	4.782	4.863	4.945	5.027	5.109	5.193	5.277	5.362	4.3
4.4	4.894	4.976	5.060	5.144	5.228	5.314	5.400	5.486	4.4
4.5	5.005	5.089	5.175	5.260	5.347	5.434	5.522	5.611	4.5
4.6	5.116	5.202	5.290	5.377	5.466	5.555	5.645	5.736	4.6
4.7	5.227	5.316	5.405	5.494	5.585	5.676	5.768	5.860	4.7
4.8	5.339	5.429	5.520	5.611	5.703	5.797	5.890	5.985	4.8
4.9	5.450	5.542	5.635	5.728	5.822	5.917	6.013	6.110	4.9
5.0	5.561	5.655	5.750	5.845	5.941	6.038	6.136	6.234	5.0
5.1	5.672	5.768	5.864	5.962	6.060	6.159	6.259	6.359	5.1
5.2	5.783	5.881	5.979	6.079	6.179	6.280	6.381	6.484	5.2
5.3	5.895	5.994	6.094	6.196	6.298	6.400	6.504	6.609	5.3
5.4	6.006	6.107	6.209	6.313	6.416	6.521	6.627	6.733	5.4

VOLUME IN CUBIC METRES

Length in Metres	Mid-diameter in centimetres								Length in Metres
	119	120	121	122	123	124	125	126	
5.5	6.117	6.220	6.324	6.429	6.535	6.642	6.750	6.858	5.5
5.6	6.228	6.333	6.439	6.546	6.654	6.763	6.872	6.983	5.6
5.7	6.340	6.447	6.554	6.663	6.773	6.883	6.995	7.107	5.7
5.8	6.451	6.560	6.669	6.780	6.892	7.004	7.118	7.232	5.8
5.9	6.562	6.673	6.784	6.897	7.011	7.125	7.240	7.357	5.9
6.0	6.673	6.786	6.899	7.014	7.129	7.246	7.363	7.481	6.0
6.1	6.784	6.899	7.014	7.131	7.248	7.367	7.486	7.606	6.1
6.2	6.896	7.012	7.129	7.248	7.367	7.487	7.609	7.731	6.2
6.3	7.007	7.125	7.244	7.365	7.486	7.608	7.731	7.855	6.3
6.4	7.118	7.238	7.359	7.482	7.605	7.729	7.854	7.980	6.4
6.5	7.229	7.351	7.474	7.598	7.723	7.850	7.977	8.105	6.5
6.6	7.341	7.464	7.589	7.715	7.842	7.970	8.099	8.230	6.6
6.7	7.452	7.578	7.704	7.832	7.961	8.091	8.222	8.354	6.7
6.8	7.563	7.691	7.819	7.949	8.080	8.212	8.345	8.479	6.8
6.9	7.674	7.804	7.934	8.066	8.199	8.333	8.468	8.604	6.9
7.0	7.785	7.917	8.049	8.183	8.318	8.453	8.590	8.728	7.0
7.1	7.897	8.030	8.164	8.300	8.436	8.574	8.713	8.853	7.1
7.2	8.008	8.143	8.279	8.417	8.555	8.695	8.836	8.978	7.2
7.3	8.119	8.256	8.394	8.534	8.674	8.816	8.958	9.102	7.3
7.4	8.230	8.369	8.509	8.650	8.793	8.936	9.081	9.227	7.4
7.5	8.342	8.482	8.624	8.767	8.912	9.057	9.204	9.352	7.5
7.6	8.453	8.595	8.739	8.884	9.031	9.178	9.327	9.476	7.6
7.7	8.564	8.708	8.854	9.001	9.149	9.299	9.449	9.601	7.7
7.8	8.675	8.822	8.969	9.118	9.268	9.419	9.572	9.726	7.8
7.9	8.786	8.935	9.084	9.235	9.387	9.540	9.695	9.850	7.9
8.0	8.898	9.048	9.199	9.352	9.506	9.661	9.817	9.975	8.0
8.1	9.009	9.161	9.314	9.469	9.625	9.782	9.940	10.10	8.1
8.2	9.120	9.274	9.429	9.586	9.743	9.903	10.06	10.22	8.2
8.3	9.231	9.387	9.544	9.703	9.862	10.02	10.19	10.35	8.3
8.4	9.342	9.500	9.659	9.819	9.981	10.14	10.31	10.47	8.4
8.5	9.454	9.613	9.774	9.936	10.10	10.26	10.43	10.60	8.5
8.6	9.565	9.726	9.889	10.05	10.22	10.39	10.55	10.72	8.6
8.7	9.676	9.839	10.00	10.17	10.34	10.51	10.68	10.85	8.7
8.8	9.787	9.953	10.12	10.29	10.46	10.63	10.80	10.97	8.8
8.9	9.899	10.07	10.23	10.40	10.58	10.75	10.92	11.10	8.9
9.0	10.01	10.18	10.35	10.52	10.69	10.87	11.04	11.22	9.0
9.1	10.12	10.29	10.46	10.64	10.81	10.99	11.17	11.35	9.1
9.2	10.23	10.40	10.58	10.75	10.93	11.11	11.29	11.47	9.2
9.3	10.34	10.52	10.69	10.87	11.05	11.23	11.41	11.60	9.3
9.4	10.45	10.63	10.81	10.99	11.17	11.35	11.54	11.72	9.4
9.5	10.57	10.74	10.92	11.11	11.29	11.47	11.66	11.85	9.5
9.6	10.68	10.86	11.04	11.22	11.41	11.59	11.78	11.97	9.6
9.7	10.79	10.97	11.15	11.34	11.53	11.71	11.90	12.09	9.7
9.8	10.90	11.08	11.27	11.46	11.64	11.83	12.03	12.22	9.8
9.9	11.01	11.20	11.38	11.57	11.76	11.96	12.15	12.34	9.9
10.0	11.12	11.31	11.50	11.69	11.88	12.08	12.27	12.47	10.0

	VOLUME IN CUBIC METRES								
Length in Metres	Mid-diameter in centimetres								Length in Metres
	127	128	129	130	131	132	133	134	
1.0	1.267	1.287	1.307	1.327	1.348	1.368	1.389	1.410	1.0
1.1	1.393	1.415	1.438	1.460	1.483	1.505	1.528	1.551	1.1
1.2	1.520	1.544	1.568	1.593	1.617	1.642	1.667	1.692	1.2
1.3	1.647	1.673	1.699	1.726	1.752	1.779	1.806	1.833	1.3
1.4	1.773	1.802	1.830	1.858	1.887	1.916	1.945	1.974	1.4
1.5	1.900	1.930	1.960	1.991	2.022	2.053	2.084	2.115	1.5
1.6	2.027	2.059	2.091	2.124	2.157	2.190	2.223	2.256	1.6
1.7	2.154	2.188	2.222	2.256	2.291	2.326	2.362	2.397	1.7
1.8	2.280	2.316	2.353	2.389	2.426	2.463	2.501	2.538	1.8
1.9	2.407	2.445	2.483	2.522	2.561	2.600	2.640	2.679	1.9
2.0	2.534	2.574	2.614	2.655	2.696	2.737	2.779	2.821	2.0
2.1	2.660	2.702	2.745	2.787	2.830	2.874	2.918	2.962	2.1
2.2	2.787	2.831	2.875	2.920	2.965	3.011	3.056	3.103	2.2
2.3	2.914	2.960	3.006	3.053	3.100	3.147	3.195	3.244	2.3
2.4	3.040	3.088	3.137	3.186	3.235	3.284	3.334	3.385	2.4
2.5	3.167	3.217	3.267	3.318	3.370	3.421	3.473	3.526	2.5
2.6	3.294	3.346	3.398	3.451	3.504	3.558	3.612	3.667	2.6
2.7	3.420	3.474	3.529	3.584	3.639	3.695	3.751	3.808	2.7
2.8	3.547	3.603	3.660	3.716	3.774	3.832	3.890	3.949	2.8
2.9	3.674	3.732	3.790	3.849	3.909	3.969	4.029	4.090	2.9
3.0	3.800	3.860	3.921	3.982	4.043	4.105	4.168	4.231	3.0
3.1	3.927	3.989	4.052	4.115	4.178	4.242	4.307	4.372	3.1
3.2	4.054	4.118	4.182	4.247	4.313	4.379	4.446	4.513	3.2
3.3	4.180	4.246	4.313	4.380	4.448	4.516	4.585	4.654	3.3
3.4	4.307	4.375	4.444	4.513	4.583	4.653	4.724	4.795	3.4
3.5	4.434	4.504	4.574	4.646	4.717	4.790	4.863	4.936	3.5
3.6	4.560	4.632	4.705	4.778	4.852	4.927	5.001	5.077	3.6
3.7	4.687	4.761	4.836	4.911	4.987	5.063	5.140	5.218	3.7
3.8	4.814	4.890	4.967	5.044	5.122	5.200	5.279	5.359	3.8
3.9	4.940	5.019	5.097	5.177	5.256	5.337	5.418	5.500	3.9
4.0	5.067	5.147	5.228	5.309	5.391	5.474	5.557	5.641	4.0
4.1	5.194	5.276	5.359	5.442	5.526	5.611	5.696	5.782	4.1
4.2	5.320	5.405	5.489	5.575	5.661	5.748	5.835	5.923	4.2
4.3	5.447	5.533	5.620	5.707	5.796	5.884	5.974	6.064	4.3
4.4	5.574	5.662	5.751	5.840	5.930	6.021	6.113	6.205	4.4
4.5	5.700	5.791	5.881	5.973	6.065	6.158	6.252	6.346	4.5
4.6	5.827	5.919	6.012	6.106	6.200	6.295	6.391	6.487	4.6
4.7	5.954	6.048	6.143	6.238	6.335	6.432	6.530	6.628	4.7
4.8	6.080	6.177	6.274	6.371	6.470	6.569	6.669	6.769	4.8
4.9	6.207	6.305	6.404	6.504	6.604	6.706	6.808	6.910	4.9
5.0	6.334	6.434	6.535	6.637	6.739	6.842	6.946	7.051	5.0
5.1	6.461	6.563	6.666	6.769	6.874	6.979	7.085	7.192	5.1
5.2	6.587	6.691	6.796	6.902	7.009	7.116	7.224	7.333	5.2
5.3	6.714	6.820	6.927	7.035	7.143	7.253	7.363	7.474	5.3
5.4	6.841	6.949	7.058	7.168	7.278	7.390	7.502	7.615	5.4

VOLUME IN CUBIC METRES

Length in Metres	Mid-diameter in centimetres								Length in Metres
	127	128	129	130	131	132	133	134	
5.5	6.967	7.077	7.188	7.300	7.413	7.527	7.641	7.756	5.5
5.6	7.094	7.206	7.319	7.433	7.548	7.663	7.780	7.897	5.6
5.7	7.221	7.335	7.450	7.566	7.683	7.800	7.919	8.038	5.7
5.8	7.347	7.463	7.580	7.698	7.817	7.937	8.058	8.180	5.8
5.9	7.474	7.592	7.711	7.831	7.952	8.074	8.197	8.321	5.9
6.0	7.601	7.721	7.842	7.964	8.087	8.211	8.336	8.462	6.0
6.1	7.727	7.849	7.973	8.097	8.222	8.348	8.475	8.603	6.1
6.2	7.854	7.978	8.103	8.229	8.356	8.485	8.614	8.744	6.2
6.3	7.981	8.107	8.234	8.362	8.491	8.621	8.753	8.885	6.3
6.4	8.107	8.235	8.365	8.495	8.626	8.758	8.891	9.026	6.4
6.5	8.234	8.364	8.495	8.628	8.761	8.895	9.030	9.167	6.5
6.6	8.361	8.493	8.626	8.760	8.896	9.032	9.169	9.308	6.6
6.7	8.487	8.622	8.757	8.893	9.030	9.169	9.308	9.449	6.7
6.8	8.614	8.750	8.887	9.026	9.165	9.306	9.447	9.590	6.8
6.9	8.741	8.879	9.018	9.159	9.300	9.442	9.586	9.731	6.9
7.0	8.867	9.008	9.149	9.291	9.435	9.579	9.725	9.872	7.0
7.1	8.994	9.136	9.280	9.424	9.570	9.716	9.864	10.01	7.1
7.2	9.121	9.265	9.410	9.557	9.704	9.853	10.00	10.15	7.2
7.3	9.247	9.394	9.541	9.689	9.839	9.990	10.14	10.29	7.3
7.4	9.374	9.522	9.672	9.822	9.974	10.13	10.28	10.44	7.4
7.5	9.501	9.651	9.802	9.955	10.11	10.26	10.42	10.58	7.5
7.6	9.627	9.780	9.933	10.09	10.24	10.40	10.56	10.72	7.6
7.7	9.754	9.908	10.06	10.22	10.38	10.54	10.70	10.86	7.7
7.8	9.881	10.04	10.19	10.35	10.51	10.67	10.84	11.00	7.8
7.9	10.01	10.17	10.33	10.49	10.65	10.81	10.98	11.14	7.9
8.0	10.13	10.29	10.46	10.62	10.78	10.95	11.11	11.28	8.0
8.1	10.26	10.42	10.59	10.75	10.92	11.08	11.25	11.42	8.1
8.2	10.39	10.55	10.72	10.88	11.05	11.22	11.39	11.56	8.2
8.3	10.51	10.68	10.85	11.02	11.19	11.36	11.53	11.71	8.3
8.4	10.64	10.81	10.98	11.15	11.32	11.50	11.67	11.85	8.4
8.5	10.77	10.94	11.11	11.28	11.46	11.63	11.81	11.99	8.5
8.6	10.89	11.07	11.24	11.41	11.59	11.77	11.95	12.13	8.6
8.7	11.02	11.20	11.37	11.55	11.73	11.91	12.09	12.27	8.7
8.8	11.15	11.32	11.50	11.68	11.86	12.04	12.23	12.41	8.8
8.9	11.27	11.45	11.63	11.81	12.00	12.18	12.36	12.55	8.9
9.0	11.40	11.58	11.76	11.95	12.13	12.32	12.50	12.69	9.0
9.1	11.53	11.71	11.89	12.08	12.27	12.45	12.64	12.83	9.1
9.2	11.65	11.84	12.02	12.21	12.40	12.59	12.78	12.97	9.2
9.3	11.78	11.97	12.15	12.34	12.53	12.73	12.92	13.12	9.3
9.4	11.91	12.10	12.29	12.48	12.67	12.86	13.06	13.26	9.4
9.5	12.03	12.22	12.42	12.61	12.80	13.00	13.20	13.40	9.5
9.6	12.16	12.35	12.55	12.74	12.94	13.14	13.34	13.54	9.6
9.7	12.29	12.48	12.68	12.88	13.07	13.27	13.48	13.68	9.7
9.8	12.41	12.61	12.81	13.01	13.21	13.41	13.62	13.82	9.8
9.9	12.54	12.74	12.94	13.14	13.34	13.55	13.75	13.96	9.9
10.0	12.67	12.87	13.07	13.27	13.48	13.68	13.89	14.10	10.0

	VOLUME IN CUBIC METRES								
Length in Metres	Mid-diameter in centimetres								Length in Metres
	135	136	137	138	139	140	141	142	
1.0	1.431	1.453	1.474	1.496	1.517	1.539	1.561	1.584	1.0
1.1	1.575	1.598	1.622	1.645	1.669	1.693	1.718	1.742	1.1
1.2	1.718	1.743	1.769	1.795	1.821	1.847	1.874	1.900	1.2
1.3	1.861	1.888	1.916	1.944	1.973	2.001	2.030	2.059	1.3
1.4	2.004	2.034	2.064	2.094	2.124	2.155	2.186	2.217	1.4
1.5	2.147	2.179	2.211	2.244	2.276	2.309	2.342	2.376	1.5
1.6	2.290	2.324	2.359	2.393	2.428	2.463	2.498	2.534	1.6
1.7	2.433	2.470	2.506	2.543	2.580	2.617	2.654	2.692	1.7
1.8	2.576	2.615	2.653	2.692	2.731	2.771	2.811	2.851	1.8
1.9	2.720	2.760	2.801	2.842	2.883	2.925	2.967	3.009	1.9
2.0	2.863	2.905	2.948	2.991	3.035	3.079	3.123	3.167	2.0
2.1	3.006	3.051	3.096	3.141	3.187	3.233	3.279	3.326	2.1
2.2	3.149	3.196	3.243	3.291	3.338	3.387	3.435	3.484	2.2
2.3	3.292	3.341	3.390	3.440	3.490	3.541	3.591	3.642	2.3
2.4	3.435	3.486	3.538	3.590	3.642	3.695	3.747	3.801	2.4
2.5	3.578	3.632	3.685	3.739	3.794	3.848	3.904	3.959	2.5
2.6	3.722	3.777	3.833	3.889	3.945	4.002	4.060	4.118	2.6
2.7	3.865	3.922	3.980	4.038	4.097	4.156	4.216	4.276	2.7
2.8	4.008	4.067	4.128	4.188	4.249	4.310	4.372	4.434	2.8
2.9	4.151	4.213	4.275	4.338	4.401	4.464	4.528	4.593	2.9
3.0	4.294	4.358	4.422	4.487	4.552	4.618	4.684	4.751	3.0
3.1	4.437	4.503	4.570	4.637	4.704	4.772	4.840	4.909	3.1
3.2	4.580	4.649	4.717	4.786	4.856	4.926	4.997	5.068	3.2
3.3	4.724	4.794	4.865	4.936	5.008	5.080	5.153	5.226	3.3
3.4	4.867	4.939	5.012	5.085	5.159	5.234	5.309	5.384	3.4
3.5	5.010	5.084	5.159	5.235	5.311	5.388	5.465	5.543	3.5
3.6	5.153	5.230	5.307	5.385	5.463	5.542	5.621	5.701	3.6
3.7	5.296	5.375	5.454	5.534	5.615	5.696	5.777	5.860	3.7
3.8	5.439	5.520	5.602	5.684	5.766	5.850	5.934	6.018	3.8
3.9	5.582	5.665	5.749	5.833	5.918	6.004	6.090	6.176	3.9
4.0	5.726	5.811	5.896	5.983	6.070	6.158	6.246	6.335	4.0
4.1	5.869	5.956	6.044	6.132	6.222	6.311	6.402	6.493	4.1
4.2	6.012	6.101	6.191	6.282	6.373	6.465	6.558	6.651	4.2
4.3	6.155	6.246	6.339	6.432	6.525	6.619	6.714	6.810	4.3
4.4	6.298	6.392	6.486	6.581	6.677	6.773	6.870	6.968	4.4
4.5	6.441	6.537	6.634	6.731	6.829	6.927	7.027	7.127	4.5
4.6	6.584	6.682	6.781	6.880	6.980	7.081	7.183	7.285	4.6
4.7	6.728	6.828	6.928	7.030	7.132	7.235	7.339	7.443	4.7
4.8	6.871	6.973	7.076	7.179	7.284	7.389	7.495	7.602	4.8
4.9	7.014	7.118	7.223	7.329	7.436	7.543	7.651	7.760	4.9
5.0	7.157	7.263	7.371	7.479	7.587	7.697	7.807	7.918	5.0
5.1	7.300	7.409	7.518	7.628	7.739	7.851	7.963	8.077	5.1
5.2	7.443	7.554	7.665	7.778	7.891	8.005	8.120	8.235	5.2
5.3	7.586	7.699	7.813	7.927	8.043	8.159	8.276	8.393	5.3
5.4	7.729	7.844	7.960	8.077	8.194	8.313	8.432	8.552	5.4

Length in Metres	VOLUME IN CUBIC METRES								Length in Metres
	Mid-diameter in centimetres								
	135	136	137	138	139	140	141	142	
5.5	7.873	7.990	8.108	8.226	8.346	8.467	8.588	8.710	5.5
5.6	8.016	8.135	8.255	8.376	8.498	8.621	8.744	8.869	5.6
5.7	8.159	8.280	8.402	8.526	8.650	8.774	8.900	9.027	5.7
5.8	8.302	8.425	8.550	8.675	8.801	8.928	9.056	9.185	5.8
5.9	8.445	8.571	8.697	8.825	8.953	9.082	9.213	9.344	5.9
6.0	8.588	8.716	8.845	8.974	9.105	9.236	9.369	9.502	6.0
6.1	8.731	8.861	8.992	9.124	9.257	9.390	9.525	9.660	6.1
6.2	8.875	9.007	9.139	9.273	9.408	9.544	9.681	9.819	6.2
6.3	9.018	9.152	9.287	9.423	9.560	9.698	9.837	9.977	6.3
6.4	9.161	9.297	9.434	9.573	9.712	9.852	9.993	10.14	6.4
6.5	9.304	9.442	9.582	9.722	9.864	10.01	10.15	10.29	6.5
6.6	9.447	9.588	9.729	9.872	10.02	10.16	10.31	10.45	6.6
6.7	9.590	9.733	9.877	10.02	10.17	10.31	10.46	10.61	6.7
6.8	9.733	9.878	10.02	10.17	10.32	10.47	10.62	10.77	6.8
6.9	9.877	10.02	10.17	10.32	10.47	10.62	10.77	10.93	6.9
7.0	10.02	10.17	10.32	10.47	10.62	10.78	10.93	11.09	7.0
7.1	10.16	10.31	10.47	10.62	10.77	10.93	11.09	11.24	7.1
7.2	10.31	10.46	10.61	10.77	10.93	11.08	11.24	11.40	7.2
7.3	10.45	10.60	10.76	10.92	11.08	11.24	11.40	11.56	7.3
7.4	10.59	10.75	10.91	11.07	11.23	11.39	11.55	11.72	7.4
7.5	10.74	10.90	11.06	11.22	11.38	11.55	11.71	11.88	7.5
7.6	10.88	11.04	11.20	11.37	11.53	11.70	11.87	12.04	7.6
7.7	11.02	11.19	11.35	11.52	11.68	11.85	12.02	12.19	7.7
7.8	11.16	11.33	11.50	11.67	11.84	12.01	12.18	12.35	7.8
7.9	11.31	11.48	11.65	11.82	11.99	12.16	12.34	12.51	7.9
8.0	11.45	11.62	11.79	11.97	12.14	12.32	12.49	12.67	8.0
8.1	11.59	11.77	11.94	12.12	12.29	12.47	12.65	12.83	8.1
8.2	11.74	11.91	12.09	12.26	12.44	12.62	12.80	12.99	8.2
8.3	11.88	12.06	12.24	12.41	12.59	12.78	12.96	13.14	8.3
8.4	12.02	12.20	12.38	12.56	12.75	12.93	13.12	13.30	8.4
8.5	12.17	12.35	12.53	12.71	12.90	13.08	13.27	13.46	8.5
8.6	12.31	12.49	12.68	12.86	13.05	13.24	13.43	13.62	8.6
8.7	12.45	12.64	12.82	13.01	13.20	13.39	13.58	13.78	8.7
8.8	12.60	12.78	12.97	13.16	13.35	13.55	13.74	13.94	8.8
8.9	12.74	12.93	13.12	13.31	13.51	13.70	13.90	14.09	8.9
9.0	12.88	13.07	13.27	13.46	13.66	13.85	14.05	14.25	9.0
9.1	13.03	13.22	13.41	13.61	13.81	14.01	14.21	14.41	9.1
9.2	13.17	13.36	13.56	13.76	13.96	14.16	14.37	14.57	9.2
9.3	13.31	13.51	13.71	13.91	14.11	14.32	14.52	14.73	9.3
9.4	13.46	13.66	13.86	14.06	14.26	14.47	14.68	14.89	9.4
9.5	13.60	13.80	14.00	14.21	14.42	14.62	14.83	15.04	9.5
9.6	13.74	13.95	14.15	14.36	14.57	14.78	14.99	15.20	9.6
9.7	13.88	14.09	14.30	14.51	14.72	14.93	15.15	15.36	9.7
9.8	14.03	14.24	14.45	14.66	14.87	15.09	15.30	15.52	9.8
9.9	14.17	14.38	14.59	14.81	15.02	15.24	15.46	15.68	9.9
10.0	14.31	14.53	14.74	14.96	15.17	15.39	15.61	15.84	10.0

Length in Metres	VOLUME IN CUBIC METRES								Length in Metres
	Mid-diameter in centimetres								
	143	144	145	146	147	148	149	150	
1.0	1.606	1.629	1.651	1.674	1.697	1.720	1.744	1.767	1.0
1.1	1.767	1.791	1.816	1.842	1.867	1.892	1.918	1.944	1.1
1.2	1.927	1.954	1.982	2.009	2.037	2.064	2.092	2.121	1.2
1.3	2.088	2.117	2.147	2.176	2.206	2.236	2.267	2.297	1.3
1.4	2.248	2.280	2.312	2.344	2.376	2.408	2.441	2.474	1.4
1.5	2.409	2.443	2.477	2.511	2.546	2.581	2.615	2.651	1.5
1.6	2.570	2.606	2.642	2.679	2.715	2.753	2.790	2.827	1.6
1.7	2.730	2.769	2.807	2.846	2.885	2.925	2.964	3.004	1.7
1.8	2.891	2.931	2.972	3.013	3.055	3.097	3.139	3.181	1.8
1.9	3.052	3.094	3.137	3.181	3.225	3.269	3.313	3.358	1.9
2.0	3.212	3.257	3.303	3.348	3.394	3.441	3.487	3.534	2.0
2.1	3.373	3.420	3.468	3.516	3.564	3.613	3.662	3.711	2.1
2.2	3.533	3.583	3.633	3.683	3.734	3.785	3.836	3.888	2.2
2.3	3.694	3.746	3.798	3.851	3.903	3.957	4.010	4.064	2.3
2.4	3.855	3.909	3.963	4.018	4.073	4.129	4.185	4.241	2.4
2.5	4.015	4.071	4.128	4.185	4.243	4.301	4.359	4.418	2.5
2.6	4.176	4.234	4.293	4.353	4.413	4.473	4.534	4.595	2.6
2.7	4.336	4.397	4.459	4.520	4.582	4.645	4.708	4.771	2.7
2.8	4.497	4.560	4.624	4.688	4.752	4.817	4.882	4.948	2.8
2.9	4.658	4.723	4.789	4.855	4.922	4.989	5.057	5.125	2.9
3.0	4.818	4.886	4.954	5.022	5.091	5.161	5.231	5.301	3.0
3.1	4.979	5.049	5.119	5.190	5.261	5.333	5.405	5.478	3.1
3.2	5.139	5.212	5.284	5.357	5.431	5.505	5.580	5.655	3.2
3.3	5.300	5.374	5.449	5.525	5.601	5.677	5.754	5.832	3.3
3.4	5.461	5.537	5.614	5.692	5.770	5.849	5.928	6.008	3.4
3.5	5.621	5.700	5.780	5.860	5.940	6.021	6.103	6.185	3.5
3.6	5.782	5.863	5.945	6.027	6.110	6.193	6.277	6.362	3.6
3.7	5.942	6.026	6.110	6.194	6.280	6.365	6.452	6.538	3.7
3.8	6.103	6.189	6.275	6.362	6.449	6.537	6.626	6.715	3.8
3.9	6.264	6.352	6.440	6.529	6.619	6.709	6.800	6.892	3.9
4.0	6.424	6.514	6.605	6.697	6.789	6.881	6.975	7.069	4.0
4.1	6.585	6.677	6.770	6.864	6.958	7.053	7.149	7.245	4.1
4.2	6.745	6.840	6.935	7.031	7.128	7.225	7.323	7.422	4.2
4.3	6.906	7.003	7.101	7.199	7.298	7.397	7.498	7.599	4.3
4.4	7.067	7.166	7.266	7.366	7.468	7.569	7.672	7.775	4.4
4.5	7.227	7.329	7.431	7.534	7.637	7.742	7.846	7.952	4.5
4.6	7.388	7.492	7.596	7.701	7.807	7.914	8.021	8.129	4.6
4.7	7.548	7.654	7.761	7.869	7.977	8.086	8.195	8.306	4.7
4.8	7.709	7.817	7.926	8.036	8.146	8.258	8.370	8.482	4.8
4.9	7.870	7.980	8.091	8.203	8.316	8.430	8.544	8.659	4.9
5.0	8.030	8.143	8.256	8.371	8.486	8.602	8.718	8.836	5.0
5.1	8.191	8.306	8.422	8.538	8.656	8.774	8.893	9.012	5.1
5.2	8.352	8.469	8.587	8.706	8.825	8.946	9.067	9.189	5.2
5.3	8.512	8.632	8.752	8.873	8.995	9.118	9.241	9.366	5.3
5.4	8.673	8.794	8.917	9.040	9.165	9.290	9.416	9.543	5.4

VOLUME IN CUBIC METRES

Length in Metres	Mid-diameter in centimetres								Length in Metres
	143	144	145	146	147	148	149	150	
5.5	8.833	8.957	9.082	9.208	9.334	9.462	9.590	9.719	5.5
5.6	8.994	9.120	9.247	9.375	9.504	9.634	9.764	9.896	5.6
5.7	9.155	9.283	9.412	9.543	9.674	9.806	9.939	10.07	5.7
5.8	9.315	9.446	9.578	9.710	9.844	9.978	10.11	10.25	5.8
5.9	9.476	9.609	9.743	9.878	10.01	10.15	10.29	10.43	5.9
6.0	9.636	9.772	9.908	10.04	10.18	10.32	10.46	10.60	6.0
6.1	9.797	9.934	10.07	10.21	10.35	10.49	10.64	10.78	6.1
6.2	9.958	10.10	10.24	10.38	10.52	10.67	10.81	10.96	6.2
6.3	10.12	10.26	10.40	10.55	10.69	10.84	10.99	11.13	6.3
6.4	10.28	10.42	10.57	10.71	10.86	11.01	11.16	11.31	6.4
6.5	10.44	10.59	10.73	10.88	11.03	11.18	11.33	11.49	6.5
6.6	10.60	10.75	10.90	11.05	11.20	11.35	11.51	11.66	6.6
6.7	10.76	10.91	11.06	11.22	11.37	11.53	11.68	11.84	6.7
6.8	10.92	11.07	11.23	11.38	11.54	11.70	11.86	12.02	6.8
6.9	11.08	11.24	11.39	11.55	11.71	11.87	12.03	12.19	6.9
7.0	11.24	11.40	11.56	11.72	11.88	12.04	12.21	12.37	7.0
7.1	11.40	11.56	11.72	11.89	12.05	12.21	12.38	12.55	7.1
7.2	11.56	11.73	11.89	12.05	12.22	12.39	12.55	12.72	7.2
7.3	11.72	11.89	12.05	12.22	12.39	12.56	12.73	12.90	7.3
7.4	11.88	12.05	12.22	12.39	12.56	12.73	12.90	13.08	7.4
7.5	12.05	12.21	12.38	12.56	12.73	12.90	13.08	13.25	7.5
7.6	12.21	12.38	12.55	12.72	12.90	13.07	13.25	13.43	7.6
7.7	12.37	12.54	12.71	12.89	13.07	13.25	13.43	13.61	7.7
7.8	12.53	12.70	12.88	13.06	13.24	13.42	13.60	13.78	7.8
7.9	12.69	12.87	13.05	13.23	13.41	13.59	13.77	13.96	7.9
8.0	12.85	13.03	13.21	13.39	13.58	13.76	13.95	14.14	8.0
8.1	13.01	13.19	13.38	13.56	13.75	13.93	14.12	14.31	8.1
8.2	13.17	13.35	13.54	13.73	13.92	14.11	14.30	14.49	8.2
8.3	13.33	13.52	13.71	13.90	14.09	14.28	14.47	14.67	8.3
8.4	13.49	13.68	13.87	14.06	14.26	14.45	14.65	14.84	8.4
8.5	13.65	13.84	14.04	14.23	14.43	14.62	14.82	15.02	8.5
8.6	13.81	14.01	14.20	14.40	14.60	14.79	15.00	15.20	8.6
8.7	13.97	14.17	14.37	14.57	14.77	14.97	15.17	15.37	8.7
8.8	14.13	14.33	14.53	14.73	14.94	15.14	15.34	15.55	8.8
8.9	14.29	14.49	14.70	14.90	15.10	15.31	15.52	15.73	8.9
9.0	14.45	14.66	14.86	15.07	15.27	15.48	15.69	15.90	9.0
9.1	14.62	14.82	15.03	15.23	15.44	15.66	15.87	16.08	9.1
9.2	14.78	14.98	15.19	15.40	15.61	15.83	16.04	16.26	9.2
9.3	14.94	15.15	15.36	15.57	15.78	16.00	16.22	16.43	9.3
9.4	15.10	15.31	15.52	15.74	15.95	16.17	16.39	16.61	9.4
9.5	15.26	15.47	15.69	15.90	16.12	16.34	16.56	16.79	9.5
9.6	15.42	15.63	15.85	16.07	16.29	16.52	16.74	16.96	9.6
9.7	15.58	15.80	16.02	16.24	16.46	16.69	16.91	17.14	9.7
9.8	15.74	15.96	16.18	16.41	16.63	16.86	17.09	17.32	9.8
9.9	15.90	16.12	16.35	16.57	16.80	17.03	17.26	17.49	9.9
10.0	16.06	16.29	16.51	16.74	16.97	17.20	17.44	17.67	10.0

Length in Metres	VOLUME IN CUBIC METRES								Length in Metres
	Mid-diameter in centimetres								
	151	152	153	154	155	156	157	158	
1.0	1.791	1.815	1.839	1.863	1.887	1.911	1.936	1.961	1.0
1.1	1.970	1.996	2.022	2.049	2.076	2.102	2.130	2.157	1.1
1.2	2.149	2.177	2.206	2.235	2.264	2.294	2.323	2.353	1.2
1.3	2.328	2.359	2.390	2.421	2.453	2.485	2.517	2.549	1.3
1.4	2.507	2.540	2.574	2.608	2.642	2.676	2.710	2.745	1.4
1.5	2.686	2.722	2.758	2.794	2.830	2.867	2.904	2.941	1.5
1.6	2.865	2.903	2.942	2.980	3.019	3.058	3.097	3.137	1.6
1.7	3.044	3.085	3.126	3.167	3.208	3.249	3.291	3.333	1.7
1.8	3.223	3.266	3.309	3.353	3.396	3.440	3.485	3.529	1.8
1.9	3.402	3.448	3.493	3.539	3.585	3.632	3.678	3.725	1.9
2.0	3.582	3.629	3.677	3.725	3.774	3.823	3.872	3.921	2.0
2.1	3.761	3.811	3.861	3.912	3.963	4.014	4.065	4.117	2.1
2.2	3.940	3.992	4.045	4.098	4.151	4.205	4.259	4.313	2.2
2.3	4.119	4.174	4.229	4.284	4.340	4.396	4.453	4.510	2.3
2.4	4.298	4.355	4.412	4.470	4.529	4.587	4.646	4.706	2.4
2.5	4.477	4.536	4.596	4.657	4.717	4.778	4.840	4.902	2.5
2.6	4.656	4.718	4.780	4.843	4.906	4.969	5.033	5.098	2.6
2.7	4.835	4.899	4.964	5.029	5.095	5.161	5.227	5.294	2.7
2.8	5.014	5.081	5.148	5.215	5.283	5.352	5.421	5.490	2.8
2.9	5.193	5.262	5.332	5.402	5.472	5.543	5.614	5.686	2.9
3.0	5.372	5.444	5.516	5.588	5.661	5.734	5.808	5.882	3.0
3.1	5.551	5.625	5.699	5.774	5.849	5.925	6.001	6.078	3.1
3.2	5.731	5.807	5.883	5.960	6.038	6.116	6.195	6.274	3.2
3.3	5.910	5.988	6.067	6.147	6.227	6.307	6.389	6.470	3.3
3.4	6.089	6.170	6.251	6.333	6.416	6.499	6.582	6.666	3.4
3.5	6.268	6.351	6.435	6.519	6.604	6.690	6.776	6.862	3.5
3.6	6.447	6.532	6.619	6.706	6.793	6.881	6.969	7.058	3.6
3.7	6.626	6.714	6.803	6.892	6.982	7.072	7.163	7.254	3.7
3.8	6.805	6.895	6.986	7.078	7.170	7.263	7.357	7.451	3.8
3.9	6.984	7.077	7.170	7.264	7.359	7.454	7.550	7.647	3.9
4.0	7.163	7.258	7.354	7.451	7.548	7.645	7.744	7.843	4.0
4.1	7.342	7.440	7.538	7.637	7.736	7.837	7.937	8.039	4.1
4.2	7.521	7.621	7.722	7.823	7.925	8.028	8.131	8.235	4.2
4.3	7.700	7.803	7.906	8.009	8.114	8.219	8.324	8.431	4.3
4.4	7.879	7.984	8.090	8.196	8.302	8.410	8.518	8.627	4.4
4.5	8.059	8.166	8.273	8.382	8.491	8.601	8.712	8.823	4.5
4.6	8.238	8.347	8.457	8.568	8.680	8.792	8.905	9.019	4.6
4.7	8.417	8.529	8.641	8.754	8.869	8.983	9.099	9.215	4.7
4.8	8.596	8.710	8.825	8.941	9.057	9.174	9.292	9.411	4.8
4.9	8.775	8.891	9.009	9.127	9.246	9.366	9.486	9.607	4.9
5.0	8.954	9.073	9.193	9.313	9.435	9.557	9.680	9.803	5.0
5.1	9.133	9.254	9.377	9.500	9.623	9.748	9.873	9.999	5.1
5.2	9.312	9.436	9.560	9.686	9.812	9.939	10.07	10.20	5.2
5.3	9.491	9.617	9.744	9.872	10.00	10.13	10.26	10.39	5.3
5.4	9.670	9.799	9.928	10.06	10.19	10.32	10.45	10.59	5.4

VOLUME IN CUBIC METRES

Length in Metres	Mid-diameter in centimetres								Length in Metres
	151	152	153	154	155	156	157	158	
5.5	9.849	9.980	10.11	10.24	10.38	10.51	10.65	10.78	5.5
5.6	10.03	10.16	10.30	10.43	10.57	10.70	10.84	10.98	5.6
5.7	10.21	10.34	10.48	10.62	10.76	10.89	11.03	11.18	5.7
5.8	10.39	10.52	10.66	10.80	10.94	11.09	11.23	11.37	5.8
5.9	10.57	10.71	10.85	10.99	11.13	11.28	11.42	11.57	5.9
6.0	10.74	10.89	11.03	11.18	11.32	11.47	11.62	11.76	6.0
6.1	10.92	11.07	11.22	11.36	11.51	11.66	11.81	11.96	6.1
6.2	11.10	11.25	11.40	11.55	11.70	11.85	12.00	12.16	6.2
6.3	11.28	11.43	11.58	11.73	11.89	12.04	12.20	12.35	6.3
6.4	11.46	11.61	11.77	11.92	12.08	12.23	12.39	12.55	6.4
6.5	11.64	11.79	11.95	12.11	12.26	12.42	12.58	12.74	6.5
6.6	11.82	11.98	12.13	12.29	12.45	12.61	12.78	12.94	6.6
6.7	12.00	12.16	12.32	12.48	12.64	12.81	12.97	13.14	6.7
6.8	12.18	12.34	12.50	12.67	12.83	13.00	13.16	13.33	6.8
6.9	12.36	12.52	12.69	12.85	13.02	13.19	13.36	13.53	6.9
7.0	12.54	12.70	12.87	13.04	13.21	13.38	13.55	13.72	7.0
7.1	12.71	12.88	13.05	13.22	13.40	13.57	13.75	13.92	7.1
7.2	12.89	13.06	13.24	13.41	13.59	13.76	13.94	14.12	7.2
7.3	13.07	13.25	13.42	13.60	13.77	13.95	14.13	14.31	7.3
7.4	13.25	13.43	13.61	13.78	13.96	14.14	14.33	14.51	7.4
7.5	13.43	13.61	13.79	13.97	14.15	14.34	14.52	14.70	7.5
7.6	13.61	13.79	13.97	14.16	14.34	14.53	14.71	14.90	7.6
7.7	13.79	13.97	14.16	14.34	14.53	14.72	14.91	15.10	7.7
7.8	13.97	14.15	14.34	14.53	14.72	14.91	15.10	15.29	7.8
7.9	14.15	14.34	14.52	14.71	14.91	15.10	15.29	15.49	7.9
8.0	14.33	14.52	14.71	14.90	15.10	15.29	15.49	15.69	8.0
8.1	14.51	14.70	14.89	15.09	15.28	15.48	15.68	15.88	8.1
8.2	14.68	14.88	15.08	15.27	15.47	15.67	15.87	16.08	8.2
8.3	14.86	15.06	15.26	15.46	15.66	15.86	16.07	16.27	8.3
8.4	15.04	15.24	15.44	15.65	15.85	16.06	16.26	16.47	8.4
8.5	15.22	15.42	15.63	15.83	16.04	16.25	16.46	16.67	8.5
8.6	15.40	15.61	15.81	16.02	16.23	16.44	16.65	16.86	8.6
8.7	15.58	15.79	16.00	16.21	16.42	16.63	16.84	17.06	8.7
8.8	15.76	15.97	16.18	16.39	16.60	16.82	17.04	17.25	8.8
8.9	15.94	16.15	16.36	16.58	16.79	17.01	17.23	17.45	8.9
9.0	16.12	16.33	16.55	16.76	16.98	17.20	17.42	17.65	9.0
9.1	16.30	16.51	16.73	16.95	17.17	17.39	17.62	17.84	9.1
9.2	16.48	16.69	16.91	17.14	17.36	17.58	17.81	18.04	9.2
9.3	16.65	16.88	17.10	17.32	17.55	17.78	18.00	18.23	9.3
9.4	16.83	17.06	17.28	17.51	17.74	17.97	18.20	18.43	9.4
9.5	17.01	17.24	17.47	17.70	17.93	18.16	18.39	18.63	9.5
9.6	17.19	17.42	17.65	17.88	18.11	18.35	18.58	18.82	9.6
9.7	17.37	17.60	17.83	18.07	18.30	18.54	18.78	19.02	9.7
9.8	17.55	17.78	18.02	18.25	18.49	18.73	18.97	19.21	9.8
9.9	17.73	17.96	18.20	18.44	18.68	18.92	19.17	19.41	9.9
10.0	17.91	18.15	18.39	18.63	18.87	19.11	19.36	19.61	10.0

VOLUME IN CUBIC METRES

Length in Metres	Mid-diameter in centimetres								Length in Metres
	159	160	161	162	163	164	165	166	
1.0	1.986	2.011	2.036	2.061	2.087	2.112	2.138	2.164	1.0
1.1	2.184	2.212	2.239	2.267	2.295	2.324	2.352	2.381	1.1
1.2	2.383	2.413	2.443	2.473	2.504	2.535	2.566	2.597	1.2
1.3	2.581	2.614	2.647	2.680	2.713	2.746	2.780	2.814	1.3
1.4	2.780	2.815	2.850	2.886	2.921	2.957	2.994	3.030	1.4
1.5	2.978	3.016	3.054	3.092	3.130	3.169	3.207	3.246	1.5
1.6	3.177	3.217	3.257	3.298	3.339	3.380	3.421	3.463	1.6
1.7	3.375	3.418	3.461	3.504	3.547	3.591	3.635	3.679	1.7
1.8	3.574	3.619	3.664	3.710	3.756	3.802	3.849	3.896	1.8
1.9	3.773	3.820	3.868	3.916	3.965	4.014	4.063	4.112	1.9
2.0	3.971	4.021	4.072	4.122	4.173	4.225	4.276	4.328	2.0
2.1	4.170	4.222	4.275	4.329	4.382	4.436	4.490	4.545	2.1
2.2	4.368	4.423	4.479	4.535	4.591	4.647	4.704	4.761	2.2
2.3	4.567	4.624	4.682	4.741	4.799	4.859	4.918	4.978	2.3
2.4	4.765	4.825	4.886	4.947	5.008	5.070	5.132	5.194	2.4
2.5	4.964	5.027	5.090	5.153	5.217	5.281	5.346	5.411	2.5
2.6	5.162	5.228	5.293	5.359	5.425	5.492	5.559	5.627	2.6
2.7	5.361	5.429	5.497	5.565	5.634	5.703	5.773	5.843	2.7
2.8	5.560	5.630	5.700	5.771	5.843	5.915	5.987	6.060	2.8
2.9	5.758	5.831	5.904	5.977	6.051	6.126	6.201	6.276	2.9
3.0	5.957	6.032	6.107	6.184	6.260	6.337	6.415	6.493	3.0
3.1	6.155	6.233	6.311	6.390	6.469	6.548	6.629	6.709	3.1
3.2	6.354	6.434	6.515	6.596	6.678	6.760	6.842	6.926	3.2
3.3	6.552	6.635	6.718	6.802	6.886	6.971	7.056	7.142	3.3
3.4	6.751	6.836	6.922	7.008	7.095	7.182	7.270	7.358	3.4
3.5	6.949	7.037	7.125	7.214	7.304	7.393	7.484	7.575	3.5
3.6	7.148	7.238	7.329	7.420	7.512	7.605	7.698	7.791	3.6
3.7	7.347	7.439	7.533	7.626	7.721	7.816	7.912	8.008	3.7
3.8	7.545	7.640	7.736	7.833	7.930	8.027	8.125	8.224	3.8
3.9	7.744	7.841	7.940	8.039	8.138	8.238	8.339	8.441	3.9
4.0	7.942	8.042	8.143	8.245	8.347	8.450	8.553	8.657	4.0
4.1	8.141	8.244	8.347	8.451	8.556	8.661	8.767	8.873	4.1
4.2	8.339	8.445	8.550	8.657	8.764	8.872	8.981	9.090	4.2
4.3	8.538	8.646	8.754	8.863	8.973	9.083	9.194	9.306	4.3
4.4	8.736	8.847	8.958	9.069	9.182	9.295	9.408	9.523	4.4
4.5	8.935	9.048	9.161	9.275	9.390	9.506	9.622	9.739	4.5
4.6	9.134	9.249	9.365	9.482	9.599	9.717	9.836	9.956	4.6
4.7	9.332	9.450	9.568	9.688	9.808	9.928	10.05	10.17	4.7
4.8	9.531	9.651	9.772	9.894	10.02	10.14	10.26	10.39	4.8
4.9	9.729	9.852	9.976	10.10	10.22	10.35	10.48	10.60	4.9
5.0	9.928	10.05	10.18	10.31	10.43	10.56	10.69	10.82	5.0
5.1	10.13	10.25	10.38	10.51	10.64	10.77	10.91	11.04	5.1
5.2	10.32	10.46	10.59	10.72	10.85	10.98	11.12	11.25	5.2
5.3	10.52	10.66	10.79	10.92	11.06	11.20	11.33	11.47	5.3
5.4	10.72	10.86	10.99	11.13	11.27	11.41	11.55	11.69	5.4

VOLUME IN CUBIC METRES

Length in Metres	Mid-diameter in centimetres								Length in Metres
	159	160	161	162	163	164	165	166	
5.5	10.92	11.06	11.20	11.34	11.48	11.62	11.76	11.90	5.5
5.6	11.12	11.26	11.40	11.54	11.69	11.83	11.97	12.12	5.6
5.7	11.32	11.46	11.60	11.75	11.89	12.04	12.19	12.34	5.7
5.8	11.52	11.66	11.81	11.95	12.10	12.25	12.40	12.55	5.8
5.9	11.71	11.86	12.01	12.16	12.31	12.46	12.62	12.77	5.9
6.0	11.91	12.06	12.21	12.37	12.52	12.67	12.83	12.99	6.0
6.1	12.11	12.26	12.42	12.57	12.73	12.89	13.04	13.20	6.1
6.2	12.31	12.47	12.62	12.78	12.94	13.10	13.26	13.42	6.2
6.3	12.51	12.67	12.83	12.99	13.15	13.31	13.47	13.63	6.3
6.4	12.71	12.87	13.03	13.19	13.36	13.52	13.68	13.85	6.4
6.5	12.91	13.07	13.23	13.40	13.56	13.73	13.90	14.07	6.5
6.6	13.10	13.27	13.44	13.60	13.77	13.94	14.11	14.28	6.6
6.7	13.30	13.47	13.64	13.81	13.98	14.15	14.33	14.50	6.7
6.8	13.50	13.67	13.84	14.02	14.19	14.36	14.54	14.72	6.8
6.9	13.70	13.87	14.05	14.22	14.40	14.58	14.75	14.93	6.9
7.0	13.90	14.07	14.25	14.43	14.61	14.79	14.97	15.15	7.0
7.1	14.10	14.28	14.45	14.63	14.82	15.00	15.18	15.37	7.1
7.2	14.30	14.48	14.66	14.84	15.02	15.21	15.40	15.58	7.2
7.3	14.49	14.68	14.86	15.05	15.23	15.42	15.61	15.80	7.3
7.4	14.69	14.88	15.07	15.25	15.44	15.63	15.82	16.02	7.4
7.5	14.89	15.08	15.27	15.46	15.65	15.84	16.04	16.23	7.5
7.6	15.09	15.28	15.47	15.67	15.86	16.05	16.25	16.45	7.6
7.7	15.29	15.48	15.68	15.87	16.07	16.27	16.46	16.66	7.7
7.8	15.49	15.68	15.88	16.08	16.28	16.48	16.68	16.88	7.8
7.9	15.69	15.88	16.08	16.28	16.49	16.69	16.89	17.10	7.9
8.0	15.88	16.08	16.29	16.49	16.69	16.90	17.11	17.31	8.0
8.1	16.08	16.29	16.49	16.70	16.90	17.11	17.32	17.53	8.1
8.2	16.28	16.49	16.69	16.90	17.11	17.32	17.53	17.75	8.2
8.3	16.48	16.69	16.90	17.11	17.32	17.53	17.75	17.96	8.3
8.4	16.68	16.89	17.10	17.31	17.53	17.74	17.96	18.18	8.4
8.5	16.88	17.09	17.30	17.52	17.74	17.96	18.18	18.40	8.5
8.6	17.08	17.29	17.51	17.73	17.95	18.17	18.39	18.61	8.6
8.7	17.27	17.49	17.71	17.93	18.15	18.38	18.60	18.83	8.7
8.8	17.47	17.69	17.92	18.14	18.36	18.59	18.82	19.05	8.8
8.9	17.67	17.89	18.12	18.34	18.57	18.80	19.03	19.26	8.9
9.0	17.87	18.10	18.32	18.55	18.78	19.01	19.24	19.48	9.0
9.1	18.07	18.30	18.53	18.76	18.99	19.22	19.46	19.69	9.1
9.2	18.27	18.50	18.73	18.96	19.20	19.43	19.67	19.91	9.2
9.3	18.47	18.70	18.93	19.17	19.41	19.65	19.89	20.13	9.3
9.4	18.66	18.90	19.14	19.38	19.62	19.86	20.10	20.34	9.4
9.5	18.86	19.10	19.34	19.58	19.82	20.07	20.31	20.56	9.5
9.6	19.06	19.30	19.54	19.79	20.03	20.28	20.53	20.78	9.6
9.7	19.26	19.50	19.75	19.99	20.24	20.49	20.74	20.99	9.7
9.8	19.46	19.70	19.95	20.20	20.45	20.70	20.95	21.21	9.8
9.9	19.66	19.91	20.15	20.41	20.66	20.91	21.17	21.43	9.9
10.0	19.86	20.11	20.36	20.61	20.87	21.12	21.38	21.64	10.0

VOLUME IN CUBIC METRES

Length in Metres	Top-diameter in centimetres								Length in Metres
	10	12	14	16	18	20	22	24	
1.8	0.02	0.03	0.04	0.04	0.06	0.07	0.08	0.09	1.8
1.9	0.02	0.03	0.04	0.05	0.06	0.07	0.08	0.10	1.9
2.0	0.02	0.03	0.04	0.05	0.06	0.07	0.09	0.10	2.0
2.1	0.02	0.03	0.04	0.05	0.07	0.08	0.09	0.11	2.1
2.2	0.02	0.03	0.04	0.06	0.07	0.08	0.10	0.12	2.2
2.3	0.03	0.04	0.05	0.06	0.07	0.09	0.10	0.12	2.3
2.4	0.03	0.04	0.05	0.06	0.08	0.09	0.11	0.13	2.4
2.5	0.03	0.04	0.05	0.06	0.08	0.10	0.11	0.13	2.5
2.6	0.03	0.04	0.05	0.07	0.08	0.10	0.12	0.14	2.6
2.7	0.03	0.04	0.06	0.07	0.09	0.10	0.12	0.14	2.7
2.8	0.03	0.04	0.06	0.07	0.09	0.11	0.13	0.15	2.8
2.9	0.03	0.05	0.06	0.08	0.09	0.11	0.13	0.16	2.9
3.0	0.04	0.05	0.06	0.08	0.10	0.12	0.14	0.16	3.0
3.1	0.04	0.05	0.06	0.08	0.10	0.12	0.14	0.17	3.1
3.2	0.04	0.05	0.07	0.08	0.10	0.13	0.15	0.17	3.2
3.3	0.04	0.05	0.07	0.09	0.11	0.13	0.15	0.18	3.3
3.4	0.04	0.06	0.07	0.09	0.11	0.13	0.16	0.19	3.4
3.5	0.04	0.06	0.07	0.09	0.12	0.14	0.16	0.19	3.5
3.6	0.04	0.06	0.08	0.10	0.12	0.14	0.17	0.20	3.6
3.7	0.05	0.06	0.08	0.10	0.12	0.15	0.18	0.20	3.7
3.8	0.05	0.06	0.08	0.10	0.13	0.15	0.18	0.21	3.8
3.9	0.05	0.07	0.08	0.11	0.13	0.16	0.19	0.22	3.9
4.0	0.05	0.07	0.09	0.11	0.13	0.16	0.19	0.22	4.0
4.1	0.05	0.07	0.09	0.11	0.14	0.17	0.20	0.23	4.1
4.2	0.05	0.07	0.09	0.12	0.14	0.17	0.20	0.24	4.2
4.3	0.06	0.07	0.10	0.12	0.15	0.18	0.21	0.24	4.3
4.4	0.06	0.08	0.10	0.12	0.15	0.18	0.21	0.25	4.4
4.5	0.06	0.08	0.10	0.13	0.15	0.18	0.22	0.26	4.5
4.6	0.06	0.08	0.10	0.13	0.16	0.19	0.22	0.26	4.6
4.7	0.06	0.08	0.11	0.13	0.16	0.19	0.23	0.27	4.7
4.8	0.06	0.08	0.11	0.14	0.17	0.20	0.24	0.27	4.8
4.9	0.07	0.09	0.11	0.14	0.17	0.20	0.24	0.28	4.9
5.0	0.07	0.09	0.11	0.14	0.17	0.21	0.25	0.29	5.0

VOLUME IN CUBIC METRES

Length in Metres	Top-diameter in centimetres								Length in Metres
	10	12	14	16	18	20	22	24	
5.1	0.07	0.09	0.12	0.15	0.18	0.21	0.25	0.29	5.1
5.2	0.07	0.09	0.12	0.15	0.18	0.22	0.26	0.30	5.2
5.3	0.07	0.10	0.12	0.15	0.19	0.22	0.26	0.31	5.3
5.4	0.07	0.10	0.13	0.16	0.19	0.23	0.27	0.31	5.4
5.5	0.08	0.10	0.13	0.16	0.20	0.23	0.28	0.32	5.5
5.6	0.08	0.10	0.13	0.16	0.20	0.24	0.28	0.33	5.6
5.7	0.08	0.11	0.14	0.17	0.20	0.24	0.29	0.34	5.7
5.8	0.08	0.11	0.14	0.17	0.21	0.25	0.29	0.34	5.8
5.9	0.08	0.11	0.14	0.18	0.21	0.25	0.30	0.35	5.9
6.0	0.09	0.11	0.14	0.18	0.22	0.26	0.31	0.36	6.0
6.1	0.09	0.12	0.15	0.18	0.22	0.27	0.31	0.36	6.1
6.2	0.09	0.12	0.15	0.19	0.23	0.27	0.32	0.37	6.2
6.3	0.09	0.12	0.15	0.19	0.23	0.28	0.32	0.38	6.3
6.4	0.09	0.12	0.16	0.19	0.24	0.28	0.33	0.38	6.4
6.5	0.10	0.13	0.16	0.20	0.24	0.29	0.34	0.39	6.5
6.6	0.10	0.13	0.16	0.20	0.25	0.29	0.34	0.40	6.6
6.7	0.10	0.13	0.17	0.21	0.25	0.30	0.35	0.41	6.7
6.8	0.10	0.13	0.17	0.21	0.25	0.30	0.36	0.41	6.8
6.9	0.10	0.14	0.17	0.21	0.26	0.31	0.36	0.42	6.9
7.0	0.11	0.14	0.18	0.22	0.26	0.31	0.37	0.43	7.0
7.1	0.11	0.14	0.18	0.22	0.27	0.32	0.38	0.44	7.1
7.2	0.11	0.14	0.18	0.23	0.27	0.33	0.38	0.44	7.2
7.3	0.11	0.15	0.19	0.23	0.28	0.33	0.39	0.45	7.3
7.4	0.12	0.15	0.19	0.23	0.28	0.34	0.40	0.46	7.4
7.5	0.12	0.15	0.19	0.24	0.29	0.34	0.40	0.47	7.5
7.6	0.12	0.16	0.20	0.24	0.29	0.35	0.41	0.47	7.6
7.7	0.12	0.16	0.20	0.25	0.30	0.35	0.42	0.48	7.7
7.8	0.12	0.16	0.20	0.25	0.30	0.36	0.42	0.49	7.8
7.9	0.13	0.16	0.21	0.26	0.31	0.37	0.43	0.50	7.9
8.0	0.13	0.17	0.21	0.26	0.31	0.37	0.44	0.50	8.0
8.1	0.13	0.17	0.21	0.26	0.32	0.38	0.44	0.51	8.1
8.2	0.13	0.17	0.22	0.27	0.32	0.38	0.45	0.52	8.2
8.3	0.14	0.18	0.22	0.27	0.33	0.39	0.46	0.53	8.3

	VOLUME IN CUBIC METRES								
Length in Metres	Top-diameter in centimetres								Length in Metres
	26	28	30	32	34	36	38	40	
1.8	0.11	0.13	0.14	0.16	0.18	0.20	0.22	0.25	1.8
1.9	0.12	0.13	0.15	0.17	0.19	0.21	0.24	0.26	1.9
2.0	0.12	0.14	0.16	0.18	0.20	0.22	0.25	0.27	2.0
2.1	0.13	0.15	0.17	0.19	0.21	0.24	0.26	0.29	2.1
2.2	0.13	0.15	0.18	0.20	0.22	0.25	0.28	0.30	2.2
2.3	0.14	0.16	0.18	0.21	0.23	0.26	0.29	0.32	2.3
2.4	0.15	0.17	0.19	0.22	0.24	0.27	0.30	0.33	2.4
2.5	0.15	0.18	0.20	0.23	0.26	0.28	0.31	0.35	2.5
2.6	0.16	0.18	0.21	0.24	0.27	0.30	0.33	0.36	2.6
2.7	0.17	0.19	0.22	0.25	0.28	0.31	0.34	0.38	2.7
2.8	0.17	0.20	0.23	0.26	0.29	0.32	0.35	0.39	2.8
2.9	0.18	0.21	0.24	0.27	0.30	0.33	0.37	0.41	2.9
3.0	0.19	0.22	0.25	0.28	0.31	0.34	0.38	0.42	3.0
3.1	0.19	0.22	0.25	0.29	0.32	0.36	0.40	0.44	3.1
3.2	0.20	0.23	0.26	0.30	0.33	0.37	0.41	0.45	3.2
3.3	0.21	0.24	0.27	0.31	0.34	0.38	0.42	0.47	3.3
3.4	0.22	0.25	0.28	0.32	0.35	0.39	0.44	0.48	3.4
3.5	0.22	0.26	0.29	0.33	0.37	0.41	0.45	0.50	3.5
3.6	0.23	0.26	0.30	0.34	0.38	0.42	0.46	0.51	3.6
3.7	0.24	0.27	0.31	0.35	0.39	0.43	0.48	0.53	3.7
3.8	0.24	0.28	0.32	0.36	0.40	0.44	0.49	0.54	3.8
3.9	0.25	0.29	0.33	0.37	0.41	0.46	0.51	0.56	3.9
4.0	0.26	0.30	0.34	0.38	0.42	0.47	0.52	0.57	4.0
4.1	0.27	0.30	0.34	0.39	0.43	0.48	0.53	0.59	4.1
4.2	0.27	0.31	0.35	0.40	0.45	0.50	0.55	0.60	4.2
4.3	0.28	0.32	0.36	0.41	0.46	0.51	0.56	0.62	4.3
4.4	0.29	0.33	0.37	0.42	0.47	0.52	0.58	0.63	4.4
4.5	0.29	0.34	0.38	0.43	0.48	0.53	0.59	0.65	4.5
4.6	0.30	0.35	0.39	0.44	0.49	0.55	0.60	0.67	4.6
4.7	0.31	0.35	0.40	0.45	0.50	0.56	0.62	0.68	4.7
4.8	0.32	0.36	0.41	0.46	0.52	0.57	0.63	0.70	4.8
4.9	0.32	0.37	0.42	0.47	0.53	0.59	0.65	0.71	4.9
5.0	0.33	0.38	0.43	0.48	0.54	0.60	0.66	0.73	5.0

Length in Metres	26	28	30	32	34	36	38	40	Length in Metres
	VOLUME IN CUBIC METRES								
	Top-diameter in centimetres								
5.1	0.34	0.39	0.44	0.49	0.55	0.61	0.68	0.74	5.1
5.2	0.35	0.40	0.45	0.51	0.56	0.63	0.69	0.76	5.2
5.3	0.36	0.41	0.46	0.52	0.58	0.64	0.71	0.78	5.3
5.4	0.36	0.41	0.47	0.53	0.59	0.65	0.72	0.79	5.4
5.5	0.37	0.42	0.48	0.54	0.60	0.67	0.74	0.81	5.5
5.6	0.38	0.43	0.49	0.55	0.61	0.68	0.75	0.83	5.6
5.7	0.39	0.44	0.50	0.56	0.63	0.69	0.77	0.84	5.7
5.8	0.39	0.45	0.51	0.57	0.64	0.71	0.78	0.86	5.8
5.9	0.40	0.46	0.52	0.58	0.65	0.72	0.80	0.88	5.9
6.0	0.41	0.47	0.53	0.59	0.66	0.74	0.81	0.89	6.0
6.1	0.42	0.48	0.54	0.61	0.68	0.75	0.83	0.91	6.1
6.2	0.43	0.49	0.55	0.62	0.69	0.76	0.84	0.92	6.2
6.3	0.43	0.49	0.56	0.63	0.70	0.78	0.86	0.94	6.3
6.4	0.44	0.50	0.57	0.64	0.71	0.79	0.87	0.96	6.4
6.5	0.45	0.51	0.58	0.65	0.73	0.80	0.89	0.98	6.5
6.6	0.46	0.52	0.59	0.66	0.74	0.82	0.90	0.99	6.6
6.7	0.47	0.53	0.60	0.67	0.75	0.83	0.92	1.01	6.7
6.8	0.48	0.54	0.61	0.69	0.76	0.85	0.93	1.03	6.8
6.9	0.48	0.55	0.62	0.70	0.78	0.86	0.95	1.04	6.9
7.0	0.49	0.56	0.63	0.71	0.79	0.88	0.97	1.06	7.0
7.1	0.50	0.57	0.64	0.72	0.80	0.89	0.98	1.08	7.1
7.2	0.51	0.58	0.65	0.73	0.82	0.90	1.00	1.09	7.2
7.3	0.52	0.59	0.66	0.74	0.83	0.92	1.01	1.11	7.3
7.4	0.53	0.60	0.68	0.76	0.84	0.93	1.03	1.13	7.4
7.5	0.53	0.61	0.69	0.77	0.86	0.95	1.05	1.15	7.5
7.6	0.54	0.62	0.70	0.78	0.87	0.96	1.06	1.16	7.6
7.7	0.55	0.63	0.71	0.79	0.88	0.98	1.08	1.18	7.7
7.8	0.56	0.64	0.72	0.81	0.90	0.99	1.09	1.20	7.8
7.9	0.57	0.65	0.73	0.82	0.91	1.01	1.11	1.22	7.9
8.0	0.58	0.66	0.74	0.83	0.92	1.02	1.13	1.23	8.0
8.1	0.59	0.67	0.75	0.84	0.94	1.04	1.14	1.25	8.1
8.2	0.60	0.68	0.76	0.85	0.95	1.05	1.16	1.27	8.2
8.3	0.60	0.69	0.77	0.87	0.96	1.07	1.18	1.29	8.3

	VOLUME IN CUBIC METRES								
Length in Metres	Top-diameter in centimetres								Length in Metres
	42	44	46	48	50	52	54	56	
1.8	0.27	0.30	0.32	0.35	0.38	0.41	0.44	0.47	1.8
1.9	0.29	0.31	0.34	0.37	0.40	0.43	0.46	0.50	1.9
2.0	0.30	0.33	0.36	0.39	0.42	0.46	0.49	0.53	2.0
2.1	0.32	0.35	0.38	0.41	0.44	0.48	0.51	0.55	2.1
2.2	0.33	0.36	0.40	0.43	0.47	0.50	0.54	0.58	2.2
2.3	0.35	0.38	0.42	0.45	0.49	0.53	0.57	0.61	2.3
2.4	0.36	0.40	0.43	0.47	0.51	0.55	0.59	0.63	2.4
2.5	0.38	0.42	0.45	0.49	0.53	0.57	0.62	0.66	2.5
2.6	0.40	0.43	0.47	0.51	0.55	0.60	0.64	0.69	2.6
2.7	0.41	0.45	0.49	0.53	0.58	0.62	0.67	0.72	2.7
2.8	0.43	0.47	0.51	0.55	0.60	0.65	0.69	0.74	2.8
2.9	0.45	0.49	0.53	0.57	0.62	0.67	0.72	0.77	2.9
3.0	0.46	0.50	0.55	0.59	0.64	0.69	0.75	0.80	3.0
3.1	0.48	0.52	0.57	0.62	0.67	0.72	0.77	0.83	3.1
3.2	0.49	0.54	0.59	0.64	0.69	0.74	0.80	0.86	3.2
3.3	0.51	0.56	0.61	0.66	0.71	0.77	0.82	0.88	3.3
3.4	0.53	0.58	0.63	0.68	0.73	0.79	0.85	0.91	3.4
3.5	0.54	0.59	0.65	0.70	0.76	0.82	0.88	0.94	3.5
3.6	0.56	0.61	0.67	0.72	0.78	0.84	0.90	0.97	3.6
3.7	0.58	0.63	0.68	0.74	0.80	0.86	0.93	1.00	3.7
3.8	0.59	0.65	0.70	0.76	0.83	0.89	0.96	1.02	3.8
3.9	0.61	0.67	0.72	0.79	0.85	0.91	0.98	1.05	3.9
4.0	0.63	0.68	0.74	0.81	0.87	0.94	1.01	1.08	4.0
4.1	0.64	0.70	0.76	0.83	0.89	0.96	1.04	1.11	4.1
4.2	0.66	0.72	0.78	0.85	0.92	0.99	1.06	1.14	4.2
4.3	0.68	0.74	0.80	0.87	0.94	1.01	1.09	1.17	4.3
4.4	0.69	0.76	0.82	0.89	0.96	1.04	1.12	1.20	4.4
4.5	0.71	0.78	0.84	0.91	0.99	1.06	1.14	1.23	4.5
4.6	0.73	0.80	0.86	0.94	1.01	1.09	1.17	1.25	4.6
4.7	0.75	0.81	0.88	0.96	1.04	1.11	1.20	1.28	4.7
4.8	0.76	0.83	0.91	0.98	1.06	1.14	1.22	1.31	4.8
4.9	0.78	0.85	0.93	1.00	1.08	1.17	1.25	1.34	4.9
5.0	0.80	0.87	0.95	1.02	1.11	1.19	1.28	1.37	5.0

VOLUME IN CUBIC METRES

ength in etres	Top-diameter in centimetres 42	44	46	48	50	52	54	56	Length in Metres
.1	0.82	0.89	0.97	1.05	1.13	1.22	1.31	1.40	5.1
.2	0.83	0.91	0.99	1.07	1.15	1.24	1.33	1.43	5.2
.3	0.85	0.93	1.01	1.09	1.18	1.27	1.36	1.46	5.3
.4	0.87	0.95	1.03	1.11	1.20	1.29	1.39	1.49	5.4
.5	0.89	0.97	1.05	1.14	1.23	1.32	1.42	1.52	5.5
.6	0.90	0.99	1.07	1.16	1.25	1.35	1.45	1.55	5.6
.7	0.92	1.00	1.09	1.18	1.28	1.37	1.47	1.58	5.7
.8	0.94	1.02	1.11	1.20	1.30	1.40	1.50	1.61	5.8
.9	0.96	1.04	1.13	1.23	1.32	1.43	1.53	1.64	5.9
.0	0.98	1.06	1.15	1.25	1.35	1.45	1.56	1.67	6.0
.1	0.99	1.08	1.18	1.27	1.37	1.48	1.59	1.70	6.1
.2	1.01	1.10	1.20	1.30	1.40	1.50	1.61	1.73	6.2
.3	1.03	1.12	1.22	1.32	1.42	1.53	1.64	1.76	6.3
.4	1.05	1.14	1.24	1.34	1.45	1.56	1.67	1.79	6.4
.5	1.07	1.16	1.26	1.36	1.47	1.58	1.70	1.82	6.5
.6	1.08	1.18	1.28	1.39	1.50	1.61	1.73	1.85	6.6
.7	1.10	1.20	1.30	1.41	1.52	1.64	1.76	1.88	6.7
.8	1.12	1.22	1.33	1.43	1.55	1.66	1.79	1.91	6.8
.9	1.14	1.24	1.35	1.46	1.57	1.69	1.82	1.94	6.9
.0	1.16	1.26	1.37	1.48	1.60	1.72	1.84	1.97	7.0
.1	1.18	1.28	1.39	1.51	1.62	1.75	1.87	2.00	7.1
.2	1.20	1.30	1.41	1.53	1.65	1.77	1.90	2.04	7.2
.3	1.22	1.32	1.44	1.55	1.67	1.80	1.93	2.07	7.3
.4	1.23	1.34	1.46	1.58	1.70	1.83	1.96	2.10	7.4
.5	1.25	1.36	1.48	1.60	1.73	1.86	1.99	2.13	7.5
.6	1.27	1.38	1.50	1.62	1.75	1.88	2.02	2.16	7.6
.7	1.29	1.41	1.52	1.65	1.78	1.91	2.05	2.19	7.7
.8	1.31	1.43	1.55	1.67	1.80	1.94	2.08	2.22	7.8
.9	1.33	1.45	1.57	1.70	1.83	1.97	2.11	2.26	7.9
.0	1.35	1.47	1.59	1.72	1.85	1.99	2.14	2.29	8.0
.1	1.37	1.49	1.61	1.75	1.88	2.02	2.17	2.32	8.1
.2	1.39	1.51	1.64	1.77	1.91	2.05	2.20	2.35	8.2
.3	1.41	1.53	1.66	1.79	1.93	2.08	2.23	2.38	8.3

	VOLUME IN CUBIC METRES								
Length in Metres	Top-diameter in centimetres								Length in Metres
	58	60	62	64	66	68	70	72	
1.8	0.50	0.54	0.57	0.61	0.65	0.69	0.73	0.77	1.8
1.9	0.53	0.57	0.61	0.65	0.69	0.73	0.77	0.81	1.9
2.0	0.56	0.60	0.64	0.68	0.72	0.77	0.81	0.86	2.0
2.1	0.59	0.63	0.67	0.72	0.76	0.81	0.85	0.90	2.1
2.2	0.62	0.66	0.71	0.75	0.80	0.84	0.89	0.94	2.2
2.3	0.65	0.69	0.74	0.79	0.83	0.88	0.94	0.99	2.3
2.4	0.68	0.72	0.77	0.82	0.87	0.92	0.98	1.03	2.4
2.5	0.71	0.76	0.81	0.86	0.91	0.96	1.02	1.08	2.5
2.6	0.74	0.79	0.84	0.89	0.95	1.00	1.06	1.12	2.6
2.7	0.77	0.82	0.87	0.93	0.98	1.04	1.10	1.17	2.7
2.8	0.80	0.85	0.91	0.96	1.02	1.08	1.15	1.21	2.8
2.9	0.83	0.88	0.94	1.00	1.06	1.12	1.19	1.25	2.9
3.0	0.86	0.91	0.97	1.03	1.10	1.16	1.23	1.30	3.0
3.1	0.89	0.94	1.01	1.07	1.14	1.20	1.27	1.34	3.1
3.2	0.91	0.98	1.04	1.11	1.17	1.24	1.31	1.39	3.2
3.3	0.94	1.01	1.07	1.14	1.21	1.28	1.36	1.43	3.3
3.4	0.97	1.04	1.11	1.18	1.25	1.32	1.40	1.48	3.4
3.5	1.00	1.07	1.14	1.21	1.29	1.36	1.44	1.52	3.5
3.6	1.03	1.10	1.18	1.25	1.33	1.41	1.49	1.57	3.6
3.7	1.07	1.14	1.21	1.29	1.37	1.45	1.53	1.61	3.7
3.8	1.10	1.17	1.24	1.32	1.40	1.49	1.57	1.66	3.8
3.9	1.13	1.20	1.28	1.36	1.44	1.53	1.62	1.71	3.9
4.0	1.16	1.23	1.31	1.40	1.48	1.57	1.66	1.75	4.0
4.1	1.19	1.27	1.35	1.43	1.52	1.61	1.70	1.80	4.1
4.2	1.22	1.30	1.38	1.47	1.56	1.65	1.75	1.84	4.2
4.3	1.25	1.33	1.42	1.51	1.60	1.69	1.79	1.89	4.3
4.4	1.28	1.36	1.45	1.54	1.64	1.73	1.83	1.94	4.4
4.5	1.31	1.40	1.49	1.58	1.68	1.78	1.88	1.98	4.5
4.6	1.34	1.43	1.52	1.62	1.72	1.82	1.92	2.03	4.6
4.7	1.37	1.46	1.56	1.65	1.76	1.86	1.96	2.07	4.7
4.8	1.40	1.50	1.59	1.69	1.79	1.90	2.01	2.12	4.8
4.9	1.43	1.53	1.63	1.73	1.83	1.94	2.05	2.17	4.9
5.0	1.47	1.56	1.66	1.77	1.87	1.98	2.10	2.21	5.0

Length in Metres	VOLUME IN CUBIC METRES								Length in Metres
	Top-diameter in centimetres								
	58	60	62	64	66	68	70	72	
5.1	1.50	1.60	1.70	1.80	1.91	2.03	2.14	2.26	5.1
5.2	1.53	1.63	1.73	1.84	1.95	2.07	2.19	2.31	5.2
5.3	1.56	1.66	1.77	1.88	1.99	2.11	2.23	2.35	5.3
5.4	1.59	1.70	1.81	1.92	2.03	2.15	2.28	2.40	5.4
5.5	1.62	1.73	1.84	1.96	2.07	2.20	2.32	2.45	5.5
5.6	1.65	1.76	1.88	1.99	2.11	2.24	2.37	2.50	5.6
5.7	1.69	1.80	1.91	2.03	2.15	2.28	2.41	2.54	5.7
5.8	1.72	1.83	1.95	2.07	2.20	2.32	2.46	2.59	5.8
5.9	1.75	1.87	1.99	2.11	2.24	2.37	2.50	2.64	5.9
6.0	1.78	1.90	2.02	2.15	2.28	2.41	2.55	2.69	6.0
6.1	1.81	1.93	2.06	2.19	2.32	2.45	2.59	2.73	6.1
6.2	1.85	1.97	2.09	2.22	2.36	2.50	2.64	2.78	6.2
6.3	1.88	2.00	2.13	2.26	2.40	2.54	2.68	2.83	6.3
6.4	1.91	2.04	2.17	2.30	2.44	2.58	2.73	2.88	6.4
6.5	1.94	2.07	2.20	2.34	2.48	2.63	2.77	2.93	6.5
6.6	1.98	2.11	2.24	2.38	2.52	2.67	2.82	2.97	6.6
6.7	2.01	2.14	2.28	2.42	2.56	2.71	2.87	3.02	6.7
6.8	2.04	2.18	2.31	2.46	2.60	2.76	2.91	3.07	6.8
6.9	2.07	2.21	2.35	2.50	2.65	2.80	2.96	3.12	6.9
7.0	2.11	2.25	2.39	2.54	2.69	2.84	3.00	3.17	7.0
7.1	2.14	2.28	2.43	2.58	2.73	2.89	3.05	3.22	7.1
7.2	2.17	2.32	2.46	2.61	2.77	2.93	3.10	3.27	7.2
7.3	2.21	2.35	2.50	2.65	2.81	2.98	3.14	3.32	7.3
7.4	2.24	2.39	2.54	2.69	2.85	3.02	3.19	3.36	7.4
7.5	2.27	2.42	2.58	2.73	2.90	3.06	3.24	3.41	7.5
7.6	2.31	2.46	2.61	2.77	2.94	3.11	3.28	3.46	7.6
7.7	2.34	2.49	2.65	2.81	2.98	3.15	3.33	3.51	7.7
7.8	2.37	2.53	2.69	2.85	3.02	3.20	3.38	3.56	7.8
7.9	2.41	2.56	2.73	2.89	3.07	3.24	3.42	3.61	7.9
8.0	2.44	2.60	2.76	2.93	3.11	3.29	3.47	3.66	8.0
8.1	2.48	2.64	2.80	2.97	3.15	3.33	3.52	3.71	8.1
8.2	2.51	2.67	2.84	3.01	3.19	3.38	3.57	3.76	8.2
8.3	2.54	2.71	2.88	3.06	3.24	3.42	3.61	3.81	8.3

VOLUME IN CUBIC METRES PER 100 PIECES

Length in Metres	Top-diameter in centimetres					Length in Metres
	4	5	6	7	8	
0.5	0.07	0.11	0.16	0.21	0.27	0.5
0.6	0.09	0.14	0.19	0.26	0.33	0.6
0.7	0.11	0.16	0.23	0.30	0.39	0.7
0.8	0.13	0.19	0.26	0.35	0.45	0.8
0.9	0.15	0.22	0.30	0.40	0.52	0.9
1.0	0.17	0.25	0.34	0.45	0.58	1.0
1.1	0.19	0.28	0.38	0.51	0.65	1.1
1.2	0.21	0.31	0.42	0.56	0.72	1.2
1.3	0.23	0.34	0.47	0.62	0.79	1.3
1.4	0.26	0.37	0.51	0.67	0.86	1.4
1.5	0.28	0.41	0.56	0.73	0.93	1.5
1.6	0.31	0.45	0.61	0.79	1.01	1.6
1.7	0.34	0.48	0.66	0.86	1.08	1.7
1.8	0.36	0.52	0.71	0.92	1.16	1.8
1.9	0.39	0.56	0.76	0.99	1.24	1.9
2.0	0.42	0.60	0.81	1.05	1.33	2.0
2.1	0.45	0.64	0.87	1.12	1.41	2.1
2.2	0.49	0.69	0.92	1.19	1.50	2.2
2.3	0.52	0.73	0.98	1.27	1.59	2.3
2.4	0.56	0.78	1.04	1.34	1.68	2.4
2.5	0.59	0.83	1.10	1.41	1.77	2.5
2.6	0.63	0.88	1.16	1.49	1.86	2.6
2.7	0.67	0.93	1.23	1.57	1.96	2.7
2.8	0.71	0.98	1.29	1.65	2.05	2.8
2.9	0.75	1.03	1.36	1.73	2.15	2.9
3.0	0.79	1.08	1.43	1.82	2.26	3.0
3.1	0.83	1.14	1.50	1.90	2.36	3.1
3.2	0.88	1.20	1.57	1.99	2.47	3.2
3.3	0.92	1.26	1.64	2.08	2.57	3.3
3.4	0.97	1.32	1.72	2.17	2.68	3.4
3.5	1.02	1.38	1.80	2.27	2.79	3.5
3.6	1.07	1.44	1.87	2.36	2.91	3.6
3.7	1.12	1.51	1.96	2.46	3.02	3.7
3.8	1.17	1.57	2.04	2.56	3.14	3.8
3.9	1.22	1.64	2.12	2.66	3.26	3.9
4.0	1.28	1.71	2.21	2.76	3.39	4.0

VOLUME IN CUBIC METRES PER 100 PIECES

Length in Metres	Top-diameter in centimetres					Length in Metres
	9	10	11	12	13	
0.5	0.34	0.42	0.50	0.59	0.69	0.5
0.6	0.41	0.51	0.61	0.72	0.84	0.6
0.7	0.49	0.60	0.72	0.85	0.99	0.7
0.8	0.56	0.69	0.83	0.98	1.14	0.8
0.9	0.64	0.78	0.94	1.11	1.30	0.9
1.0	0.72	0.88	1.06	1.25	1.45	1.0
1.1	0.81	0.98	1.17	1.38	1.61	1.1
1.2	0.89	1.08	1.29	1.52	1.77	1.2
1.3	0.98	1.19	1.42	1.67	1.94	1.3
1.4	1.06	1.29	1.54	1.81	2.10	1.4
1.5	1.15	1.40	1.67	1.96	2.27	1.5
1.6	1.24	1.51	1.80	2.11	2.45	1.6
1.7	1.34	1.62	1.93	2.26	2.62	1.7
1.8	1.43	1.73	2.06	2.42	2.80	1.8
1.9	1.53	1.85	2.20	2.57	2.98	1.9
2.0	1.63	1.97	2.33	2.73	3.16	2.0
2.1	1.73	2.09	2.48	2.90	3.35	2.1
2.2	1.84	2.21	2.62	3.06	3.54	2.2
2.3	1.94	2.33	2.76	3.23	3.73	2.3
2.4	2.05	2.46	2.91	3.40	3.92	2.4
2.5	2.16	2.59	3.06	3.57	4.12	2.5
2.6	2.27	2.72	3.22	3.75	4.32	2.6
2.7	2.39	2.86	3.37	3.93	4.52	2.7
2.8	2.50	2.99	3.53	4.11	4.73	2.8
2.9	2.62	3.13	3.69	4.29	4.94	2.9
3.0	2.74	3.27	3.85	4.48	5.15	3.0
3.1	2.86	3.42	4.02	4.67	5.37	3.1
3.2	2.99	3.56	4.19	4.86	5.58	3.2
3.3	3.12	3.71	4.36	5.05	5.80	3.3
3.4	3.25	3.86	4.53	5.25	6.03	3.4
3.5	3.38	4.01	4.71	5.45	6.25	3.5
3.6	3.51	4.17	4.88	5.66	6.48	3.6
3.7	3.65	4.33	5.07	5.86	6.72	3.7
3.8	3.79	4.49	5.25	6.07	6.95	3.8
3.9	3.93	4.65	5.44	6.28	7.19	3.9
4.0	4.07	4.82	5.63	6.50	7.43	4.0

Table 66 (contd)

VOLUME IN CUBIC METRES PER 100 PIECES

Length in Metres	Top-diameter in centimetres					Length in Metres
	14	15	16	17	18	
0.5	0.80	0.92	1.04	1.17	1.31	0.5
0.6	0.97	1.11	1.26	1.42	1.59	0.6
0.7	1.14	1.31	1.48	1.67	1.86	0.7
0.8	1.32	1.50	1.71	1.92	2.14	0.8
0.9	1.49	1.71	1.93	2.17	2.43	0.9
1.0	1.67	1.91	2.16	2.43	2.72	1.0
1.1	1.86	2.12	2.40	2.69	3.01	1.1
1.2	2.04	2.33	2.63	2.96	3.30	1.2
1.3	2.23	2.54	2.87	3.23	3.60	1.3
1.4	2.42	2.76	3.12	3.50	3.90	1.4
1.5	2.61	2.98	3.36	3.77	4.21	1.5
1.6	2.81	3.20	3.61	4.05	4.51	1.6
1.7	3.01	3.42	3.86	4.33	4.83	1.7
1.8	3.21	3.65	4.12	4.62	5.14	1.8
1.9	3.42	3.88	4.38	4.91	5.46	1.9
2.0	3.62	4.12	4.64	5.20	5.78	2.0
2.1	3.84	4.36	4.91	5.49	6.11	2.1
2.2	4.05	4.60	5.18	5.79	6.44	2.2
2.3	4.27	4.84	5.45	6.10	6.78	2.3
2.4	4.49	5.09	5.73	6.40	7.12	2.4
2.5	4.71	5.34	6.01	6.71	7.46	2.5
2.6	4.94	5.59	6.29	7.02	7.80	2.6
2.7	5.17	5.85	6.57	7.34	8.15	2.7
2.8	5.40	6.11	6.86	7.66	8.51	2.8
2.9	5.63	6.37	7.16	7.99	8.86	2.9
3.0	5.87	6.64	7.45	8.32	9.22	3.0
3.1	6.11	6.91	7.75	8.65	9.59	3.1
3.2	6.36	7.18	8.06	8.98	9.96	3.2
3.3	6.61	7.46	8.36	9.32	10.33	3.3
3.4	6.86	7.74	8.67	9.66	10.71	3.4
3.5	7.11	8.02	8.99	10.01	11.09	3.5
3.6	7.37	8.31	9.31	10.36	11.47	3.6
3.7	7.63	8.60	9.63	10.72	11.86	3.7
3.8	7.89	8.89	9.95	11.07	12.25	3.8
3.9	8.16	9.19	10.28	11.43	12.65	3.9
4.0	8.43	9.49	10.61	11.80	13.05	4.0

VOLUME IN CUBIC METRES PER 100 PIECES

Length in Metres	Top-diameter in centimetres					Length in Metres
	19	20	21	22	23	
0.5	1.46	1.62	1.78	1.95	2.13	0.5
0.6	1.77	1.95	2.15	2.36	2.57	0.6
0.7	2.07	2.29	2.52	2.76	3.01	0.7
0.8	2.38	2.63	2.90	3.17	3.46	0.8
0.9	2.70	2.98	3.28	3.59	3.92	0.9
1.0	3.02	3.33	3.66	4.01	4.37	1.0
1.1	3.34	3.69	4.05	4.43	4.83	1.1
1.2	3.66	4.04	4.44	4.86	5.30	1.2
1.3	3.99	4.41	4.84	5.30	5.77	1.3
1.4	4.33	4.77	5.24	5.73	6.25	1.4
1.5	4.66	5.14	5.65	6.17	6.73	1.5
1.6	5.00	5.52	6.06	6.62	7.21	1.6
1.7	5.35	5.89	6.47	7.07	7.70	1.7
1.8	5.70	6.28	6.89	7.53	8.19	1.8
1.9	6.05	6.66	7.31	7.98	8.69	1.9
2.0	6.40	7.05	7.73	8.45	9.19	2.0
2.1	6.76	7.45	8.17	8.92	9.70	2.1
2.2	7.13	7.85	8.60	9.39	10.21	2.2
2.3	7.49	8.25	9.04	9.87	10.73	2.3
2.4	7.87	8.66	9.48	10.35	11.25	2.4
2.5	8.24	9.07	9.93	10.83	11.77	2.5
2.6	8.62	9.48	10.38	11.32	12.31	2.6
2.7	9.01	9.90	10.84	11.82	12.84	2.7
2.8	9.39	10.32	11.30	12.32	13.38	2.8
2.9	9.78	10.75	11.76	12.82	13.93	2.9
3.0	10.18	11.18	12.23	13.33	14.47	3.0
3.1	10.58	11.62	12.71	13.84	15.03	3.1
3.2	10.98	12.06	13.19	14.36	15.59	3.2
3.3	11.39	12.50	13.67	14.88	16.15	3.3
3.4	11.80	12.95	14.16	15.41	16.72	3.4
3.5	12.22	13.41	14.65	15.94	17.30	3.5
3.6	12.64	13.86	15.14	16.48	17.87	3.6
3.7	13.06	14.32	15.64	17.02	18.46	3.7
3.8	13.49	14.79	16.15	17.57	19.05	3.8
3.9	13.92	15.26	16.66	18.12	19.64	3.9
4.0	14.36	15.74	17.17	18.67	20.24	4.0

Pitwood
(100 pieces)

Length in Metres	VOLUME IN CUBIC METRES PER 100 PIECES					Length in Metres
	Top-diameter in centimetres					
	6	7	8	9	10	
0.375	0.114	0.154	0.199			0.375
0.400	0.122	0.165	0.213			0.400
0.450	0.139	0.187	0.242	0.304		0.450
0.500	0.156	0.209	0.270	0.339		0.500
0.525	0.164	0.220	0.285	0.358	0.439	0.525
0.550	0.173	0.232	0.300	0.376	0.461	0.550
0.600	0.190	0.255	0.329	0.413	0.505	0.600
0.650	0.208	0.279	0.359	0.450	0.551	0.650
0.675	0.217	0.290	0.374	0.469	0.574	0.675
0.750	0.245	0.327	0.420	0.526	0.643	0.750
0.825	0.273	0.364	0.467	0.584	0.713	0.825
0.875	0.292	0.389	0.499	0.623	0.761	0.875
0.900	0.302	0.401	0.515	0.643	0.785	0.900
0.975	0.332	0.440	0.564	0.703	0.857	0.975
1.025	0.352	0.466	0.597	0.743	0.906	1.025
1.050	0.362	0.479	0.613	0.764	0.931	1.050
1.125	0.393	0.520	0.664	0.826	1.006	1.125
1.175	0.414	0.547	0.698	0.868	1.056	1.175
1.200	0.425	0.561	0.716	0.889	1.082	1.200
1.275	0.457	0.603	0.768	0.954	1.159	1.275
1.350	0.491	0.646	0.822	1.019	1.238	1.350
1.425	0.525	0.689	0.876	1.085	1.317	1.425
1.500	0.560	0.734	0.932	1.153	1.398	1.500
1.575	0.595	0.779	0.988	1.222	1.480	1.575
1.600	0.607	0.795	1.007	1.245	1.507	1.600
1.650	0.632	0.826	1.046	1.291	1.563	1.650
1.800	0.707	0.921	1.163	1.434	1.733	1.800
1.950	0.785	1.020	1.285	1.581	1.908	1.950
2.100	0.867	1.123	1.411	1.733	2.087	2.100
2.250	0.952	1.229	1.541	1.889	2.272	2.250
2.400	1.040	1.339	1.676	2.050	2.462	2.400
2.550		1.453	1.814	2.216	2.657	2.550
2.700			1.957	2.386	2.857	2.700
2.850			2.105	2.561	3.062	2.850
3.000				2.741	3.273	3.000
3.200				2.989	3.562	3.200
3.400					3.861	3.400
3.600						3.600
3.800						3.800
4.000						4.000

VOLUME IN CUBIC METRES PER 100 PIECES

Length in Metres	Top-diameter in centimetres					Length in Metres
	11	12	13	14	15	
0.375						0.375
0.400						0.400
0.450						0.450
0.500						0.500
0.525						0.525
0.550	0.554					0.550
0.600	0.608					0.600
0.650	0.662	0.783				0.650
0.675	0.689	0.815				0.675
0.750	0.772	0.913	1.065			0.750
0.825	0.856	1.011	1.179	1.361		0.825
0.875	0.912	1.077	1.256	1.449		0.875
0.900	0.941	1.111	1.295	1.493	1.706	0.900
0.975	1.027	1.212	1.412	1.628	1.859	0.975
1.025	1.085	1.280	1.491	1.718	1.962	1.025
1.050	1.114	1.314	1.531	1.764	2.013	1.050
1.125	1.203	1.418	1.651	1.901	2.170	1.125
1.175	1.263	1.488	1.732	1.994	2.275	1.175
1.200	1.293	1.524	1.773	2.041	2.327	1.200
1.275	1.385	1.630	1.896	2.181	2.487	1.275
1.350	1.477	1.738	2.020	2.324	2.648	1.350
1.425	1.571	1.848	2.146	2.467	2.811	1.425
1.500	1.666	1.958	2.274	2.613	2.976	1.500
1.575	1.763	2.070	2.403	2.760	3.142	1.575
1.600	1.795	2.108	2.446	2.810	3.198	1.600
1.650	1.861	2.184	2.533	2.909	3.310	1.650
1.800	2.060	2.416	2.799	3.211	3.651	1.800
1.950	2.265	2.653	3.071	3.520	4.000	1.950
2.100	2.475	2.896	3.349	3.836	4.355	2.100
2.250	2.691	3.144	3.634	4.158	4.718	2.250
2.400	2.912	3.399	3.924	4.487	5.087	2.400
2.550	3.138	3.660	4.221	4.823	5.464	2.550
2.700	3.370	3.926	4.525	5.165	5.848	2.700
2.850	3.608	4.199	4.835	5.515	6.240	2.850
3.000	3.852	4.478	5.151	5.871	6.639	3.000
3.200	4.185	4.859	5.583	6.358	7.182	3.200
3.400	4.529	5.252	6.027	6.856	7.739	3.400
3.600	4.884	5.655	6.483	7.368	8.309	3.600
3.800	5.249	6.071	6.952	7.893	8.893	3.800
4.000		6.497	7.432	8.430	9.491	4.000

Pitwood
(100 pieces), *contd.*

top diam. 16-20 cm.

VOLUME IN CUBIC METRES PER 100 PIECES

Length in Metres	Top-diameter in centimetres 16	17	18	19	20	Length in Metres
0.375						0.375
0.400						0.400
0.450						0.450
0.500						0.500
0.525						0.525
0.550						0.550
0.600						0.600
0.650						0.650
0.675						0.675
0.750						0.750
0.825						0.825
0.875						0.875
0.900						0.900
0.975	2.105					0.975
1.025	2.221					1.025
1.050	2.279	2.562				1.050
1.125	2.455	2.759	3.080			1.125
1.175	2.574	2.891	3.227	3.581		1.175
1.200	2.633	2.957	3.301	3.663		1.200
1.275	2.812	3.158	3.524	3.910	4.315	1.275
1.350	2.994	3.361	3.749	4.158	4.589	1.350
1.425	3.177	3.565	3.976	4.409	4.865	1.425
1.500	3.362	3.772	4.205	4.662	5.143	1.500
1.575	3.549	3.980	4.436	4.917	5.423	1.575
1.600	3.611	4.050	4.514	5.003	5.517	1.600
1.650	3.737	4.190	4.669	5.174	5.705	1.650
1.800	4.120	4.617	5.142	5.695	6.277	1.800
1.950	4.510	5.051	5.623	6.225	6.858	1.950
2.100	4.908	5.493	6.112	6.763	7.448	2.100
2.250	5.313	5.943	6.609	7.310	8.047	2.250
2.400	5.726	6.402	7.115	7.866	8.655	2.400
2.550	6.146	6.868	7.629	8.431	9.273	2.550
2.700	6.574	7.342	8.152	9.005	9.900	2.700
2.850	7.010	7.824	8.684	9.588	10.537	2.850
3.000	7.453	8.315	9.224	10.180	11.183	3.000
3.200	8.057	8.982	9.958	10.983	12.059	3.200
3.400	8.675	9.664	10.707	11.803	12.952	3.400
3.600	9.307	10.361	11.472	12.639	13.863	3.600
3.800	9.953	11.073	12.253	13.492	14.791	3.800
4.000	10.614	11.800	13.050	14.362	15.736	4.000

Pitwood
(100 lineal metres)

top diam. 6-10 cm

VOLUME IN CUBIC METRES PER 100 LINEAL METRES

Length in Metres	Top-diameter in centimetres					Length in Metres
	6	7	8	9	10	
0.375	0.304	0.410	0.531			0.375
0.400	0.306	0.411	0.533			0.400
0.450	0.309	0.415	0.537	0.675		0.450
0.500	0.311	0.418	0.541	0.679		0.500
0.525	0.313	0.420	0.543	0.681	0.835	0.525
0.550	0.314	0.422	0.545	0.683	0.838	0.550
0.600	0.317	0.425	0.549	0.688	0.842	0.600
0.650	0.320	0.429	0.552	0.692	0.847	0.650
0.675	0.322	0.430	0.554	0.694	0.850	0.675
0.750	0.326	0.435	0.560	0.701	0.857	0.750
0.825	0.331	0.441	0.566	0.707	0.864	0.825
0.875	0.334	0.444	0.570	0.712	0.869	0.875
0.900	0.335	0.446	0.572	0.714	0.872	0.900
0.975	0.340	0.451	0.578	0.721	0.879	0.975
1.025	0.343	0.455	0.582	0.725	0.884	1.025
1.050	0.345	0.457	0.584	0.728	0.887	1.050
1.125	0.349	0.462	0.590	0.734	0.894	1.125
1.175	0.353	0.466	0.594	0.739	0.899	1.175
1.200	0.354	0.467	0.596	0.741	0.902	1.200
1.275	0.359	0.473	0.603	0.748	0.909	1.275
1.350	0.364	0.478	0.609	0.755	0.917	1.350
1.425	0.368	0.484	0.615	0.762	0.924	1.425
1.500	0.373	0.489	0.621	0.769	0.932	1.500
1.575	0.378	0.495	0.627	0.776	0.940	1.575
1.600	0.380	0.497	0.629	0.778	0.942	1.600
1.650	0.383	0.500	0.634	0.783	0.947	1.650
1.800	0.393	0.512	0.646	0.797	0.963	1.800
1.950	0.403	0.523	0.659	0.811	0.978	1.950
2.100	0.413	0.535	0.672	0.825	0.994	2.100
2.250	0.423	0.546	0.685	0.840	1.010	2.250
2.400	0.433	0.558	0.698	0.854	1.026	2.400
2.550		0.570	0.711	0.869	1.042	2.550
2.700			0.725	0.884	1.058	2.700
2.850			0.738	0.899	1.074	2.850
3.000				0.914	1.091	3.000
3.200				0.934	1.113	3.200
3.400					1.135	3.400
3.600						3.600
3.800						3.800
4.000						4.000

Pitwood
(100 lineal metres), *contd.*

VOLUME IN CUBIC METRES PER 100 LINEAL METRES

Length in Metres	Top-diameter in centimetres 11	12	13	14	15	Length in Metres
0.375						0.375
0.400						0.400
0.450						0.450
0.500						0.500
0.525						0.525
0.550	1.008					0.550
0.600	1.013					0.600
0.650	1.018	1.205				0.650
0.675	1.021	1.208				0.675
0.750	1.029	1.217	1.420			0.750
0.825	1.037	1.225	1.429	1.649		0.825
0.875	1.042	1.231	1.436	1.656		0.875
0.900	1.045	1.234	1.439	1.659	1.896	0.900
0.975	1.053	1.243	1.448	1.670	1.907	0.975
1.025	1.059	1.249	1.455	1.676	1.914	1.025
1.050	1.061	1.252	1.458	1.680	1.917	1.050
1.125	1.070	1.261	1.468	1.690	1.928	1.125
1.175	1.075	1.267	1.474	1.697	1.936	1.175
1.200	1.078	1.270	1.477	1.700	1.939	1.200
1.275	1.086	1.279	1.487	1.711	1.950	1.275
1.350	1.094	1.288	1.496	1.721	1.962	1.350
1.425	1.103	1.297	1.506	1.732	1.973	1.425
1.500	1.111	1.306	1.516	1.742	1.984	1.500
1.575	1.119	1.315	1.526	1.752	1.995	1.575
1.600	1.122	1.318	1.529	1.756	1.999	1.600
1.650	1.128	1.324	1.535	1.763	2.006	1.650
1.800	1.144	1.342	1.555	1.784	2.029	1.800
1.950	1.161	1.360	1.575	1.805	2.051	1.950
2.100	1.179	1.379	1.595	1.827	2.074	2.100
2.250	1.196	1.398	1.615	1.848	2.097	2.250
2.400	1.213	1.416	1.635	1.870	2.120	2.400
2.550	1.231	1.435	1.655	1.891	2.143	2.550
2.700	1.248	1.454	1.676	1.913	2.166	2.700
2.850	1.266	1.473	1.696	1.935	2.189	2.850
3.000	1.284	1.493	1.717	1.957	2.213	3.000
3.200	1.308	1.519	1.745	1.987	2.244	3.200
3.400	1.332	1.545	1.773	2.017	2.276	3.400
3.600	1.357	1.571	1.801	2.047	2.308	3.600
3.800	1.381	1.598	1.829	2.077	2.340	3.800
4.000		1.624	1.858	2.107	2.373	4.000

VOLUME IN CUBIC METRES PER 100 LINEAL METRES

Length in Metres	16	17	18	19	20	Length in Metres
	Top-diameter in centimetres					
0.375						0.375
0.400						0.400
0.450						0.450
0.500						0.500
0.525						0.525
0.550						0.550
0.600						0.600
0.650						0.650
0.675						0.675
0.750						0.750
0.825						0.825
0.875						0.875
0.900						0.900
0.975	2.159					0.975
1.025	2.167					1.025
1.050	2.171	2.440				1.050
1.125	2.182	2.452	2.738			1.125
1.175	2.190	2.460	2.746	3.048		1.175
1.200	2.194	2.465	2.751	3.052		1.200
1.275	2.206	2.477	2.764	3.066	3.385	1.275
1.350	2.218	2.489	2.777	3.080	3.399	1.350
1.425	2.229	2.502	2.790	3.094	3.414	1.425
1.500	2.241	2.514	2.803	3.108	3.428	1.500
1.575	2.253	2.527	2.817	3.122	3.443	1.575
1.600	2.257	2.531	2.821	3.127	3.448	1.600
1.650	2.265	2.540	2.830	3.136	3.458	1.650
1.800	2.289	2.565	2.857	3.164	3.487	1.800
1.950	2.313	2.590	2.883	3.192	3.517	1.950
2.100	2.337	2.616	2.910	3.221	3.547	2.100
2.250	2.361	2.642	2.937	3.249	3.576	2.250
2.400	2.386	2.667	2.965	3.278	3.606	2.400
2.550	2.410	2.693	2.992	3.306	3.637	2.550
2.700	2.435	2.719	3.019	3.335	3.667	2.700
2.850	2.460	2.745	3.047	3.364	3.697	2.850
3.000	2.484	2.772	3.075	3.393	3.728	3.000
3.200	2.518	2.807	3.112	3.432	3.768	3.200
3.400	2.551	2.842	3.149	3.471	3.810	3.400
3.600	2.585	2.878	3.187	3.511	3.851	3.600
3.800	2.619	2.914	3.224	3.551	3.892	3.800
4.000	2.654	2.950	3.262	3.590	3.934	4.000

dbh cm	VOLUME IN CUBIC METRES ÓVERBARK											dbh cm
	Tariff Number											
	0	1	2	3	4	5	6	7	8	9	10	
7	0.00	0.005	0.005	0.005	0.005	0.005	0.005	0.005	0.005	0.005	0.005	7
8	0.00	0.005	0.006	0.006	0.006	0.007	0.007	0.008	0.008	0.008	0.009	8
9	0.00	0.006	0.007	0.007	0.008	0.009	0.010	0.010	0.011	0.012	0.013	9
10	0.00	0.006	0.007	0.009	0.010	0.011	0.012	0.014	0.015	0.016	0.017	10
11	0.00	0.007	0.008	0.010	0.012	0.014	0.015	0.017	0.019	0.021	0.023	11
12	0.00	0.007	0.009	0.012	0.014	0.016	0.019	0.021	0.024	0.026	0.028	12
13	0.00	0.008	0.011	0.014	0.017	0.019	0.022	0.025	0.028	0.031	0.034	13
14	0.00	0.008	0.012	0.015	0.019	0.023	0.026	0.030	0.034	0.037	0.041	14
15	0.00	0.009	0.013	0.018	0.022	0.026	0.031	0.035	0.039	0.044	0.048	15
16	0.00	0.009	0.015	0.020	0.025	0.030	0.035	0.040	0.045	0.050	0.056	16
17	0.00	0.010	0.016	0.022	0.028	0.034	0.040	0.046	0.052	0.058	0.064	17
18	0.00	0.011	0.018	0.025	0.031	0.038	0.045	0.052	0.059	0.065	0.072	18
19	0.00	0.012	0.019	0.027	0.035	0.043	0.050	0.058	0.066	0.073	0.081	19
20	0.00	0.013	0.021	0.030	0.039	0.047	0.056	0.065	0.073	0.082	0.091	20
21	0.00	0.01	0.02	0.03	0.04	0.05	0.06	0.07	0.08	0.09	0.10	21
22	0.00	0.01	0.03	0.04	0.05	0.06	0.07	0.08	0.09	0.10	0.11	22
23	0.00	0.02	0.03	0.04	0.05	0.06	0.07	0.09	0.10	0.11	0.12	23
24	0.00	0.02	0.03	0.04	0.06	0.07	0.08	0.09	0.11	0.12	0.13	24
25	0.00	0.02	0.03	0.05	0.06	0.07	0.09	0.10	0.12	0.13	0.15	25
26	0.00	0.02	0.03	0.05	0.06	0.08	0.10	0.11	0.13	0.14	0.16	26
27	0.00	0.02	0.04	0.05	0.07	0.09	0.10	0.12	0.14	0.15	0.17	27
28	0.00	0.02	0.04	0.06	0.08	0.09	0.11	0.13	0.15	0.17	0.18	28
29	0.00	0.02	0.04	0.06	0.08	0.10	0.12	0.14	0.16	0.18	0.20	29
30	0.00	0.02	0.04	0.07	0.09	0.11	0.13	0.15	0.17	0.19	0.21	30

dbh cm	VOLUME IN CUBIC METRES OVERBARK										
	Tariff Number										
	10	11	12	13	14	15	16	17	18	19	20
7	0.005	0.005	0.005	0.005	0.005	0.005	0.005	0.005	0.005	0.005	0.005
8	0.009	0.009	0.009	0.010	0.010	0.011	0.011	0.011	0.012	0.012	0.012
9	0.013	0.014	0.014	0.015	0.016	0.017	0.018	0.018	0.019	0.020	0.021
10	0.017	0.019	0.020	0.021	0.023	0.024	0.025	0.026	0.028	0.029	0.030
11	0.023	0.024	0.026	0.028	0.030	0.032	0.033	0.035	0.037	0.039	0.040
12	0.028	0.031	0.033	0.035	0.038	0.040	0.042	0.045	0.047	0.049	0.052
13	0.034	0.037	0.040	0.043	0.046	0.049	0.052	0.055	0.058	0.061	0.064
14	0.041	0.045	0.048	0.052	0.055	0.059	0.063	0.066	0.070	0.074	0.077
15	0.048	0.052	0.057	0.061	0.065	0.070	0.074	0.078	0.083	0.087	0.092
16	0.056	0.061	0.066	0.071	0.076	0.081	0.086	0.091	0.097	0.102	0.107
17	0.064	0.070	0.075	0.081	0.087	0.093	0.099	0.105	0.111	0.117	0.123
18	0.072	0.079	0.086	0.093	0.099	0.106	0.113	0.120	0.127	0.133	0.140
19	0.081	0.089	0.097	0.104	0.112	0.120	0.127	0.135	0.143	0.151	0.158
20	0.091	0.099	0.108	0.117	0.125	0.134	0.143	0.151	0.160	0.169	0.178
21	0.10	0.11	0.12	0.13	0.14	0.15	0.16	0.17	0.18	0.19	0.20
22	0.11	0.12	0.13	0.14	0.15	0.16	0.18	0.19	0.20	0.21	0.22
23	0.12	0.13	0.15	0.16	0.17	0.18	0.19	0.21	0.22	0.23	0.24
24	0.13	0.15	0.16	0.17	0.19	0.20	0.21	0.22	0.24	0.25	0.26
25	0.15	0.16	0.17	0.19	0.20	0.22	0.23	0.25	0.26	0.27	0.29
26	0.16	0.17	0.19	0.20	0.22	0.24	0.25	0.27	0.28	0.30	0.31
27	0.17	0.19	0.20	0.22	0.24	0.26	0.27	0.29	0.31	0.32	0.34
28	0.18	0.20	0.22	0.24	0.26	0.28	0.29	0.31	0.33	0.35	0.37
29	0.20	0.22	0.24	0.26	0.28	0.30	0.32	0.34	0.36	0.37	0.39
30	0.21	0.23	0.25	0.28	0.30	0.32	0.34	0.36	0.38	0.40	0.42
31	0.23	0.25	0.27	0.30	0.32	0.34	0.36	0.39	0.41	0.43	0.45
32	0.24	0.27	0.29	0.32	0.34	0.36	0.39	0.41	0.44	0.46	0.48
33	0.26	0.28	0.31	0.34	0.36	0.39	0.41	0.44	0.46	0.49	0.52
34	0.28	0.30	0.33	0.36	0.38	0.41	0.44	0.47	0.49	0.52	0.55
35	0.29	0.32	0.35	0.38	0.41	0.44	0.47	0.50	0.52	0.55	0.58
36	0.31	0.34	0.37	0.40	0.43	0.46	0.49	0.53	0.56	0.59	0.62
37	0.33	0.36	0.39	0.43	0.46	0.49	0.52	0.56	0.59	0.62	0.65
38	0.35	0.38	0.41	0.45	0.48	0.52	0.55	0.59	0.62	0.66	0.69
39	0.36	0.40	0.44	0.47	0.51	0.55	0.58	0.62	0.66	0.69	0.73
40	0.38	0.42	0.46	0.50	0.54	0.58	0.61	0.65	0.69	0.73	0.77
41	0.40	0.44	0.48	0.52	0.56	0.61	0.65	0.69	0.73	0.77	0.81
42	0.42	0.47	0.51	0.55	0.59	0.64	0.68	0.72	0.76	0.81	0.85
43	0.44	0.49	0.53	0.58	0.62	0.67	0.71	0.76	0.80	0.85	0.89
44	0.47	0.51	0.56	0.61	0.65	0.70	0.75	0.79	0.84	0.89	0.93
45	0.49	0.54	0.58	0.63	0.68	0.73	0.78	0.83	0.88	0.93	0.98
46	0.51	0.56	0.61	0.66	0.71	0.77	0.82	0.87	0.92	0.97	1.02
47	0.53	0.59	0.64	0.69	0.75	0.80	0.85	0.91	0.96	1.01	1.07
48	0.56	0.61	0.67	0.72	0.78	0.83	0.89	0.95	1.00	1.06	1.11
49	0.58	0.64	0.70	0.75	0.81	0.87	0.93	0.99	1.04	1.10	1.16
50	0.60	0.66	0.72	0.78	0.85	0.91	0.97	1.03	1.09	1.15	1.21

dbh cm	VOLUME IN CUBIC METRES OVERBARK											dbh cm
	Tariff Number											
	10	11	12	13	14	15	16	17	18	19	20	
51	0.63	0.69	0.75	0.82	0.88	0.94	1.01	1.07	1.13	1.20	1.26	51
52	0.65	0.72	0.78	0.85	0.92	0.98	1.05	1.11	1.18	1.24	1.31	52
53	0.68	0.75	0.82	0.88	0.95	1.02	1.09	1.16	1.22	1.29	1.36	53
54	0.70	0.78	0.85	0.92	0.99	1.06	1.13	1.20	1.27	1.34	1.41	54
55	0.73	0.80	0.88	0.95	1.03	1.10	1.17	1.25	1.32	1.39	1.47	55
56	0.76	0.83	0.91	0.99	1.06	1.14	1.22	1.29	1.37	1.45	1.52	56
57	0.79	0.86	0.94	1.02	1.10	1.18	1.26	1.34	1.42	1.50	1.58	57
58	0.81	0.90	0.98	1.06	1.14	1.22	1.31	1.39	1.47	1.55	1.63	58
59	0.84	0.93	1.01	1.10	1.18	1.27	1.35	1.44	1.52	1.61	1.69	59
60	0.87	0.96	1.05	1.14	1.22	1.31	1.40	1.49	1.57	1.66	1.75	60
61	0.90	0.99	1.08	1.17	1.26	1.36	1.45	1.54	1.63	1.72	1.81	61
62	0.93	1.02	1.12	1.21	1.31	1.40	1.49	1.59	1.68	1.78	1.87	62
63	0.96	1.06	1.16	1.25	1.35	1.45	1.54	1.64	1.74	1.83	1.93	63
64	0.99	1.09	1.19	1.29	1.39	1.49	1.59	1.69	1.79	1.89	1.99	64
65	1.02	1.13	1.23	1.33	1.44	1.54	1.64	1.75	1.85	1.95	2.06	65
66	1.06	1.16	1.27	1.38	1.48	1.59	1.70	1.80	1.91	2.01	2.12	66
67	1.09	1.20	1.31	1.42	1.53	1.64	1.75	1.86	1.97	2.08	2.19	67
68	1.12	1.23	1.35	1.46	1.57	1.69	1.80	1.91	2.03	2.14	2.25	68
69	1.15	1.27	1.39	1.50	1.62	1.74	1.85	1.97	2.09	2.20	2.32	69
70	1.19	1.31	1.43	1.55	1.67	1.79	1.91	2.03	2.15	2.27	2.39	70
71	1.22	1.35	1.47	1.59	1.72	1.84	1.96	2.09	2.21	2.33	2.46	71
72	1.26	1.38	1.51	1.64	1.77	1.89	2.02	2.15	2.27	2.40	2.53	72
73	1.29	1.42	1.55	1.69	1.82	1.95	2.08	2.21	2.34	2.47	2.60	73
74	1.33	1.46	1.60	1.73	1.87	2.00	2.13	2.27	2.40	2.54	2.67	74
75	1.37	1.50	1.64	1.78	1.92	2.06	2.19	2.33	2.47	2.61	2.75	75
76	1.40	1.54	1.69	1.83	1.97	2.11	2.25	2.39	2.54	2.68	2.82	76
77	1.44	1.59	1.73	1.88	2.02	2.17	2.31	2.46	2.60	2.75	2.89	77
78	1.48	1.63	1.78	1.93	2.07	2.22	2.37	2.52	2.67	2.82	2.97	78
79	1.52	1.67	1.82	1.98	2.13	2.28	2.44	2.59	2.74	2.89	3.05	79
80	1.55	1.71	1.87	2.03	2.18	2.34	2.50	2.65	2.81	2.97	3.13	80

dbh cm	VOLUME IN CUBIC METRES OVERBARK											dbh cm
	Tariff Number											
	20	21	22	23	24	25	26	27	28	29	30	
7	0.005	0.005	0.005	0.005	0.005	0.005	0.005	0.005	0.005	0.005	0.005	7
8	0.012	0.013	0.013	0.014	0.014	0.014	0.015	0.015	0.015	0.016	0.016	8
9	0.021	0.022	0.022	0.023	0.024	0.025	0.026	0.026	0.027	0.028	0.029	9
10	0.030	0.031	0.033	0.034	0.035	0.036	0.038	0.039	0.040	0.041	0.043	10
11	0.040	0.042	0.044	0.046	0.048	0.049	0.051	0.053	0.055	0.056	0.058	11
12	0.052	0.054	0.056	0.059	0.061	0.063	0.066	0.068	0.071	0.073	0.075	12
13	0.064	0.067	0.070	0.073	0.076	0.079	0.082	0.085	0.088	0.091	0.094	13
14	0.077	0.081	0.085	0.088	0.092	0.095	0.099	0.103	0.106	0.110	0.114	14
15	0.092	0.096	0.100	0.105	0.109	0.113	0.118	0.122	0.126	0.131	0.135	15
16	0.107	0.112	0.117	0.122	0.127	0.132	0.138	0.143	0.148	0.153	0.158	16
17	0.123	0.129	0.135	0.141	0.147	0.153	0.159	0.165	0.170	0.176	0.182	17
18	0.140	0.147	0.154	0.161	0.167	0.174	0.181	0.188	0.195	0.201	0.208	18
19	0.158	0.166	0.174	0.182	0.189	0.197	0.205	0.212	0.220	0.228	0.236	19
20	0.178	0.186	0.195	0.204	0.212	0.221	0.230	0.238	0.247	0.256	0.264	20
21	0.20	0.21	0.22	0.23	0.24	0.25	0.26	0.27	0.28	0.28	0.29	21
22	0.22	0.23	0.24	0.25	0.26	0.27	0.28	0.29	0.30	0.32	0.33	22
23	0.24	0.25	0.26	0.28	0.29	0.30	0.31	0.32	0.34	0.35	0.36	23
24	0.26	0.28	0.29	0.30	0.32	0.33	0.34	0.36	0.37	0.38	0.39	24
25	0.29	0.30	0.32	0.33	0.35	0.36	0.37	0.39	0.40	0.42	0.43	25
26	0.31	0.33	0.34	0.36	0.38	0.39	0.41	0.42	0.44	0.45	0.47	26
27	0.34	0.36	0.37	0.39	0.41	0.42	0.44	0.46	0.47	0.49	0.51	27
28	0.37	0.38	0.40	0.42	0.44	0.46	0.48	0.49	0.51	0.53	0.55	28
29	0.39	0.41	0.43	0.45	0.47	0.49	0.51	0.53	0.55	0.57	0.59	29
30	0.42	0.44	0.47	0.49	0.51	0.53	0.55	0.57	0.59	0.61	0.63	30
31	0.45	0.48	0.50	0.52	0.54	0.57	0.59	0.61	0.63	0.66	0.68	31
32	0.48	0.51	0.53	0.56	0.58	0.60	0.63	0.65	0.68	0.70	0.73	32
33	0.52	0.54	0.57	0.59	0.62	0.64	0.67	0.70	0.72	0.75	0.77	33
34	0.55	0.58	0.60	0.63	0.66	0.69	0.71	0.74	0.77	0.80	0.82	34
35	0.58	0.61	0.64	0.67	0.70	0.73	0.76	0.79	0.82	0.84	0.87	35
36	0.62	0.65	0.68	0.71	0.74	0.77	0.80	0.83	0.86	0.90	0.93	36
37	0.65	0.69	0.72	0.75	0.78	0.82	0.85	0.88	0.92	0.95	0.98	37
38	0.69	0.73	0.76	0.79	0.83	0.86	0.90	0.93	0.97	1.00	1.04	38
39	0.73	0.76	0.80	0.84	0.87	0.91	0.95	0.98	1.02	1.06	1.09	39
40	0.77	0.81	0.84	0.88	0.92	0.96	1.00	1.04	1.07	1.11	1.15	40
41	0.81	0.85	0.89	0.93	0.97	1.01	1.05	1.09	1.13	1.17	1.21	41
42	0.85	0.89	0.93	0.98	1.02	1.06	1.10	1.14	1.19	1.23	1.27	42
43	0.89	0.93	0.98	1.02	1.07	1.11	1.16	1.20	1.25	1.29	1.33	43
44	0.93	0.98	1.03	1.07	1.12	1.17	1.21	1.26	1.31	1.35	1.40	44
45	0.98	1.02	1.07	1.12	1.17	1.22	1.27	1.32	1.37	1.42	1.47	45
46	1.02	1.07	1.12	1.17	1.23	1.28	1.33	1.38	1.43	1.48	1.53	46
47	1.07	1.12	1.17	1.23	1.28	1.33	1.39	1.44	1.49	1.55	1.60	47
48	1.11	1.17	1.22	1.28	1.34	1.39	1.45	1.50	1.56	1.62	1.67	48
49	1.16	1.22	1.28	1.34	1.39	1.45	1.51	1.57	1.63	1.68	1.74	49
50	1.21	1.27	1.33	1.39	1.45	1.51	1.57	1.63	1.69	1.76	1.82	50

VOLUME IN CUBIC METRES OVERBARK

dbh cm	Tariff Number 20	21	22	23	24	25	26	27	28	29	30	dbh cm
51	1.26	1.32	1.39	1.45	1.51	1.57	1.64	1.70	1.76	1.83	1.89	51
52	1.31	1.38	1.44	1.51	1.57	1.64	1.70	1.77	1.84	1.90	1.97	52
53	1.36	1.43	1.50	1.57	1.63	1.70	1.77	1.84	1.91	1.98	2.04	53
54	1.41	1.48	1.56	1.63	1.70	1.77	1.84	1.91	1.98	2.05	2.12	54
55	1.47	1.54	1.61	1.69	1.76	1.84	1.91	1.98	2.06	2.13	2.20	55
56	1.52	1.60	1.67	1.75	1.83	1.90	1.98	2.06	2.13	2.21	2.29	56
57	1.58	1.66	1.74	1.82	1.89	1.97	2.05	2.13	2.21	2.29	2.37	57
58	1.63	1.72	1.80	1.88	1.96	2.04	2.13	2.21	2.29	2.37	2.45	58
59	1.69	1.78	1.86	1.95	2.03	2.12	2.20	2.29	2.37	2.46	2.54	59
60	1.75	1.84	1.93	2.01	2.10	2.19	2.28	2.37	2.45	2.54	2.63	60
61	1.81	1.90	1.99	2.08	2.17	2.26	2.35	2.45	2.54	2.63	2.72	61
62	1.87	1.96	2.06	2.15	2.25	2.34	2.43	2.53	2.62	2.72	2.81	62
63	1.93	2.03	2.13	2.22	2.32	2.42	2.51	2.61	2.71	2.80	2.90	63
64	1.99	2.09	2.19	2.29	2.39	2.49	2.59	2.69	2.79	2.90	3.00	64
65	2.06	2.16	2.26	2.37	2.47	2.57	2.68	2.78	2.88	2.99	3.09	65
66	2.12	2.23	2.33	2.44	2.55	2.65	2.76	2.87	2.97	3.08	3.19	66
67	2.19	2.30	2.41	2.52	2.63	2.74	2.85	2.96	3.07	3.18	3.29	67
68	2.25	2.37	2.48	2.59	2.71	2.82	2.93	3.05	3.16	3.27	3.39	68
69	2.32	2.44	2.55	2.67	2.79	2.90	3.02	3.14	3.25	3.37	3.49	69
70	2.39	2.51	2.63	2.75	2.87	2.99	3.11	3.23	3.35	3.47	3.59	70
71	2.46	2.58	2.71	2.83	2.95	3.08	3.20	3.32	3.45	3.57	3.69	71
72	2.53	2.66	2.78	2.91	3.04	3.16	3.29	3.42	3.54	3.67	3.80	72
73	2.60	2.73	2.86	2.99	3.12	3.25	3.38	3.51	3.64	3.78	3.91	73
74	2.67	2.81	2.94	3.07	3.21	3.34	3.48	3.61	3.75	3.88	4.01	74
75	2.75	2.88	3.02	3.16	3.30	3.44	3.57	3.71	3.85	3.99	4.12	75
76	2.82	2.96	3.10	3.24	3.39	3.53	3.67	3.81	3.95	4.09	4.24	76
77	2.89	3.04	3.19	3.33	3.48	3.62	3.77	3.91	4.06	4.20	4.35	77
78	2.97	3.12	3.27	3.42	3.57	3.72	3.87	4.02	4.17	4.31	4.46	78
79	3.05	3.20	3.35	3.51	3.66	3.81	3.97	4.12	4.27	4.43	4.58	79
80	3.13	3.28	3.44	3.60	3.75	3.91	4.07	4.23	4.38	4.54	4.70	80
81	3.21	3.37	3.53	3.69	3.85	4.01	4.17	4.33	4.49	4.66	4.82	81
82	3.29	3.45	3.62	3.78	3.95	4.11	4.28	4.44	4.61	4.77	4.94	82
83	3.37	3.54	3.70	3.87	4.04	4.21	4.38	4.55	4.72	4.89	5.06	83
84	3.45	3.62	3.80	3.97	4.14	4.32	4.49	4.66	4.84	5.01	5.18	84
85	3.53	3.71	3.89	4.06	4.24	4.42	4.60	4.77	4.95	5.13	5.31	85
86	3.62	3.80	3.98	4.16	4.34	4.52	4.71	4.89	5.07	5.25	5.43	86
87	3.70	3.89	4.07	4.26	4.44	4.63	4.82	5.00	5.19	5.38	5.56	87
88	3.79	3.98	4.17	4.36	4.55	4.74	4.93	5.12	5.31	5.50	5.69	88
89	3.87	4.07	4.26	4.46	4.65	4.85	5.04	5.24	5.43	5.63	5.82	89
90	3.96	4.16	4.36	4.56	4.76	4.96	5.16	5.36	5.56	5.75	5.95	90
91	4.05	4.25	4.46	4.66	4.87	5.07	5.27	5.48	5.68	5.88	6.09	91
92	4.14	4.35	4.56	4.76	4.97	5.18	5.39	5.60	5.81	6.01	6.22	92
93	4.23	4.44	4.66	4.87	5.08	5.30	5.51	5.72	5.93	6.15	6.36	93
94	4.32	4.54	4.76	4.98	5.19	5.41	5.63	5.85	6.06	6.28	6.50	94
95	4.42	4.64	4.86	5.08	5.30	5.53	5.75	5.97	6.19	6.41	6.64	95
96	4.51	4.74	4.96	5.19	5.42	5.64	5.87	6.10	6.32	6.55	6.78	96
97	4.60	4.84	5.07	5.30	5.53	5.76	5.99	6.23	6.46	6.69	6.92	97
98	4.70	4.94	5.17	5.41	5.65	5.88	6.12	6.36	6.59	6.83	7.06	98
99	4.80	5.04	5.28	5.52	5.76	6.00	6.25	6.49	6.73	6.97	7.21	99
100	4.90	5.14	5.39	5.63	5.88	6.13	6.37	6.62	6.86	7.11	7.36	100

dbh cm	VOLUME IN CUBIC METRES OVERBARK											dbh cm
	Tariff Number											
	30	31	32	33	34	35	36	37	38	39	40	
7	0.005	0.005	0.005	0.005	0.005	0.005	0.005	0.005	0.005	0.005	0.005	7
8	0.016	0.017	0.017	0.017	0.018	0.018	0.018	0.019	0.019	0.019	0.020	8
9	0.029	0.029	0.030	0.031	0.032	0.033	0.033	0.034	0.035	0.036	0.037	9
10	0.043	0.044	0.045	0.047	0.048	0.049	0.050	0.052	0.053	0.054	0.055	10
11	0.058	0.060	0.062	0.064	0.065	0.067	0.069	0.071	0.072	0.074	0.076	11
12	0.075	0.078	0.080	0.082	0.085	0.087	0.089	0.092	0.094	0.096	0.099	12
13	0.094	0.097	0.100	0.103	0.106	0.109	0.112	0.114	0.117	0.120	0.123	13
14	0.114	0.117	0.121	0.125	0.128	0.132	0.135	0.139	0.143	0.146	0.150	14
15	0.135	0.139	0.144	0.148	0.153	0.157	0.161	0.166	0.170	0.174	0.179	15
16	0.158	0.163	0.168	0.173	0.178	0.184	0.189	0.194	0.199	0.204	0.209	16
17	0.182	0.188	0.194	0.200	0.206	0.212	0.218	0.224	0.230	0.236	0.242	17
18	0.208	0.215	0.222	0.229	0.235	0.242	0.249	0.256	0.263	0.269	0.276	18
19	0.236	0.243	0.251	0.259	0.266	0.274	0.282	0.290	0.297	0.305	0.313	19
20	0.264	0.273	0.282	0.290	0.299	0.308	0.316	0.325	0.334	0.343	0.351	20
21	0.29	0.30	0.31	0.32	0.33	0.34	0.35	0.36	0.37	0.38	0.39	21
22	0.33	0.34	0.35	0.36	0.37	0.38	0.39	0.40	0.41	0.42	0.43	22
23	0.36	0.37	0.38	0.40	0.41	0.42	0.43	0.44	0.45	0.47	0.48	23
24	0.39	0.41	0.42	0.43	0.45	0.46	0.47	0.49	0.50	0.51	0.52	24
25	0.43	0.44	0.46	0.47	0.49	0.50	0.52	0.53	0.54	0.56	0.57	25
26	0.47	0.48	0.50	0.51	0.53	0.55	0.56	0.58	0.59	0.61	0.62	26
27	0.51	0.52	0.54	0.56	0.57	0.59	0.61	0.63	0.64	0.66	0.68	27
28	0.55	0.57	0.58	0.60	0.62	0.64	0.66	0.68	0.69	0.71	0.73	28
29	0.59	0.61	0.63	0.65	0.67	0.69	0.71	0.73	0.75	0.77	0.79	29
30	0.63	0.65	0.68	0.70	0.72	0.74	0.76	0.78	0.80	0.82	0.84	30
31	0.68	0.70	0.72	0.75	0.77	0.79	0.81	0.84	0.86	0.88	0.90	31
32	0.73	0.75	0.77	0.80	0.82	0.85	0.87	0.89	0.92	0.94	0.97	32
33	0.77	0.80	0.82	0.85	0.88	0.90	0.93	0.95	0.98	1.01	1.03	33
34	0.82	0.85	0.88	0.91	0.93	0.96	0.99	1.01	1.04	1.07	1.10	34
35	0.87	0.90	0.93	0.96	0.99	1.02	1.05	1.08	1.11	1.14	1.16	35
36	0.93	0.96	0.99	1.02	1.05	1.08	1.11	1.14	1.17	1.20	1.23	36
37	0.98	1.01	1.05	1.08	1.11	1.14	1.18	1.21	1.24	1.27	1.31	37
38	1.04	1.07	1.10	1.14	1.17	1.21	1.24	1.28	1.31	1.35	1.38	38
39	1.09	1.13	1.17	1.20	1.24	1.27	1.31	1.35	1.38	1.42	1.46	39
40	1.15	1.19	1.23	1.27	1.30	1.34	1.38	1.42	1.46	1.50	1.53	40
41	1.21	1.25	1.29	1.33	1.37	1.41	1.45	1.49	1.53	1.57	1.61	41
42	1.27	1.31	1.36	1.40	1.44	1.48	1.53	1.57	1.61	1.65	1.70	42
43	1.33	1.38	1.42	1.47	1.51	1.56	1.60	1.65	1.69	1.74	1.78	43
44	1.40	1.45	1.49	1.54	1.59	1.63	1.68	1.73	1.77	1.82	1.87	44
45	1.47	1.51	1.56	1.61	1.66	1.71	1.76	1.81	1.86	1.91	1.95	45
46	1.53	1.58	1.63	1.69	1.74	1.79	1.84	1.89	1.94	1.99	2.04	46
47	1.60	1.65	1.71	1.76	1.81	1.87	1.92	1.98	2.03	2.08	2.14	47
48	1.67	1.73	1.78	1.84	1.89	1.95	2.01	2.06	2.12	2.17	2.23	48
49	1.74	1.80	1.86	1.92	1.98	2.03	2.09	2.15	2.21	2.27	2.32	49
50	1.82	1.88	1.94	2.00	2.06	2.12	2.18	2.24	2.30	2.36	2.42	50

VOLUME IN CUBIC METRES OVERBARK

dbh cm	Tariff Number 30	31	32	33	34	35	36	37	38	39	40	dbh cm
51	1.89	1.95	2.02	2.08	2.14	2.21	2.27	2.33	2.40	2.46	2.52	51
52	1.97	2.03	2.10	2.16	2.23	2.30	2.36	2.43	2.49	2.56	2.62	52
53	2.04	2.11	2.18	2.25	2.32	2.39	2.45	2.52	2.59	2.66	2.73	53
54	2.12	2.19	2.27	2.34	2.41	2.48	2.55	2.62	2.69	2.76	2.83	54
55	2.20	2.28	2.35	2.42	2.50	2.57	2.65	2.72	2.79	2.87	2.94	55
56	2.29	2.36	2.44	2.52	2.59	2.67	2.74	2.82	2.90	2.97	3.05	56
57	2.37	2.45	2.53	2.61	2.69	2.77	2.84	2.92	3.00	3.08	3.16	57
58	2.45	2.54	2.62	2.70	2.78	2.86	2.95	3.03	3.11	3.19	3.27	58
59	2.54	2.63	2.71	2.80	2.88	2.97	3.05	3.14	3.22	3.31	3.39	59
60	2.63	2.72	2.80	2.89	2.98	3.07	3.16	3.24	3.33	3.42	3.51	60
61	2.72	2.81	2.90	2.99	3.08	3.17	3.26	3.35	3.44	3.54	3.63	61
62	2.81	2.90	3.00	3.09	3.18	3.28	3.37	3.47	3.56	3.65	3.75	62
63	2.90	3.00	3.10	3.19	3.29	3.39	3.48	3.58	3.68	3.77	3.87	63
64	3.00	3.10	3.20	3.30	3.40	3.50	3.60	3.70	3.80	3.90	4.00	64
65	3.09	3.19	3.30	3.40	3.50	3.61	3.71	3.81	3.92	4.02	4.12	65
66	3.19	3.29	3.40	3.51	3.61	3.72	3.83	3.93	4.04	4.15	4.25	66
67	3.29	3.40	3.51	3.62	3.73	3.83	3.94	4.05	4.16	4.27	4.38	67
68	3.39	3.50	3.61	3.72	3.84	3.95	4.06	4.18	4.29	4.40	4.52	68
69	3.49	3.60	3.72	3.84	3.95	4.07	4.19	4.30	4.42	4.54	4.65	69
70	3.59	3.71	3.83	3.95	4.07	4.19	4.31	4.43	4.55	4.67	4.79	70
71	3.69	3.82	3.94	4.06	4.19	4.31	4.43	4.56	4.68	4.81	4.93	71
72	3.80	3.93	4.05	4.18	4.31	4.43	4.56	4.69	4.82	4.94	5.07	72
73	3.91	4.04	4.17	4.30	4.43	4.56	4.69	4.82	4.95	5.08	5.21	73
74	4.01	4.15	4.28	4.42	4.55	4.69	4.82	4.95	5.09	5.22	5.36	74
75	4.12	4.26	4.40	4.54	4.68	4.81	4.95	5.09	5.23	5.37	5.50	75
76	4.24	4.38	4.52	4.66	4.80	4.95	5.09	5.23	5.37	5.51	5.65	76
77	4.35	4.50	4.64	4.79	4.93	5.08	5.22	5.37	5.51	5.66	5.80	77
78	4.46	4.61	4.76	4.91	5.06	5.21	5.36	5.51	5.66	5.81	5.96	78
79	4.58	4.73	4.89	5.04	5.19	5.35	5.50	5.65	5.81	5.96	6.11	79
80	4.70	4.85	5.01	5.17	5.33	5.48	5.64	5.80	5.95	6.11	6.27	80
81	4.82	4.98	5.14	5.30	5.46	5.62	5.78	5.94	6.11	6.27	6.43	81
82	4.94	5.10	5.27	5.43	5.60	5.76	5.93	6.09	6.26	6.42	6.59	82
83	5.06	5.23	5.40	5.57	5.74	5.91	6.07	6.24	6.41	6.58	6.75	83
84	5.18	5.36	5.53	5.70	5.88	6.05	6.22	6.40	6.57	6.74	6.92	84
85	5.31	5.48	5.66	5.84	6.02	6.19	6.37	6.55	6.73	6.91	7.08	85
86	5.43	5.62	5.80	5.98	6.16	6.34	6.52	6.71	6.89	7.07	7.25	86
87	5.56	5.75	5.93	6.12	6.31	6.49	6.68	6.86	7.05	7.24	7.42	87
88	5.69	5.88	6.07	6.26	6.45	6.64	6.83	7.02	7.21	7.40	7.59	88
89	5.82	6.02	6.21	6.41	6.60	6.80	6.99	7.18	7.38	7.57	7.77	89
90	5.95	6.15	6.35	6.55	6.75	6.95	7.15	7.35	7.55	7.75	7.95	90
91	6.09	6.29	6.49	6.70	6.90	7.11	7.31	7.51	7.72	7.92	8.12	91
92	6.22	6.43	6.64	6.85	7.06	7.26	7.47	7.68	7.89	8.10	8.30	92
93	6.36	6.57	6.78	7.00	7.21	7.42	7.64	7.85	8.06	8.27	8.49	93
94	6.50	6.71	6.93	7.15	7.37	7.58	7.80	8.02	8.24	8.45	8.67	94
95	6.64	6.86	7.08	7.30	7.53	7.75	7.97	8.19	8.41	8.64	8.86	95
96	6.78	7.00	7.23	7.46	7.69	7.91	8.14	8.37	8.59	8.82	9.05	96
97	6.92	7.15	7.38	7.62	7.85	8.08	8.31	8.54	8.77	9.01	9.24	97
98	7.06	7.30	7.54	7.77	8.01	8.25	8.48	8.72	8.96	9.19	9.43	98
99	7.21	7.45	7.69	7.93	8.18	8.42	8.66	8.90	9.14	9.38	9.62	99
100	7.36	7.60	7.85	8.10	8.34	8.59	8.83	9.08	9.33	9.57	9.82	100

dbh cm	40	41	42	43	44	45	46	47	48	49	50	dbh cm
	VOLUME IN CUBIC METRES OVERBARK											
	Tariff Number											
7	0.005	0.005	0.005	0.005	0.005	0.005	0.005	0.005	0.005	0.005	0.005	7
8	0.020	0.020	0.021	0.021	0.021	0.022	0.022	0.022	0.023	0.023	0.024	8
9	0.037	0.037	0.038	0.039	0.040	0.041	0.041	0.042	0.043	0.044	0.045	9
10	0.055	0.057	0.058	0.059	0.060	0.062	0.063	0.064	0.065	0.067	0.068	10
11	0.076	0.078	0.080	0.081	0.083	0.085	0.087	0.089	0.090	0.092	0.094	11
12	0.099	0.101	0.103	0.106	0.108	0.110	0.113	0.115	0.118	0.120	0.122	12
13	0.123	0.126	0.129	0.132	0.135	0.138	0.141	0.144	0.147	0.150	0.153	13
14	0.150	0.154	0.157	0.161	0.165	0.168	0.172	0.175	0.179	0.183	0.186	14
15	0.179	0.183	0.187	0.192	0.196	0.200	0.205	0.209	0.213	0.218	0.222	15
16	0.209	0.214	0.219	0.225	0.230	0.235	0.240	0.245	0.250	0.255	0.260	16
17	0.242	0.248	0.254	0.260	0.266	0.271	0.277	0.283	0.289	0.295	0.301	17
18	0.276	0.283	0.290	0.297	0.303	0.310	0.317	0.324	0.331	0.338	0.344	18
19	0.313	0.320	0.328	0.336	0.344	0.351	0.359	0.367	0.375	0.382	0.390	19
20	0.351	0.360	0.369	0.377	0.386	0.395	0.403	0.412	0.421	0.429	0.438	20
21	0.39	0.40	0.41	0.42	0.43	0.44	0.45	0.46	0.47	0.48	0.49	21
22	0.43	0.44	0.46	0.47	0.48	0.49	0.50	0.51	0.52	0.53	0.54	22
23	0.48	0.49	0.50	0.51	0.53	0.54	0.55	0.56	0.57	0.59	0.60	23
24	0.52	0.54	0.55	0.56	0.58	0.59	0.60	0.62	0.63	0.64	0.66	24
25	0.57	0.59	0.60	0.62	0.63	0.64	0.66	0.67	0.69	0.70	0.72	25
26	0.62	0.64	0.65	0.67	0.69	0.70	0.72	0.73	0.75	0.76	0.78	26
27	0.68	0.69	0.71	0.73	0.74	0.76	0.78	0.79	0.81	0.83	0.84	27
28	0.73	0.75	0.77	0.78	0.80	0.82	0.84	0.86	0.88	0.89	0.91	28
29	0.79	0.81	0.83	0.84	0.86	0.88	0.90	0.92	0.94	0.96	0.98	29
30	0.84	0.87	0.89	0.91	0.93	0.95	0.97	0.99	1.01	1.03	1.05	30
31	0.90	0.93	0.95	0.97	0.99	1.02	1.04	1.06	1.09	1.11	1.13	31
32	0.97	0.99	1.01	1.04	1.06	1.09	1.11	1.14	1.16	1.18	1.21	32
33	1.03	1.06	1.08	1.11	1.13	1.16	1.19	1.21	1.24	1.26	1.29	33
34	1.10	1.12	1.15	1.18	1.21	1.23	1.26	1.29	1.32	1.34	1.37	34
35	1.16	1.19	1.22	1.25	1.28	1.31	1.34	1.37	1.40	1.43	1.46	35
36	1.23	1.27	1.30	1.33	1.36	1.39	1.42	1.45	1.48	1.51	1.54	36
37	1.31	1.34	1.37	1.40	1.44	1.47	1.50	1.54	1.57	1.60	1.63	37
38	1.38	1.42	1.45	1.48	1.52	1.55	1.59	1.62	1.66	1.69	1.73	38
39	1.46	1.49	1.53	1.57	1.60	1.64	1.68	1.71	1.75	1.78	1.82	39
40	1.53	1.57	1.61	1.65	1.69	1.73	1.77	1.80	1.84	1.88	1.92	40
41	1.61	1.66	1.70	1.74	1.78	1.82	1.86	1.90	1.94	1.98	2.02	41
42	1.70	1.74	1.78	1.82	1.87	1.91	1.95	1.99	2.04	2.08	2.12	42
43	1.78	1.82	1.87	1.91	1.96	2.00	2.05	2.09	2.14	2.18	2.23	43
44	1.87	1.91	1.96	2.01	2.05	2.10	2.15	2.19	2.24	2.29	2.33	44
45	1.95	2.00	2.05	2.10	2.15	2.20	2.25	2.30	2.35	2.39	2.44	45
46	2.04	2.09	2.15	2.20	2.25	2.30	2.35	2.40	2.45	2.50	2.56	46
47	2.14	2.19	2.24	2.30	2.35	2.40	2.46	2.51	2.56	2.62	2.67	47
48	2.23	2.28	2.34	2.40	2.45	2.51	2.56	2.62	2.68	2.73	2.79	48
49	2.32	2.38	2.44	2.50	2.56	2.62	2.67	2.73	2.79	2.85	2.91	49
50	2.42	2.48	2.54	2.60	2.67	2.73	2.79	2.85	2.91	2.97	3.03	50

VOLUME IN CUBIC METRES OVERBARK

dbh cm	Tariff Number 40	41	42	43	44	45	46	47	48	49	50	dbh cm
51	2.52	2.59	2.65	2.71	2.77	2.84	2.90	2.96	3.03	3.09	3.15	51
52	2.62	2.69	2.76	2.82	2.89	2.95	3.02	3.08	3.15	3.21	3.28	52
53	2.73	2.80	2.86	2.93	3.00	3.07	3.14	3.21	3.27	3.34	3.41	53
54	2.83	2.90	2.97	3.05	3.12	3.19	3.26	3.33	3.40	3.47	3.54	54
55	2.94	3.01	3.09	3.16	3.23	3.31	3.38	3.46	3.53	3.60	3.68	55
56	3.05	3.13	3.20	3.28	3.36	3.43	3.51	3.58	3.66	3.74	3.81	56
57	3.16	3.24	3.32	3.40	3.48	3.56	3.64	3.72	3.79	3.87	3.95	57
58	3.27	3.36	3.44	3.52	3.60	3.68	3.77	3.85	3.93	4.01	4.09	58
59	3.39	3.47	3.56	3.64	3.73	3.81	3.90	3.98	4.07	4.15	4.24	59
60	3.51	3.60	3.68	3.77	3.86	3.95	4.03	4.12	4.21	4.30	4.39	60
61	3.63	3.72	3.81	3.90	3.99	4.08	4.17	4.26	4.35	4.44	4.54	61
62	3.75	3.84	3.94	4.03	4.12	4.22	4.31	4.41	4.50	4.59	4.69	62
63	3.87	3.97	4.07	4.16	4.26	4.36	4.45	4.55	4.65	4.74	4.84	63
64	4.00	4.10	4.20	4.30	4.40	4.50	4.60	4.70	4.80	4.90	5.00	64
65	4.12	4.23	4.33	4.43	4.54	4.64	4.74	4.85	4.95	5.05	5.16	65
66	4.25	4.36	4.47	4.57	4.68	4.79	4.89	5.00	5.11	5.21	5.32	66
67	4.38	4.49	4.60	4.71	4.82	4.93	5.04	5.15	5.26	5.37	5.48	67
68	4.52	4.63	4.74	4.86	4.97	5.08	5.20	5.31	5.42	5.54	5.65	68
69	4.65	4.77	4.89	5.00	5.12	5.24	5.35	5.47	5.59	5.70	5.82	69
70	4.79	4.91	5.03	5.15	5.27	5.39	5.51	5.63	5.75	5.87	5.99	70
71	4.93	5.05	5.18	5.30	5.42	5.55	5.67	5.79	5.92	6.04	6.16	71
72	5.07	5.20	5.32	5.45	5.58	5.70	5.83	5.96	6.09	6.21	6.34	72
73	5.21	5.34	5.47	5.60	5.74	5.87	6.00	6.13	6.26	6.39	6.52	73
74	5.36	5.49	5.63	5.76	5.89	6.03	6.16	6.30	6.43	6.57	6.70	74
75	5.50	5.64	5.78	5.92	6.06	6.19	6.33	6.47	6.61	6.75	6.88	75
76	5.65	5.80	5.94	6.08	6.22	6.36	6.50	6.65	6.79	6.93	7.07	76
77	5.80	5.95	6.10	6.24	6.39	6.53	6.68	6.82	6.97	7.11	7.26	77
78	5.96	6.11	6.26	6.41	6.55	6.70	6.85	7.00	7.15	7.30	7.45	78
79	6.11	6.27	6.42	6.57	6.73	6.88	7.03	7.18	7.34	7.49	7.64	79
80	6.27	6.43	6.58	6.74	6.90	7.05	7.21	7.37	7.53	7.68	7.84	80
81	6.43	6.59	6.75	6.91	7.07	7.23	7.39	7.56	7.72	7.88	8.04	81
82	6.59	6.75	6.92	7.08	7.25	7.41	7.58	7.74	7.91	8.08	8.24	82
83	6.75	6.92	7.09	7.26	7.43	7.60	7.77	7.94	8.11	8.27	8.44	83
84	6.92	7.09	7.26	7.44	7.61	7.78	7.96	8.13	8.30	8.48	8.65	84
85	7.08	7.26	7.44	7.62	7.79	7.97	8.15	8.33	8.50	8.68	8.86	85
86	7.25	7.43	7.61	7.80	7.98	8.16	8.34	8.52	8.71	8.89	9.07	86
87	7.42	7.61	7.79	7.98	8.17	8.35	8.54	8.72	8.91	9.10	9.28	87
88	7.59	7.78	7.98	8.17	8.36	8.55	8.74	8.93	9.12	9.31	9.50	88
89	7.77	7.96	8.16	8.35	8.55	8.74	8.94	9.13	9.33	9.52	9.72	89
90	7.95	8.14	8.34	8.54	8.74	8.94	9.14	9.34	9.54	9.74	9.94	90
91	8.12	8.33	8.53	8.74	8.94	9.14	9.35	9.55	9.75	9.96	10.2	91
92	8.30	8.51	8.72	8.93	9.14	9.35	9.55	9.76	9.97	10.2	10.4	92
93	8.49	8.70	8.91	9.13	9.34	9.55	9.76	9.98	10.2	10.4	10.6	93
94	8.67	8.89	9.11	9.32	9.54	9.76	9.98	10.2	10.4	10.6	10.8	94
95	8.86	9.08	9.30	9.52	9.75	9.97	10.2	10.4	10.6	10.9	11.1	95
96	9.05	9.27	9.50	9.73	9.95	10.2	10.4	10.6	10.9	11.1	11.3	96
97	9.24	9.47	9.70	9.93	10.2	10.4	10.6	10.9	11.1	11.3	11.6	97
98	9.43	9.67	9.90	10.1	10.4	10.6	10.8	11.1	11.3	11.6	11.8	98
99	9.62	9.86	10.1	10.3	10.6	10.8	11.1	11.3	11.6	11.8	12.0	99
100	9.82	10.1	10.3	10.6	10.8	11.1	11.3	11.5	11.8	12.0	12.3	100

dbh cm	VOLUME IN CUBIC METRES OVERBARK											dbh cm
	Tariff Number											
	50	51	52	53	54	55	56	57	58	59	60	
21	0.49	0.50	0.51	0.52	0.53	0.54	0.55	0.56	0.57	0.58	0.59	21
22	0.54	0.55	0.56	0.57	0.58	0.60	0.61	0.62	0.63	0.64	0.65	22
23	0.60	0.61	0.62	0.63	0.64	0.66	0.67	0.68	0.69	0.70	0.72	23
24	0.66	0.67	0.68	0.69	0.71	0.72	0.73	0.75	0.76	0.77	0.79	24
25	0.72	0.73	0.74	0.76	0.77	0.79	0.80	0.82	0.83	0.84	0.86	25
26	0.78	0.79	0.81	0.83	0.84	0.86	0.87	0.89	0.90	0.92	0.93	26
27	0.84	0.86	0.88	0.89	0.91	0.93	0.94	0.96	0.98	1.00	1.01	27
28	0.91	0.93	0.95	0.97	0.98	1.00	1.02	1.04	1.06	1.08	1.09	28
29	0.98	1.00	1.02	1.04	1.06	1.08	1.10	1.12	1.14	1.16	1.18	29
30	1.05	1.08	1.10	1.12	1.14	1.16	1.18	1.20	1.22	1.24	1.27	30
31	1.13	1.15	1.18	1.20	1.22	1.24	1.27	1.29	1.31	1.33	1.36	31
32	1.21	1.23	1.26	1.28	1.30	1.33	1.35	1.38	1.40	1.43	1.45	32
33	1.29	1.31	1.34	1.37	1.39	1.42	1.44	1.47	1.49	1.52	1.55	33
34	1.37	1.40	1.43	1.45	1.48	1.51	1.54	1.56	1.59	1.62	1.64	34
35	1.46	1.49	1.51	1.54	1.57	1.60	1.63	1.66	1.69	1.72	1.75	35
36	1.54	1.57	1.61	1.64	1.67	1.70	1.73	1.76	1.79	1.82	1.85	36
37	1.63	1.67	1.70	1.73	1.76	1.80	1.83	1.86	1.89	1.93	1.96	37
38	1.73	1.76	1.80	1.83	1.86	1.90	1.93	1.97	2.00	2.04	2.07	38
39	1.82	1.86	1.89	1.93	1.97	2.00	2.04	2.08	2.11	2.15	2.19	39
40	1.92	1.96	2.00	2.03	2.07	2.11	2.15	2.19	2.23	2.26	2.30	40
41	2.02	2.06	2.10	2.14	2.18	2.22	2.26	2.30	2.34	2.38	2.42	41
42	2.12	2.16	2.21	2.25	2.29	2.33	2.38	2.42	2.46	2.50	2.55	42
43	2.23	2.27	2.31	2.36	2.40	2.45	2.49	2.54	2.58	2.63	2.67	43
44	2.33	2.38	2.43	2.47	2.52	2.57	2.61	2.66	2.71	2.75	2.80	44
45	2.44	2.49	2.54	2.59	2.64	2.69	2.74	2.79	2.83	2.88	2.93	45
46	2.56	2.61	2.66	2.71	2.76	2.81	2.86	2.91	2.96	3.02	3.07	46
47	2.67	2.72	2.78	2.83	2.88	2.94	2.99	3.04	3.10	3.15	3.20	47
48	2.79	2.84	2.90	2.95	3.01	3.07	3.12	3.18	3.23	3.29	3.35	48
49	2.91	2.96	3.02	3.08	3.14	3.20	3.26	3.31	3.37	3.43	3.49	49
50	3.03	3.09	3.15	3.21	3.27	3.33	3.39	3.45	3.51	3.57	3.64	50
51	3.15	3.22	3.28	3.34	3.41	3.47	3.53	3.60	3.66	3.72	3.78	51
52	3.28	3.35	3.41	3.48	3.54	3.61	3.67	3.74	3.81	3.87	3.94	52
53	3.41	3.48	3.55	3.62	3.68	3.75	3.82	3.89	3.96	4.02	4.09	53
54	3.54	3.61	3.68	3.75	3.83	3.90	3.97	4.04	4.11	4.18	4.25	54
55	3.68	3.75	3.82	3.90	3.97	4.04	4.12	4.19	4.27	4.34	4.41	55
56	3.81	3.89	3.97	4.04	4.12	4.20	4.27	4.35	4.42	4.50	4.58	56
57	3.95	4.03	4.11	4.19	4.27	4.35	4.43	4.51	4.59	4.67	4.74	57
58	4.09	4.18	4.26	4.34	4.42	4.51	4.59	4.67	4.75	4.83	4.92	58
59	4.24	4.32	4.41	4.49	4.58	4.66	4.75	4.83	4.92	5.00	5.09	59
60	4.39	4.47	4.56	4.65	4.74	4.83	4.91	5.00	5.09	5.18	5.26	60
61	4.54	4.63	4.72	4.81	4.90	4.99	5.08	5.17	5.26	5.35	5.44	61
62	4.69	4.78	4.87	4.97	5.06	5.16	5.25	5.34	5.44	5.53	5.63	62
63	4.84	4.94	5.04	5.13	5.23	5.33	5.42	5.52	5.62	5.71	5.81	63
64	5.00	5.10	5.20	5.30	5.40	5.50	5.60	5.70	5.80	5.90	6.00	64
65	5.16	5.26	5.36	5.47	5.57	5.67	5.78	5.88	5.98	6.09	6.19	65
66	5.32	5.43	5.53	5.64	5.75	5.85	5.96	6.06	6.17	6.28	6.38	66
67	5.48	5.59	5.70	5.81	5.92	6.03	6.14	6.25	6.36	6.47	6.58	67
68	5.65	5.76	5.88	5.99	6.10	6.22	6.33	6.44	6.56	6.67	6.78	68
69	5.82	5.93	6.05	6.17	6.28	6.40	6.52	6.63	6.75	6.87	6.98	69
70	5.99	6.11	6.23	6.35	6.47	6.59	6.71	6.83	6.95	7.07	7.19	70

VOLUME IN CUBIC METRES OVERBARK

dbh cm	Tariff Number 50	51	52	53	54	55	56	57	58	59	60	dbh cm
71	6.16	6.29	6.41	6.53	6.66	6.78	6.90	7.03	7.15	7.28	7.40	71
72	6.34	6.47	6.59	6.72	6.85	6.98	7.10	7.23	7.36	7.48	7.61	72
73	6.52	6.65	6.78	6.91	7.04	7.17	7.30	7.43	7.56	7.69	7.83	73
74	6.70	6.83	6.97	7.10	7.24	7.37	7.51	7.64	7.77	7.91	8.04	74
75	6.88	7.02	7.16	7.30	7.44	7.57	7.71	7.85	7.99	8.13	8.26	75
76	7.07	7.21	7.35	7.50	7.64	7.78	7.92	8.06	8.20	8.35	8.49	76
77	7.26	7.40	7.55	7.70	7.84	7.99	8.13	8.28	8.42	8.57	8.71	77
78	7.45	7.60	7.75	7.90	8.05	8.20	8.35	8.50	8.65	8.79	8.94	78
79	7.64	7.80	7.95	8.10	8.26	8.41	8.56	8.72	8.87	9.02	9.18	79
80	7.84	8.00	8.15	8.31	8.47	8.63	8.78	8.94	9.10	9.25	9.41	80
81	8.04	8.20	8.36	8.52	8.68	8.84	9.01	9.17	9.33	9.49	9.65	81
82	8.24	8.41	8.57	8.74	8.90	9.07	9.23	9.40	9.56	9.73	9.89	82
83	8.44	8.61	8.78	8.95	9.12	9.29	9.46	9.63	9.80	9.97	10.1	83
84	8.65	8.82	9.00	9.17	9.34	9.52	9.69	9.86	10.0	10.2	10.4	84
85	8.86	9.04	9.21	9.39	9.57	9.75	9.92	10.1	10.3	10.5	10.6	85
86	9.07	9.25	9.43	9.61	9.80	9.98	10.2	10.3	10.5	10.7	10.9	86
87	9.28	9.47	9.65	9.84	10.0	10.2	10.4	10.6	10.8	11.0	11.1	87
88	9.50	9.69	9.88	10.1	10.3	10.5	10.6	10.8	11.0	11.2	11.4	88
89	9.72	9.91	10.1	10.3	10.5	10.7	10.9	11.1	11.3	11.5	11.7	89
90	9.94	10.1	10.3	10.5	10.7	10.9	11.1	11.3	11.5	11.7	11.9	90
91	10.2	10.4	10.6	10.8	11.0	11.2	11.4	11.6	11.8	12.0	12.2	91
92	10.4	10.6	10.8	11.0	11.2	11.4	11.6	11.8	12.1	12.3	12.5	92
93	10.6	10.8	11.0	11.3	11.5	11.7	11.9	12.1	12.3	12.5	12.7	93
94	10.8	11.1	11.3	11.5	11.7	11.9	12.2	12.4	12.6	12.8	13.0	94
95	11.1	11.3	11.5	11.7	12.0	12.2	12.4	12.6	12.9	13.1	13.3	95
96	11.3	11.5	11.8	12.0	12.2	12.4	12.7	12.9	13.1	13.4	13.6	96
97	11.6	11.8	12.0	12.2	12.5	12.7	12.9	13.2	13.4	13.6	13.9	97
98	11.8	12.0	12.3	12.5	12.7	13.0	13.2	13.4	13.7	13.9	14.2	98
99	12.0	12.3	12.5	12.8	13.0	13.2	13.5	13.7	14.0	14.2	14.4	99
100	12.3	12.5	12.8	13.0	13.3	13.5	13.8	14.0	14.3	14.5	14.7	100
101	12.5	12.8	13.0	13.3	13.5	13.8	14.0	14.3	14.5	14.8	15.0	101
102	12.8	13.0	13.3	13.5	13.8	14.1	14.3	14.6	14.8	15.1	15.3	102
103	13.0	13.3	13.6	13.8	14.1	14.3	14.6	14.9	15.1	15.4	15.6	103
104	13.3	13.6	13.8	14.1	14.4	14.6	14.9	15.2	15.4	15.7	16.0	104
105	13.5	13.8	14.1	14.4	14.6	14.9	15.2	15.4	15.7	16.0	16.3	105
106	13.8	14.1	14.4	14.6	14.9	15.2	15.5	15.7	16.0	16.3	16.6	106
107	14.1	14.4	14.6	14.9	15.2	15.5	15.8	16.0	16.3	16.6	16.9	107
108	14.3	14.6	14.9	15.2	15.5	15.8	16.1	16.3	16.6	16.9	17.2	108
109	14.6	14.9	15.2	15.5	15.8	16.1	16.4	16.7	16.9	17.2	17.5	109
110	14.9	15.2	15.5	15.8	16.1	16.4	16.7	17.0	17.3	17.6	17.9	110
111	15.1	15.4	15.8	16.1	16.4	16.7	17.0	17.3	17.6	17.9	18.2	111
112	15.4	15 7	16.0	16.3	16.7	17.0	17.3	17.6	17.9	18.2	18.5	112
113	15.7	16.0	16.3	16.6	17.0	17.3	17.6	17.9	18.2	18.5	18.8	113
114	16.0	16.3	16.6	16.9	17.3	17.6	17.9	18.2	18.5	18.9	19.2	114
115	16.3	16.6	16.9	17.2	17.6	17.9	18.2	18.5	18.9	19.2	19.5	115
116	16.5	16.9	17.2	17.5	17.9	18.2	18.5	18.9	19.2	19.5	19.9	116
117	16.8	17.2	17.5	17.8	18.2	18.5	18.9	19.2	19.5	19.9	20.2	117
118	17.1	17.5	17.8	18.2	18.5	18.8	19.2	19.5	19.9	20.2	20.6	118
119	17.4	17.8	18.1	18.5	18.8	19.2	19.5	19.9	20.2	20.6	20.9	119
120	17.7	18.1	18.4	18.8	19.1	19.5	19.8	20.2	20.6	20.9	21.3	120

SELECTED INDEX

N.B.
Some of the terms listed below occur very frequently in the text of the handbook. The page number(s) indicated for each term refer to the part of the text either defining the term or covering its principal use.

Further information is available from:

1. Forestry Commission Publications

Bulletin 14 Forestry Practice (1985)
Booklet 26 Mid Diameter Sawlog Tables (1985)
Booklet 37 Volume Tables for Smallwood and Round Pitwood (1973)
Booklet 47 Investment Appraisal in Forestry (1980)
Booklet 48 Yield Models for Forest Management (1981)
Booklet 49 Timber Measurement—A Field Guide (1983)
Field Book 1 Top Diameter Sawlog Tables (1988) *Formerly Booklet 31*
Field Book 2 Thinning Control (1988) *Formerly Booklet 54*

Note This publication (Booklet 39) includes the contents of Booklets 26, 36*, 37, part of 49, and Field Book 1.

Forestry Commission publications are available from the Publications Section (address below), from HMSO or any good bookshop, excepting Booklets 37 and 48 which are available only from the Forestry Commission Publications Section.

2. Advice on any matter relating to timber measurement is available from the Mensuration Officer, Forestry Commission Research Station, Alice Holt Lodge, Wrecclesham, Farnham, Surrey, GU10 4LH. Tel: Bentley (0420) 22255.

*Now out of print

Printed in the United Kingdom for Her Majesty's Stationery Office
Dd290894 9/88 C40 G443 10170